P9-DFW-611

François-Vincent

RASPAIL

1794–1878

Scientist and Reformer

RASPAIL

SCIENTIST

AND REFORMER

by Dora B. Weiner

WITH A CHAPTER BY SIMONE RASPAIL

Columbia University Press

NEW YORK AND LONDON

1968

Dora B. Weiner is Associate Professor of History at Manhattanville College and Research Associate in the History of Science, Graduate History Department, Columbia University.

Acknowledgment is made of the kind permission of Dr. R. Wegman of Paris to reprint material included in "François-Vincent Raspail, fondateur de l'histochimie; aperçu historique de sa réputation en France," *Annales d'histochimie*, VI, No. 1 (1961), 1–11; and of permission from Mr. Marvin Brown to use most of "F.-V. Raspail: Physician to the Poor," *French Historical Studies*, I, No. 2 (1959), 149–71.

Copyright © 1968 Columbia University Press
Library of Congress Catalog Card Number: 68–19761
Printed in the United States of America

for E. B. with love

A l'époque où vivait Raspail, la Grande
Révolution était encore pour les républicains
une chose magique. Chacun d'eux se choisissait
parmi les ancêtres disparus quelque exemple
à suivre, quelque modèle à imiter. Louis
Blanc admirait Robespierre. Raspail
s'imaginait continuer Marat.

Albert Mathiez

. . . the national energy and the great social
ferment that overthrew the Old Régime . . .
found its greatest cultural expression in
scientific accomplishment.

Henri Guerlac

La cellule est toute française, et
appartient à Monsieur Raspail.

Paul Broca

Raspail at the age of forty
(Courtesy M. Jacques Raspail) Photo Bulloz

PREFACE

WRITING A BIOGRAPHY is full of surprises. A man as versatile as Raspail will lead his biographer far afield—into treason and murder trials and many prisons, into the history of chemistry, biology, and medicine, into exile and the Chamber of Deputies, into the history of Provence and the practice of pharmacy.

From the point of view of methodology this biography presented difficulties: the historian might easily succumb to the loyalty of the biographer; the historian of science and the cultural historian might be at odds. Some liberties have been taken with chronology—for the sake of clarity and objectivity, it is hoped, and not to their detriment. Chapters IV–VI deal with Raspail's scientific and medical work, essentially between 1820 and 1850; Chapters VII–VIII cover the same period, but focus on civil liberties and politics. In Chapters IX and X these two themes coalesce, since in Raspail's mind scientific progress and democratic emancipation were but two variations of the same motif; but the biographer must consider them separately.

It is hoped that some light has been shed on that frontier between the sciences and the humanities where both the historian and the scientist tread with such care. An attempt has been made to analyze the thought of a man committed both to science and to politics: to assess the extent to which Raspail reasoned in politics like a scientific experimenter and allowed his political passions to determine his scientific thought. His popularity and effectiveness derived from the unique tone thus imparted to his utterances. It is hoped that this tone has not been entirely lost through translation into another idiom. That would be too high a price to pay for the advantage of better perspective which geographic distance affords.

Pursuing some of these topics into the relevant French libraries, archives, museums, and family closets was often rewarding and sometimes frustrating: librarians, administrators, curators, and great-grandchildren were helpful or reticent, it would seem, according to their opinions about Raspail's politics. No one knew much about Raspail, but all recognized a Man of the Left.

My happiest discovery in France was Mademoiselle Simone Raspail, my collaborator for Chapter IV and the section on camphor in Chapter VI. She is the contributor of an original aspect of this book: the performing of some of Raspail's experiments with his own microscope by a modern biologist and pharmacist, incidentally his own great-granddaughter.

M. Jacques Raspail of Paris permitted the microfilming of a hitherto unknown autobiographical fragment covering the years 1794–1835, the perusal of hundreds of family letters exchanged among Raspail's children, and the photographing of the imposing painting, not known until now, which appears on page vii of this book. It would seem that in M. Jacques Raspail's cellar there stands a trunk, in it, perhaps, that "box containing the materials for my memoirs" referred to in Raspail's Will, likely the very trunk shipped early in this century from Benjamin Raspail to his brother Xavier, Raspail's last surviving son. All attempts by this biographer to gain access to that trunk have been fruitless.

Other pursuits were more rewarding. In Paris there are small, hitherto unpublished *Fonds Raspail* at the Archives nationales, at the Bibliothèque du Muséum d'histoire naturelle, and a voluminous collection—Deputy Benjamin Raspail's papers—at the Archives du Département de la Seine et de la Ville de Paris. I should like to thank M. René Marquant, Mme Bertrand Gille, Dr. Jean Théodoridès, MM. Yves Laissus, de Vaux de Foletier, and Michel Fleury for facilitating the use of these materials. Also in Paris, M. l'Abbé Noye, Chief Archivist of the Order of St. Sulpice, most generously helped me trace Raspail's Sulpician education.

I was granted access and insight into the Pharmacie Raspail in Paris, the Hospice Raspail in Cachan, still housing much of Raspail's library, furniture, and instruments, and the Etablissements Raspail in Arcueil where the Liqueur Raspail is still being distilled. In Vaucluse, the departmental archives in Avignon proved rather impenetrable, the Musée Calvet rewarding; in Carpentras, Raspail's native town, the Bibliothèque Inguimbertine owns few but important manuscripts, such as his Will, and the Museum revealed some treasures. M. Henri Dubled, the librarian, was most helpful in making these available.

Echoes of the Raspail legend could be discerned in conversations with senior scholars: the late Georges Bourgin of Paris, Professor Gilbert Chinard of Princeton, and above all "Majoral Jouve" of Carpentras, a local celebrity living at the Hôtel-Dieu in his nine-tieth year, who recounted stories and anecdotes of his youth, and led me through the winding streets of Carpentras, bringing Raspail back to life.

I have incurred many debts to the staffs of the following libraries: the New York Academy of Medicine, Columbia University, the New York Public Library, the Library of Congress, the National Library of Medicine, the Bibliothèque nationale, and the Bibliothèque historique de la Ville de Paris.

Travel to France and free time for research and writing were granted through the generous help of the following institutions: the American Association of University Women (National Fellowship, 1956–1957), American Council of Learned Societies (Grant-in-Aid, 1962), National Institute of General Medical Sciences, United States Public Health Service (Research Grant GM 10328-01-02, 1962–1965). Work was carried out during appointments as Research Associate at the Albert Einstein College of Medicine (1962–1964) and Columbia University (1964–1966).

I should like to express my thanks to the following colleagues who have read all or part of this manuscript and saved me from many errors: Professor Dr. Erwin H. Ackerknecht, Director of the

Medizinhistorische Institut, Zürich; Professor Alex Berman, Department of Pharmacy, University of Texas; Professor Paul Gerbod, Department of History, Nanterre Division, University of Paris; Professor Louis Girard of the Sorbonne; Professor Frederick L. Holmes, Department of the History of Science and Medicine, Yale University; Professor David H. Pinkney, Department of History, University of Washington; Dr. Francis Schiller, University of California Medical School, and Professor Shepard B. Clough, Department of History, Columbia University.

A special debt has been incurred, over the years, to Dr. Richard H. Shryock who, as Director of the Institute of the History of Medicine, the Johns Hopkins University, guided my work as Fellow in 1956–1957; to Professor Jacques Barzun of Columbia University to whose masterful critique this book owes whatever scholarly economy and lucidity of style it may possess; to Dr. Herbert Weiner, my husband, Professor of Psychiatry, Albert Einstein College of Medicine, whose knowledge of medicine and science have proved indispensable; and to our three young sons without whose forbearance and high spirits this book would not have been completed. The translations and shortcomings of the book are of my own making.

Dora B. Weiner

Manhattanville College
Purchase, New York

Spring 1968

CONTENTS

List of Illustrations

François-Vincent

RASPAIL

1794–1878

Scientist and Reformer

"Raspail—c'est un boulevard."

I

SCIENCE'S ALLY, DEMOCRACY

WHO WAS RASPAIL? Few Frenchmen seem to know. Even those who recognize a fighter for democracy in nineteenth-century France are astonished to find an original scientist: the founder of histochemistry, an early exponent of the cell theory and of parasitology, and the author of the first treatise on microchemical technique.

Throughout Raspail's agitated life, which began under the Terror in 1794 and ended eighty-four years later under the Third Republic, runs the theme of a double commitment: to science and to democracy. His triumphs, his failures, his significance for our scientific age derive from a lifelong allegiance to these two ideals. As a scientist he combined a talent for original observation with ingenuity in experimentation and boundless energy. As a democratic leader he was equally well endowed. A spellbinding orator and a prolific writer, he drew strength from a belief in the common man and in the sanctity of the democratic faith. Groping for

1

a way to couple his pursuit of science and democracy, he eventually found a goal that embodied his objectives: social medicine.[1] Under the Second and Third Republics his writings were widely read, and as a deputy he was able to urge his medical and social reforms upon the Chamber and the nation.

In his eagerness to better the human condition, it never occurred to Raspail that an adherence to both of his ideals would invalidate his commitment to science and preclude a scientific career. While his political thought gained strength and cogency from his competence as an experimenter, his involvement in politics hampered his scientific work. Had neutrality in politics left him free to give science his undivided attention, his knowledge, drive, and originality might well have led to first-rate contributions. But the modern dilemma of the scientist "engaged" in politics would have lost a significant explorer.

Raspail attempted to serve two masters at a time when this was becoming impossible. In the first half of the nineteenth century, the time of his major scientific and political activity, the temper of science and politics was changing. Just as the era of the "naturalist" was drawing to a close, and the botanist, zoologist, chemist, or physicist now embarked upon a specialty, so, too, the time of the professional politician had come. True, some Frenchmen were able to hold government appointments and practice science as well— witness the careers of Arago, Berthelot, or J.-B. Dumas. But these men were in sympathy with the régimes they served. Opposition to the government was becoming less and less a part-time occupation. The impatient republican reformer, seeing no signs of progress, often turned professional, and sometimes revolutionary. His time and energy were spent on meetings and oratory, on writing books, tracts, and articles for a widening public, on lawsuits, and often in jail. In the early nineteenth century the republican scientist had to choose between science and politics.

It was impossible for Raspail to ignore the dilemma since the French government changed every few years, each revolutionary upheaval affected his scope for political action and scientific work

---

[1] The term "social medicine" is used in this book to denote comprehensive measures of prevention and cure, owed to the citizen as a part of his "natural rights," not out of charity. See *infra*, ch. X.

and therefore entailed distracting readjustments. Thus the political history of France imposed its pattern on his life, dividing it into periods of intense political activity alternating with periods of scientific pursuit. "Raspail was filled with a strong love for his studies," wrote Eugène de Mirecourt, "and this passion had somehow to fuse with his hopes for the future. This explains very well how, in the midst of the most violent revolutionary struggles, politics never totally absorbed the man of science."[2]

Under the Restoration, when he was in his thirties, Raspail worked out a satisfactory life within the limits set by reactionary politics, government-controlled science, and his own intransigence. He belonged to several secret republican organizations, yet spent most of his time pursuing independent research and writing articles for scientific journals. He was poor, but content. The Revolution of 1830 tore him away from his studies. Thereafter he never recaptured a comparable peace of mind.

Initially, in the early days of the July Monarchy, Raspail was a republican activist. In the 1840s he broadened his objectives and advocated popular and governmental involvement in sanitation and preventive medicine. Immersed in political activity during the first three months of the Second Republic, he ended up in prison, in May 1848, and eventually in exile, where research and writing were the sole occupations available to a refugee. When the Liberal Empire permitted him to return, he was soon elected a deputy. After 1869, and well into the 1870s, he could at last, as a legislator, promote freedom and health jointly. Although he did not realize it, he became less and less of a "pure" scientist as the years went by. The impatient reformer overtook the research scientist. His social conscience bade him neglect "pure" for "applied" science, and abandon even that for social service. He wrestled with problems of public health and social medicine that to this day have not been solved.

Raspail was emotionally involved in everything he undertook. An intense, personal style is discernible in his written and spoken words. Ever eager to innovate, he devised new scientific tech-

[2] E. de Mirecourt [Eugène Jacquot], "Raspail," in *Les contemporains* (Paris, 1856), 33; also published, the same year, as a booklet.

niques, original hygienic measures, and a personal brand of socialism. His need for independence was excessive, leading him to
create hurdles for himself and make enemies unnecessarily. As a
brilliant seminary student, from 1810 to 1813, he showed a fatal
independence of thought. As a scientist in the 1820s, he disdained
conventional training and examinations. As a democrat and socialist, restless under discriminatory laws, he chafed at the slowness of
social reform.

This rebellious attitude toward the Establishment partly explains
the cold reception that Raspail encountered during his life, as well
as the oblivion that has befallen him since. Professionals were as
annoyed by his injection of socialism into science and medicine as
they were bothered by the radicalism that logically resulted from
his scientific political arguments. And yet, Raspail's double emphasis on democracy and science in his quest for a happy society
did follow a well-established French tradition. He was but carrying forward the thought of some eminent Frenchmen who had
sown the seeds of reform in politics, education, and public health
during the liberal phase of the Great Revolution—men like Condorcet, Talleyrand, Lavoisier, and La Rochefoucauld-Liancourt.
Raspail, in continuing their work, won the support of the French
masses. And, despite the opposition and scorn of powerful scientists,
doctors, and politicians, he made important contributions to French
science, medicine, politics, and socialism.

As a scientist Raspail left his mark on three areas of investigation: histochemistry, cell theory, and parasitology. He founded
histochemistry by studying animal and plant tissues under the
microscope at a time when this instrument was disdained by
French biologists.[3] In 1830 he wrote an original treatise on microscopic technique. In the mid-1820s already, twelve years before
Schleiden and Schwann, he described the growing cell and accurately analyzed its contents. He studied the cell's pathology
long before Virchow. He contributed to the knowledge of scabies,
and pointed out the role of "infinitely small parasites" as agents of
communicable disease almost a quarter of a century before Pasteur.
(His colleagues were then almost all anti-contagionists.) His
capacity for work was great: witness more than fifty scientific ar-

[3] Regarding the microscope, see *infra*, pp. 83–84 and 91 ff.

ticles, nine pamphlets, eight books, and four annual publications. Some of these were ephemeral, but the famous *Health Annual* (*Manuel-annuaire*) continued for over thirty years.[4]

In medicine Raspail tended to confine himself to therapy. He knew that sickness often goes with poverty, and he was convinced that sanitary measures could help prevent disease. From practical experience he inferred that camphor had remarkable hygienic, anesthetic, and antiseptic qualities. It was also cheap and widely available. Therefore he devised a variety of camphorated salves, drugs, and lotions. Learned in medicine, although lacking a diploma, he opened a dispensary where he gave medical consultations, at no charge to the poor. For forty years he propagated his dietary, antiseptic, and anticontagionist views—known as the "Raspail system of medicine"—by means of articles, pamphlets, and books. He had a wide following, partly owing to the effectiveness of his method, partly owing to personal solicitude.

In politics Raspail criticized every government, regardless of the party in power. He was a prominent member, at times president, of democratic clubs in the 1830s and in 1848; he published two political newspapers, each short-lived, and important treatises on prison and social reform. His numerous pamphlets and speeches were often written in his own defense, for he was accused of subversion in three famous trials of the 1830s. On May 15, 1848, he was arrested as a leader of the protest march on the Constituent Assembly. Although elected to that assembly on September 22, he was not set free, parliamentary immunity being denied him. The government thus severely handicapped his candidacy for the presidency of the republic in opposition to Louis Napoleon Bonaparte. Eventually a special High Court condemned him to six years in jail. Toward the end of his life Raspail was twice elected to the legislature. During the session of 1876–1878, being the oldest member, he had the unique satisfaction of presiding over the opening ceremonies of the Chamber of Deputies.

Raspail was a socialist. He wanted society to provide for the handicapped, infants, the needy aged, widows, orphans, and foundlings. But he thought state action necessary in extreme cases only. He preferred mutual assistance or cooperative efforts under-

[4] For a list of Raspail's works, see Bibliography, pp. 295–303.

taken by small groups. Human dignity would thus be better respected. Daniel Stern, the historian and novelist,[5] confirms that
Raspail "devoted himself, with persistent ardor, to the spread of
socialist ideas." In her *History of the Revolution of 1848,* she
further writes that he was

> the steadfast defender of the principles of 1789, and pursued the better-
> ment of the suffering classes as the supreme goal of his studies. . . .
> He leaned toward communism but lacked a system formulated for im-
> mediate use. No man who espoused the cause of the people has been
> the butt of more outrages and persecution. By the daring of his opin-
> ions, the purity of his life, the irony of his language, he provoked two
> powers whose hostility was unrelenting: scholastic medicine and con-
> servative politics.[6]

Historically, Raspail belongs to that group of Utopian Socialists
who were then devising schemes for a perfect society. He did not
commit himself to any one school. Being a happily married man
with five children, he would have found life in a Fourierist pha-
lanx uncongenial. The Saint-Simonians might have appealed to
him, but he disliked their emphasis on religion and on technology.
He had no wish, either, to help an Etienne Cabet establish Utopian
"Icaria" in the United States: Raspail was a passionate patriot.
Somewhat uncritically, perhaps, he approved of all socialist efforts
as steps toward democracy.

> Raspail was less political, but more sectarian than Blanqui [commented
> Alphonse de Lamartine], owing to his name, his newspaper, and his
> club, he had a more moderate but more intimate influence on the
> faubourgs. Fifteen- to twenty-thousand men from these boroughs . . .
> attended his meetings, admired his person, and followed his advice.
> Raspail's doctrines and preaching tended to communism, but his com-
> munism was sentimental rather than subversive. It consisted of an un-
> aggressive philosophy and practical charity which aimed at equality
> through voluntary levelling, not violent expropriation. He made the
> people fanatic with hope, not with hatred against the rich and fortu-
> nate. His social philosophy did not damn society, not even the govern-
> ment; he preached patience, order, and peace. Only, he promised more
> than the republic could ever give. His vague and gilded theories were

[5] Pseudonym of Marie de Flavigny, Comtesse d'Agoult (1805–1876).
[6] D. Stern, *Histoire de la révolution de 1848* (Paris, 1878), 2nd ed., 3 vols.,
I, LX.

like clouds which present a thousand perspectives to the imagination but which one can only see, not touch.[7]

By inclination Raspail was a teacher. He never doubted the urgency of communicating his knowledge to a wide public. His message was relatively simple, aimed in particular at the proletariat —the millions of poor Frenchmen who labored in the countryside or in factories and who strove to earn a decent wage, raise their children for a better life, and act responsibly toward their neighbors.

Did his audience hear him? The evidence suggests that Raspail was indeed listened to by thousands of Frenchmen from the 1840s on.[8] Frédéric Le Play (1806–1882), for example, in his sociological classic on West European workers, describes a typical Parisian carpenter's family in 1856: the wife manages the home, supervises the children's education, administers the money, and acts as family physician—using Raspail's method:

Full of confidence in the sanitary ideas of a popular practitioner, she makes wide use of sedative lotion and camphorated medications. . . . Most of these measures are currently used in the provinces as well as among Parisian workers' wives who tend to function as family doctors and hand down certain traditional recipes.[9]

The meaning of Raspail's message is illustrated by a passage from Jules Troubat who, trying to convince the coal miners of the Gard Department to end a strike in 1882, spoke of Raspail:

As far as I am concerned [argued Troubat], I still believe in the science of *Poor Richard*—and we have one who equals his American counterpart. Our French Franklin whose books are easy to consult, who popularized science and thus made it accessible to all, is none other than F.-V. Raspail—one of the men in the whole nineteenth century who loved the people best, and who put their entire belief in this thought: do good through the propagation of science. Listen to his wise counsels:

[7] A. de Lamartine, *Histoire de la révolution de 1848* (Brussels, 1849), 2 vols., II, 107–8.

[8] "I have so much influence over these men, some of whom could crush me between their fingers," Raspail stated at a widely publicized trial, "that often a word of criticism from me has made them cry." *Procès des accusés du 15 mai devant la Haute Cour de Bourges* (Paris, 1849), 17.

[9] F. Le Play, *Les ouvriers de l'occident,* vol. V of *Les ouvriers européens* (Tours, 1878), 2nd ed., 429.

"Everyone should defend his rights through arbitration; but both sides should be careful to avoid strikes. These inconsiderate work stoppages harm everyone and only profit foreign nations, envious of French prosperity."[10]

At Raspail's death, Maurice Vachon witnessed a scene that impressed him deeply. A middle-aged worker had come to Cachan to pay his last respects to Raspail who was lying in state. Too shy to enter the house, his hand trembling too much to sign the register, he stood a long time at the door and wept.[11]

More tangible proof of Raspail's popularity is afforded by the wide sale of his books and pamphlets and by the quantities of his medicines used all over France. One may assume that those who elected him to the Constituent Assembly, the Legislative Body, and the Chamber of Deputies, or proposed him for the presidency of the republic, did believe in his message, and that the thousands who contributed to the cost of his statue in Paris mourned a trusted leader. During his lifetime their confidence was reinforced by his suffering for their cause—eight-and-a-half years in prison and nine years in exile—and by his steadfast adherence to an exacting political philosophy. These were priceless credentials for a teacher of the people.

Three motifs emerge as guidelines as one studies Raspail's philosophy and personality: rejection of the past—that of France and his own; dedication to an egalitarian, democratic, socialist future; and a fierce individualism.

In rejecting monarchy and the Church, Raspail cut loose from a childhood spent in surroundings unchanged since the Middle Ages. The French Papal States, where he was born, had belonged to the pope until three years before his birth. The political loyalties of his townsmen were merged with their religious allegiance: they made no distinction between a temporal and a religious ruler. Significantly, one of the earliest memories Raspail recalled when he wrote his autobiography at the age of seventy-seven was the anniversary of Jean-Paul Marat's murder: "I still see the scaffolding with Marat's effigy in colored cardboard; but that is all I re-

[10] J. Troubat, *Le blason de la révolution* (Paris, 1883), 190–1.

[11] M. Vachon, "F.-V. Raspail," *Galerie contemporaine, littéraire et artistique,* 3ème année (Paris, 1878).

member of a celebration which must have occurred about 1796.
. . . I can still hear my poor mother whispering to me, trying to
fill me with horror against a monster whom I later did my best to
rehabilitate." [12]

Raspail's allegiance and enthusiasm belonged wholly to the new,
revolutionary France. He never hankered after the benefits that
the old régime had bestowed on Frenchmen. The stability of a
legitimate monarchy which attracted Ernest Renan, the beauty
of medieval art and pageantry which appealed to Victor Hugo, the
mysteries of the Catholic religion which stirred Chateaubriand,
held no attraction for Raspail. At twenty he longed to reject the
medieval past of his childhood, and with it the medieval past of
his country. He quit the priesthood; but he did remain a God-
fearing man. All his life he observed a strict ethical code and
frugal habits, loved the poor, and practiced charity. He sternly
condemned sectarianism and intolerance.

When Raspail left Provence for Paris, after the Bourbon Restoration, he believed that the future belonged to democracy, socialism, science, and free thought. Soon he was involved in the struggle against the two great forces that had fashioned the France of
the old régime: monarchy and Catholicism. His severance from these
"twin principles," as Balzac called them, was so fraught with emotion that a peaceful parting became impossible. Trained for the
clergy since childhood, Raspail had formed much stronger bonds
than he realized. The separation left a deep scar. Once the step was
taken, he never returned to his native town, not even to see his
mother, whom he said he loved deeply, and who was to live another
twenty-seven years after his departure. Perhaps the passion with
which he pursued social medicine derived in part from his relief
at having found a purpose. There may even have been a desire
for revenge in the championship of his new-found cause—revenge
because "science" was widely thought of, in the nineteenth century, as the antagonist of "religion." His tone, when he addressed
the poor, sounded paternal and didactic; but he would grow enthusiastic, rhetorical, and ominous when he invoked their rights
against the powers that delayed the advent of a social republic.

Among democratic socialists Raspail stands out not only because

[12] F.-V. Raspail, *Histoire de ma vie et de mon siècle,* autogr. ms. of 287 pp.,
covering the years 1794 to 1835, in the possession of M. Jacques Raspail, 17.

of the fierce indignation he infused into his teachings, but also because of the way he used science to serve his creed. He was convinced, like many of his contemporaries, that since biology proved all men to be similarly constituted, it also pointed to their equality; that physics showed all men subject to the same laws of nature, and therefore proved them equal. He used scientific knowledge to back political arguments. Truth must be pursued systematically, by experiment. Facts are either true or false: they can be tested. Error and bias must be eliminated. Thus he reasoned in politics, heedless of the fact that people are not quantities, neither are political ideas absolutes nor constitutions experimental results arrived at by tests and logical thought only. He was convinced that monarchists were scientifically wrong, and he preached civil liberties with the certainty that they were self-evident rights.

In a revealing sketch of Jean-Paul Marat, a scientist, physician, Jacobin and, like Raspail, the editor of a newspaper called *"L'ami du peuple,"* Raspail wrote in 1864: "Being a man of science, he treated politics as if it were a science; being a radical logician, he pursued the experiment to its ultimate consequences."[13] These remarks have an autobiographical ring, including even the calm assessment of Marat's martyrdom.

Reasoning logically, Raspail argued that the inalienable rights of man should include the right to health. He realized that good health for all depends on cooperation; all must participate in the burden and the care. Personal, civic, and administrative responsibilities must coalesce. Without the citizen's concern for his own fitness, without his alertness to pathologic symptoms in his surroundings, and without his aid in prevention and therapy, medical and public authorities would be at a loss. The medical profession, in turn, requires understanding and support from the government and from the people if it is to guard the public health. The need for each citizen to contribute financially and to obey health regulations seemed the most difficult part of Raspail's plan to bring about. His success in prodding the poor into a receptive and cooperative attitude emerges as an important contribution to the progress of social democracy in France.

[13] F.-V. Raspail, *Nouvelles études scientifiques et philologiques* (Paris, 1864), 253.

Raspail's tone was often indignant and fiery. He wanted the masses to fight for their rights. But although he called for action, he never advocated bloodshed. His strategies usually stayed within legal bounds. He was committed to evolutionary change—although one could cite many instances when his language exceeded his beliefs. This explains why the masses venerated him as a man of action while the middle class feared him as a rebel. Louis Blanc described him as "a scientist notorious in the republican party for his unsociable temper and his excessive touchiness, but admired for his great intelligence and a dedication approaching heroism." [14]

Raspail's independence made him a lonely man. His associates were temporary and he had few friends. His wife and children lived in his shadow. His political followers worshiped him, and his patients respectfully complied with his therapy. His correspondence with colleagues shows him to have been mistrustful, querulous, even litigious. He provoked an endless stream of minor lawsuits with claims of priority or patent rights for his books, medicines, and inventions. One wonders whether there were really so many dishonest pharmacists, tradespeople, and writers bent on cheating Raspail. Moreover, after the "White Terror" of 1816, and especially after his first prison term in 1831, Raspail felt watched by the police and tracked by "Loyola." Several times he thought his food had been poisoned. He was pathologically suspicious.

He could not live at peace with Carpentras, the priests, the king, the scientists, or the doctors—not even with the Second and the Third Republics. Not only would he refuse to make concessions on matters of principle, but he also concurred with the minority in matters of small importance. He seemed to be drawn to the losing side. As one watches him scorn professional appointments, degrees, and honors that might have come his way, and serve long prison terms that undermined his health and work, one wonders if he did not seek martyrdom. The question is difficult to answer. He was, in many ways, his own worst enemy.

A profound identification with the disinherited, the suffering, the poor, and the outcast, doubtless spurred him on—feelings stimulated by early childhood experiences. As an infant he had lost his father: his youth was tainted by poverty and political in-

[14] L. Blanc, *Histoire de dix ans* (Paris, 1841), IV, 216.

security; the Abbé Esseyric, his "master," steered him into a career that was unsuitable; the Church, so he believed, tried to have him murdered; the monarchy persecuted him for being a republican; the republic jailed him as an extremist. There were countless other victims of injustice in France. Raspail espoused all their causes.

His isolation did not frighten him. Rather, he gained strength from the conviction that he must rely entirely on himself. In this he drew inspiration—as did many of his contemporaries—from the heroic figure of Napoleon. It is, at first sight, astonishing to discover in this passionate democrat and socialist a lifelong reverence for the Emperor. Since Raspail hated despotism the Napoleonic Empire should have been repugnant to him. Yet it was not uncommon, in that generation of Romanticism, to find young hero-worshiping liberals whom the Emperor would have disavowed. What these young men admired in Napoleon, regardless of their own politics, was his meteoric rise, his command over others by the spell of personality, his ability to organize, his titanic energy, and his belief in his own superiority, which transformed his dreams into reality. He was self-made, greater than others: a hero. "My one claim to fame," Raspail confessed at the age of fifty-two, "is to have been noticed by Napoleon when I was young. After that, no distinction seemed worth having." [15] This nostalgic veneration of the Emperor was addressed partly to the poor Corsican boy who had achieved success. Raspail the scientist might have been such a man, but he was born twenty years too late. He struggled against the tide of history—unlike Napoleon who rose to success with it. Napoleon at twenty-five, having outgrown his Corsican background, stood ready for military action at a time when France needed soldiers. Raspail at the same age, having rejected a clerical upbringing, cast his lot with science and socialism when France had returned to Catholicism and monarchy.

Raspail's ideas, ideals, achievements, and personality fit into the pattern of the Romantic revolution, which reached its violent and creative peak in France at the time of his most original work. Indeed, the Romantics wanted to destroy those narrow, neoclassical standards of beauty and excellence, those lists of accepted authori-

[15] F.-V. Raspail, *Procès et défense de F.-V. Raspail poursuivi le 19 mai 1846 en exercice illégal de la médecine* . . . (Paris, 1846), 35–36.

ties and rules for language, images, and symbols, those circumscribed areas and methods of investigation. They strove for the
individual's creative freedom.

Unfortunately for this generation of Romanticists, Raspail's
France was a country where deviation from national cultural standards was not easily tolerated. Géricault's "Raft of the Medusa," for
example, was first shown in 1819. Its startling subject matter and
style were judged unacceptable. Shakespearean drama, introduced
in 1822, was hissed off the stage because it did not conform to the
unities of time, place, and action, the country's yardstick for dramatic perfection. Official French science also tended to uniformity.
Variety of approach was not encouraged. A few isolated French
scholars, some philologists for example, who "discovered" Germany
in the early nineteenth century, marveled at the plethora of univer-
sities beyond the Rhine, and envied the Germans their freedom
from an official philosophy. In France it even proved difficult to
defend the microscope after it had officially been declared useless
to biology, to teach contagion when the country was anti-contagionist, or to urge a balanced diet and fresh air on doctors whose favorite cure was blood-letting. Raspail did win the right to follow his
own genius, but at a considerable price.

Although he took pride in his independence from convention
and in his poverty, Raspail spent his old age as an autocratic Vic-
torian patriarch on his beautiful estate near Paris. There he presided over his children and grandchildren. His influence on them
was deep and lasting. Whatever way his rebellious, pioneering
mind had explored and plotted and planned, there his children,
grandchildren, and great-grandchildren cast their professional lot.
Camille (1827–1893), his second son, and two grandsons were to
practice medicine.[16] One of the grandsons wrote his medical thesis
on the pathogenetic role of helminths, especially in infectious diseases.[17] It was prefaced with a moving dedication to the ancestor

[16] His youngest son, Xavier (1840–1926), obtained the now obsolete degree
of "health officer" and then specialized in ornithology. He wrote *Hygiène des
enfants en bas âge fondée sur les principes du système médical de F.-V. Raspail*
(Paris, 1905).

[17] Julien Raspail, *Le rôle pathogène des helminthes en général, et en particulier dans les maladies infectieuses* (Paris, 1906).

whose influence is obvious.[18] For three generations, until the First World War, two dispensaries staffed by his descendants were free to the poor.[19]

Pharmacy was the field chosen by Raspail's third son, Emile (1831–1887), and by his great-granddaughter, Simone. Emile graduated as a chemical engineer from the famous Central School and turned to the manufacture and distribution of "Raspail medicines." Simone, trained as a pharmacist and biologist, works for the national health insurance system of the French teaching profession,[20] carrying on her ancestor's social concerns as well as his interest in pharmacy.

Even politics became respectable in the Raspail family during the patriarch's lifetime. Two sons, Benjamin (1823–1899), the eldest, and Camille, the doctor, sat in the Chamber of Deputies for thirteen and eight years respectively. Benjamin and Emile served for many years as General Councillors of the Seine Department, and Emile as Mayor of Arcueil-Cachan. In office these three sons fought for wider democratic rights, social justice, and public health.[21] In 1888, after his brother Emile had died, Benjamin wrote to a friend:

We work very hard in this family, after the example set by our venerated chief, and my brother's health was not equal to the enormous la-

[18] The other grandson's thesis dealt with problems of feeding psychotic patients: François Raspail, *Contribution à l'étude de la sitiophobie chez les aliénés* (Paris, 1886). He also collaborated with Désirée Séhé on *L'éducation physique dans la famille* (Paris, 1921), which deals with hygiene, posture, gymnastics, sports, and has a preface on "Advice to mothers" written by Juliette, François' wife. In it she stresses harmonious development, the relationship of strength to beauty, and, having appealed to the Greek ideal, quotes Rousseau, John Stuart Mill, and Raspail to support her views.

[19] Camille's dispensary, 11, rue Carnot (later rue Bara), was continued by his son François till about 1920; that of Julien, 15, rue du Temple, continued until the First World War, in association with Drs. Vrain, Deshayes, and Félizet.

[20] Centre médical, Mutuelle générale de l'éducation nationale.

[21] See, e.g., Benjamin's effort to obtain a more humane treatment for the inmates of an old-age home: B. Raspail, *Une première campagne contre l'administration de l'assistance publique* (Paris, 1875); Emile's attempt to contain the spread of air pollution: E. Raspail, *Des odeurs de Paris* (Paris, 1880); or Camille's efforts to help establish a labor ministry: *Chambre des députés. Discours prononcé par M. Camille Raspail. Séance du 17 juin 1891. Discussion sur la prise en considération d'une proposition de résolution tendant à la création d'un ministère du travail* (Paris, 1891).

Cabinet Médical Raspail

sous la direction de Julien Raspail

petit fils de F. V. Raspail

14, Rue du Temple, 14

Heures des Consultations du

Cabinet Médical Raspail

(Consultations tous les jours)

JOURS	MATIN Gratuites 8 h. à 10 h.	MATIN Particulières 10 h. à midi	APRÈS-MIDI Particulières 2 h. à 5 h.	SOIR Gratuites 8 h. à 10 h.
Lundi. . . .	Dʳ Félizet	Dʳ Félizet	Dʳ Deshayes	Dʳ Vrain
Mardi. . . .	Dʳ Félizet	Dʳ Félizet	Dʳ Vrain	Dʳ Deshayes
Mercredi .	Dʳ Vrain	Dʳ Vrain	Dʳ Deshayes	Dʳ Félizet
Jeudi	Dʳ Félizet	Dʳ Félizet	Dʳ Vrain	Dʳ Deshayes
Vendredi .	Dʳ Félizet	Dʳ Félizet	Dʳ Deshayes	Dʳ Vrain
Samedi. . .	Dʳ Deshayes	Dʳ Deshayes	Dʳ Vrain	Dʳ Félizet

Dʳ   Suppléant

Consultations gratuites pour les yeux

Samedi matin de 8 h. à 10 h.

Publicity for Dr. Julien Raspail's office   (Courtesy Archives du Département de la Seine)

bors by which he managed, in the past twelve years, to transform our whole community . . . and to endow it with numerous buildings: a school museum, school buildings, kindergartens, a lay nursery school, and a lovely town hall in Louis XIII style . . .[22]

Most remarkable, perhaps, is the fact that the "Raspail method" —that is, the use of camphorated medication—is still in vogue today. The *Manuel-annuaire* has passed its first centenary and is still available. A "Pharmacie Raspail," at 20, rue Rambuteau in Paris,

[22] Autogr. ms. letter, Série biographies, dossier Raspail, Bibliothèque historique de la Ville de Paris.

does a brisk trade in camphorated medicines, even in "Raspail aspirin." Occasionally, a prescription based on the Raspail method is still presented there; but its last known practitioner, a Dr. Léon Vrain, is believed to have died before 1939. Most impressive of all the traces left by Raspail, doctor and champion of the poor, are the visiting cards which his great-grandson periodically collects on Raspail's tomb at the Père Lachaise cemetery. They carry messages of thanks for relief from pain and for the solicitude that Raspail's written word still seems to convey.[23]

Unfortunately Raspail's posthumous reputation was gravely affected by his self-righteous republicanism and by the illegality of his medical work. For over a hundred years his contribution to science has remained virtually unknown. He had irritated the scientific and political powers in France by denouncing the routine of the academies, the negligence and greed of doctors, the inequities of the jury system, the horrors of French prisons, the gagging of the press, and the lack of social equality. His exaggerated claims rendered him vulnerable to ridicule: to preach cleanliness as if it were a religious commandment sounded extravagant; to claim the discovery of a new system of medicine seemed downright absurd. And when he revealed his panacea, camphor, learned and complacent Frenchmen dismissed him as a charlatan. They were glad to be able to laugh at this disturbingly honest man.

It was only when the young Third Republic needed heroes in the 1870s that Raspail was briefly rescued from oblivion. His statue was erected in Paris on the centenary of the Revolution of 1789, and paid for by a national subscription; boulevards and avenues throughout France were baptized with his name. He appeared in a series of "great lives" for French republican children.[24] Again, during the First World War, Raspail briefly became a national hero, this time because his scientific discoveries were found to antedate German achievements. But once more the glory was short-

[23] As recently as February 27, 1911, an American adept sent Xavier Raspail a newspaper clipping from the *United States Courier,* published in Brooklyn, New York, reporting a dispute about Raspail's method. The author of the letter underlined the efficacy of the therapeutic method advocated in the *Health Annual* of ". . . the great man whose only misdeed was to teach the worker some simple preventive measures that transform parents into doctors and the kitchen into a pharmacy." Quoted in X. Raspail, *Raspail et Pasteur: Trente ans de critiques médicales et scientifiques, 1884–1914* (Paris, 1916), 454.

[24] V. Tinayre, *Raspail, Michelet, enfants* (Paris, 1881).

lived, for it subsided with French victory on the battlefield. At present, there is some renewed interest in Raspail as a consequence of lively research activity in histochemistry.

Historians and biographers have not been struck by the unity that underlies the double purpose of Raspail's life. Rather, they generally classify him according to the aspect of his work that they deem paramount. Since he was not one of the most famous men on the nineteenth-century French scene but an important member of the supporting cast, one often finds him inconspicuously cited in long lists of names. Political historians file him away as a left-wing revolutionary—together with Louis Blanc, Blanqui, Barbès, Albert —active after the Revolution of 1830 and critical of the conservatism of the Second Republic. Social historians associate him with the Utopians, because he advocated far-reaching reforms and social medicine—not unlike Etienne Cabet, Ulysse Trélat, and Jules Guérin. For historians of science he is an early exponent of the cell theory, like Turpin or Dutrochet.

These labels are exact enough, but this partial treatment of Raspail's life and personality destroys the subject. The scientist and the democrat in him were inseparable. Therefore the biographer must do justice to a consciously scientific democrat and a militantly democratic scientist. To ignore the scientist and present only the democrat is to depict but half a man. "He found incomparable tools in natural history and in chemistry," wrote Georges Weill who understood and appreciated Raspail, "for the emancipation of the working classes, for curing the physical and moral ills of the poor, for solving problems of social economy." [25]

The literature about this prolific writer can be read in a day. It consists, first, of two long biographical essays, one by Jean Saint-Martin,[26] an acquaintance of Raspail, the other by his daughter-in-law, who is excessively loyal.[27] The best sketches can be found

[25] G. Weill, *Histoire du parti républicain en France, 1814–1870* (Paris, 1928), 41–42.

[26] J. Saint-Martin [Paulin Capmal], *F.-V. Raspail* (Paris, 1877).

[27] G. Raspail (Madame Xavier Raspail), *La vie et l'oeuvre scientifique de F.-V. Raspail* (Paris, 1926). The author uses as the unquestioned source of her information the autobiography written by the seventy-seven-year-old Raspail, and his defense before the *Cour d'assises de la Seine*, on February 12, 1874. See *infra*, pp. 261–63.

in Mirecourt's *Contemporains* and in Spuller's *Figures disparues*.[28]
Three French biographical series include: a *Raspail* in *Vies roma-
nesques: aventuriers, sorciers, rebelles, magiciens, conquérants, pi-
rates, corsaires, démoniaques* which is unscholarly and tends to
sensationalism;[29] secondly, a brief *Raspail* by Jean Bossu in the collection *Les grandes figures d'hier et d'aujourd'hui*;[30] and a third
essay, occasioned by the centenary of the 1848 Revolution, which
focuses on that upheaval, neglecting other topics of equal interest.[31]
The motive for a short sketch published in Buenos Aires in 1946
remains a mystery.[32] A few local patriots in the Vaucluse Department have devoted essays to Raspail over the years.[33] His jail sentences, his election as a deputy and candidacy for the presidency
of the Second Republic in 1848, the death of his wife and his own
death, and the unveiling of his statue created ripples of excitement.[34] Outstanding for its clarity and comprehensiveness is an
essay by Raphaël Blanchard, a professor at the Faculty of Medicine
in Paris at the turn of the century and a member of the Academy
of Medicine.[35] He offers valuable guidance through Raspail's scientific and medical work, which was also discussed at times by

[28] E. de Mirecourt, "Raspail" in *Les contemporains* (Paris, 1856). E. Spuller,
Figures disparues. Portraits contemporains, politique set littéraires (Paris ,1891),
3 vols., II, 55–65.

[29] J. Wogue, *Raspail* (Paris, 1939).

[30] J. Bossu, *Raspail: sa vie ardente et chevaleresque* (Paris, n.d. [post 1934]).

[31] G. Duveau, *Raspail* (Paris, 1948). The centenary was also the occasion for
including "F.-V. Raspail" in H. Poulaille, *Maintenant* (Paris, 1948), 33–66.

[32] A. J. Bengolea, *Raspail: Historia de una conciencia* (Buenos Aires, 1946).

[33] M. C. Gaubert, "Un éminent Carpentrassien: F.-V. Raspail," *Rencontres,
Revue mensuelle des arts, lettres, spectacles, et tendances artistiques de la région
carpentrassienne*, No. 12 (Dec., 1959), 1ère année, 32–36. A. Martin, "Raspail,"
Grandes figures vauclusiennes (Avignon, 1936), 41–75. F. Martin-Ginovier,
"Raspail et Napoléon Ier," *Revue mondiale*, CXLVI (Jan.–Feb. 1922), 63–74.

[34] E. Gouget, *Raspail: Poésie dite à l'inauguration de sa statue* (Paris, 1889).
C. Marchal, *Biographie de F.-V. Raspail, représentant du peuple* (Paris, 1848).
L. Rogier, *Biographie de Raspail* (n.p. [Paris], n.d. [1849]). J. Troubat, *Un
lutteur des temps héroïques: F.-V. Raspail* (Paris, 1907). M. Vachon, "F.-V.
Raspail" in *Galerie contemporaine littéraire, artistique*, 3ème année (Paris,
1878). A. Vermorel, *Biographies contemporaines: M. F.-V. Raspail* (Paris, n.d.
[1869]). S. Wassermann, "Le Club de Raspail en 1848," *La révolution de 1848*,
V (1908–1909), 589–605; 655–74; 748–62.

[35] R. Blanchard, "Notice biographique: F.-V. Raspail," *Archives de parasitologie*, VIII (1903–1904), 5–87.

others.[36] Lastly, friends of the family have occasionally contributed articles.[37] One should especially mention Raspail's youngest son Xavier, who continued to publish the *Health Annual* after his father's death. In his annual Introduction he always reviewed contemporary medical activities in the context of his father's work.[38] No information on Raspail is available in English.[39]

The need for a full-length portrait of François-Vincent Raspail hardly needs argument. What arrests the biographer's attention is the peculiarly modern conflict that his life exemplifies. This scientist was shunted by political pressures from research into social action. Once he turned into a "doer," reality looked different to him, even through the microscope. At first, he treated each grass embryo as an individual entity that deserved days of study. Later he tended to generalize, neglecting microscopic research to focus on medicine: from physiology to pathology to therapy. He declared that conta-

[36] C.-A. Breton, *F.-V. Raspail: Sa méthode et ses oeuvres, ses détracteurs et ses partisans* (Marseille, 1868). H. Castel, *Les bienfaits de la méthode Raspail à Roubaix* (Roubaix, 1875). Gilbert [Pasteur] et Miliau [Docteur], "Raspail médecin," *Paris médical,* LX (1926), 56–61: J. Guiart, "La vérité sur Raspail," *Le Fureteur,* 3ème année, No. 5 (July 1944), 99–103. E. Marquet, *De F.-V. Raspail considéré comme réformateur en médecine et de la méthode nouvelle* (Paris, n.d. [1851]). J. Schoenfeld, *Raspail et la médecine* (Paris, 1933). J. Thoulet, "La microchimie et la cristallographie dans les trauvaux de F.-V. Raspail," *Revue scientifique,* No. XVII (April 1877), 522–28. D. B. Weiner, "F.-V. Raspail, fondateur de l'histochimie; aperçu historique de sa réputation en France," *Annales d'histochimie,* VI, No. 1 (1961), 1–11.

[37] T. Grimm, *Un grand méconnu: F.-V. Raspail* (Paris, 1910).

[38] X. Raspail, *Raspail et Pasteur: Trente ans de critiques médicales et scientifiques, 1884–1914* (Paris, 1916). This book is marred by Xavier's annoyed protests against the excessive acclaim and acceptance of Pasteur's work since microbes were, after all, so he believed, none other than Raspail's "infinitely small" parasites. Xavier insisted that Raspail's aim to "render healthy and pure" should triumph over Pasteur's which was to "render weak and putrid." For was not Pasteur poisoning man's blood, "weakening the race" (p. XI) and committing a "crime of lese humanity" by transforming man into "a sewer full of multi-colored vaccines?" (XV–XVI).

Both Raspail's grandson, Dr. François, and his great-granddaughter Simone, spoke in public about their ancestor. See F. Raspail, *Biographie de F.-V. Raspail par son petit-fils le Docteur François Raspail* (Carpentras, 1908); S. Raspail, "Un pionnier de la science: Raspail," *Cahiers laïques,* LXV–LXVI (Sept.–Dec. 1961), 168–88; and *Un savant et un républicain au XIXème siècle: François-Vincent Raspail* (n.p., n.d. [1966]), 78 pp.

[39] Except for D. B. Weiner, "F.-V. Raspail: Physician to the Poor," *French Historical Studies,* I, No. 2 (1959), 149–71.

gion was the cause of many illnesses, and pressed for preventive measures. Social problems demanded that he provide scientific generalizations and mass therapy. Exact science lost another adept.

But French socialism thereby gained a powerful champion, and the masses a beloved teacher. This was Raspail's special role in nineteenth-century French history: that he entered the political arena armed with knowledge as a scientist and medical practitioner; and, as a deputy, he pursued the people's right to health. The abolition of penal colonies, forced labor, and imprisonment were his goal; also the modernization of army barracks, schools, and apartment houses; the state's active participation in preventive medicine and public health.

He was laughed out of court by the deputies, prosecuted by the physicians, ignored by the scientists. To a large extent, he called down this punishment on himself, for he was combative, contentious, and sometimes wrong. But his voice was a powerful factor for democracy in France—for a democracy that assumes an active role in medical care, not out of charity but in response to the citizenry's justified demand.

Watch this young man, he will go far.
Napoleon Bonaparte

II

THE YOUTH FROM

VAUCLUSE

POLITICAL PASSIONS WERE AFLAME in France at the time of Raspail's birth in January 1794. Robespierre was then attempting to impose a radical, rational republic. The Catholic religion was to be excised from French hearts. Inequalities were to be legislated away.

The citizens of the Vaucluse Department were divided over politics and religion. Avignon, the ancient, beautiful capital of the French Papal States, had taken the lead, in 1791, in petitioning the National Assembly in Paris for annexation. Avignon was republican. Not so its modest but determined rival Carpentras, Raspail's birthplace. The residents of Carpentras were deeply loyal to their sovereign of half a millennium, the pope. They were, at best, apathetic and nostalgic citizens of the First Republic. Early in his life, François-Vincent Raspail was exposed to bonapartist feelings as well. Two of his stepbrothers became officers under Napoleon. The royalist townsmen of Carpentras waited and watched: during

21

the White Terror of 1815–1816 they would harry Raspail out of town.

Political passions surging around this youth were compounded by rival religious tenets. He was destined for the Church by his pious Roman Catholic mother, who chose the Abbé François-Siffrein Esseyric (1745–1822) as his main teacher. Either she was unaware of this priest's deep Jansenist convictions, or she was too unsophisticated to realize the conflicts he might arouse in the boy. From Esseyric Raspail learned at an early age that the pope had condemned his beloved teacher's religious sect and that the Jesuits were responsible for this act. Raspail's faith in papal wisdom was thus effectively shaken at a tender age. Only after painful and prolonged self-examination would he make his confessional and professional commitment. His choice was complicated by the power struggle in which he was a pawn: the fight waged in Avignon under the Empire between the constitutional, bonapartist Bishop Périer and M. Sollier, the independent, ultramontanist Superior of the Seminary St. Charles where Raspail was then a student. When, after Waterloo, Raspail reached Paris and chose his life's path, there was but one political passion left in him: hatred of all authority, political and religious, coupled with a deep desire for personal freedom and political equality.

Raspail's youth and adolescence can thus serve to illustrate a highly complex and dramatic situation in modern French history: the struggle to integrate the centuries-old papal enclave of Avignon into the French state; the transfer of the people's loyalty from a religious head of state to a lay government; the education of a child for the priesthood under a godless republic and an anti-papal empire.

During his childhood Raspail shared his townsmen's fond and grateful awareness of papal power and munificence. The connection of the pope with Carpentras had been established in the fourteenth century when the pope was a "captive" in neighboring Avignon for seventy years. The presence of the papal court at Avignon —and often at Carpentras—brought unwonted political importance to the region, and attracted to it lawyers, merchants, diplomats, and scholars. Among them was the family of Francesco Petrarca (1304–1374) who studied the humanities at Carpentras between 1315 and 1319 and returned there often in later years.

Increased business and proximity to world affairs roused Carpentras from its medieval slumber. "The gold of Christendom flowed into Avignon; well-being and luxury extended to its people."[1]

Carpentras treasured its Roman victory arch, its cathedral of Saint-Siffrein—part Romanesque, part Gothic—its Jewish temple, today the oldest in France. Three major monasteries and two convents, the Abbeys of Saint Bernard and Sainte Madeleine, bore witness to the town's active religious life. Under the old régime, several secular fraternities had undertaken charitable and nursing work or met to celebrate religious festivals. Thus, one hundred of Carpentras' citizens, grouped in a "Legion of Our Lady of Good Health," would march to the cathedral each July 10, wearing uniforms and carrying arms. The Brotherhood of Saint Mark included workers and farmers; the Brotherhood of Crossbowmen and three Brotherhoods of Penitents—Grey, White, and Black, dating back to the Reformation—reminded the citizens of the ardor with which their forefathers had defended the Catholic faith.[2]

During the Renaissance the great humanist scholar Jacopo Sadoleto (1477–1547), the friend of Erasmus, was made Bishop of Carpentras by Pope Leo X. Though he spent much time in Rome, especially when the Council of Trent was being prepared, he always returned to Carpentras. His major scholarly works, a treatise on education and a long letter to John Calvin, were composed there. A college, opened in Carpentras by the Dominicans in 1594, was taken over by the Jesuits in 1606 and soon became known for its excellence. It was closed in 1764 when the Jesuits were expelled from France. The munificent Inguimbert, who became Bishop of Carpentras in the eighteenth century, financed and supervised the building of a large town hall, a beautiful hospital and home for the aged, the Hôtel-Dieu, and a richly endowed library, the Bibliothèque Inguimbertine, which today remains astonishing for its wealth of manuscripts.

The market, still held on Fridays, had attracted the neighboring farmers since the Middle Ages. They would herd their cattle

---

[1] J. Courtet, *Dictionnaire géographique, géologique, historique, archéologique et biographique des communes du Département de Vaucluse* (Avignon, 1876), 34.

[2] J. Liabastres, *Histoire de Carpentras* (Carpentras, 1891), 55–75, *passim*.

through the winding streets of the old town and would carry hides, wool, wax, and honey. Depending on the season they would sell grain, wine, almonds, artichokes, truffles, and saffron. In later years they would bring cocoons of silk and roots of the madder plant, which was introduced into Provence in the eighteenth century and was a source of rich harvests. The completion of a monumental aqueduct in 1734 made the region of Carpentras yet more fertile. Two annual fairs had been held since the thirteenth century— under religious auspices, of course. Catholicism and devotion to the papal sovereign were thus woven deeply into the history of the town.

When Raspail was born and Robespierre ruled France, the political behavior of Carpentras gave the Jacobins every reason for distrust. The city government, elected in May 1790, was sympathetic to a constitutional monarchy. But the citizens of Carpentras found a unique implementation for such a régime: they did adopt a constitution, just like their French neighbors, but chose the pope as their sovereign. They founded a national guard, abolished feudalism, voted taxes. . . . But they could not ignore forever the action of nearby Avignon which was even then dealing with the Constituent Assembly in Paris in the name of the whole Comtat Venaissin. Feeling ran high between Avignon and Carpentras, and to this day rivalry and even hostility mark their relations. In 1791 several pitched battles were fought. But Carpentras lacked support; Pope Pius VI rejected the constitutional régime especially built for him. It would be half a century before a pope would grant a constitution. France annexed the whole Comtat Venaissin on September 14, 1791, dividing it into fragments that were incorporated into neighboring departments. Carpentras became, and has remained, a *"chef lieu d'arondissement,"* a simple county seat.

Five days after his birth on January 25, 1794, François-Vincent Raspail was secretly baptized by a non-juring priest. Catholic baptism could evidently be procured in Carpentras without trouble, even at the height of Jacobin rule. Fate struck this infant when he could barely talk: his father Joseph, who owned a restaurant in Carpentras and had invested his savings in mortgages, was ruined by the forcible conversion of his holdings into *assignats,* the revolutionary paper money. He died in 1795 "of sorrow, because he was financially ruined," writes his grandson.[3] Raspail's memoirs imply that his father's death may have been connected with the departure from their household of an aristocratic young woman, the Comtesse de Vento, whom they had sheltered for four years after the elder Raspail had rescued her from the revolutionary police.

In 1796 [sic] my father's mood suddenly turned somber though his health remained excellent and although France seemed to return to the noble ideas of 1789. The countess had recovered her property after her husband's name had been stricken from the official list of émigrés. [My father] appeared sad, depressed, answering only in monosyllables; even my mother asked in vain for the reason of his melancholy; he would get up, as if to hide his tears, take his hat and go for a walk. Within two weeks he was dead, without having been sick or in pain."[4]

The widow was left without resources, responsible for six children.[5] Her three stepsons, whom Joseph Raspail had fathered in his first marriage, were over twenty years old. They were no burden to her—nor do they seem to have been of any assistance.[6] The rest of the family may have tried to help; the Raspails were a prolific clan and had lived in the Papal States for three hundred years. The community also might have assisted Madame Raspail; a few

[3] Dr. F. Raspail, *Biographie de F.-V. Raspail par son petit-fils, le Dr. François Raspail* (Carpentras, 1908), 3. "Sorrow," needless to say, is not necessarily fatal.

[4] F.-V. Raspail, *Histoire de ma vie et de mon siècle*, 21–22. According to his great-great-grandson Jacques, Joseph Raspail, after his bills were paid, left 703 francs and 15 centimes.

[5] She had actually borne eight children, but two had died in infancy.

[6] After Waterloo, both Victor and Saint-Ange Raspail returned to Carpentras, to the delight of young François-Vincent whose bonapartism they nurtured with the stories of their exploits. Captain Victor Raspail, full of "the candor of courage and heroism," had helped defend Corfu and Novara, and had received the Legion of Honor from Napoleon in person. He had twenty-five serious wounds, was a cataplectic, and died by suicide. F.-V. Raspail, *Histoire de ma vie . . . ,* 165–77, *passim.*

"St.-Ange Raspail, a lieutenant-colonel, was a very handsome man until his old age; this had been detrimental to his advancement, for all the wives and mistresses of his chiefs fell in love with him; he used the name of 'St.-Ange,' thus covering the plebeïan 'Raspail' with his given name which had the sound of nobility." *Ibid.*, 164.

A third brother, Louis Marcellin (1762–1831), an antique dealer, tried to dispossess his stepmother at his father's death; his machinations were eventually foiled.

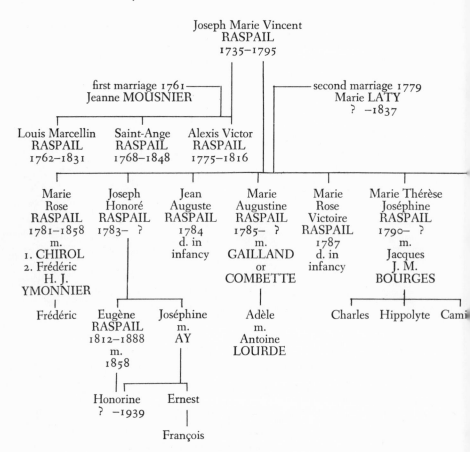

Joseph Marie Vincent
RASPAIL
1735–1795

first marriage 1761
Jeanne MOUSNIER

second marriage 1779
Marie LATY
? –1837

Louis Marcellin
RASPAIL
1762–1831

Saint-Ange
RASPAIL
1768–1848

Alexis Victor
RASPAIL
1775–1816

Marie
Rose
RASPAIL
1781–1858
m.
1. CHIROL
2. Frédéric
H. J.
YMONNIER

Joseph
Honoré
RASPAIL
1783– ?

Jean
Auguste
RASPAIL
1784
d. in
infancy

Marie
Augustine
RASPAIL
1785– ?
m.
GAILLAND
or
COMBETTE

Marie
Rose
Victoire
RASPAIL
1787
d. in
infancy

Marie Thérèse
Joséphine
RASPAIL
1790– ?
m.
Jacques
J. M.
BOURGES

Frédéric

Eugène
RASPAIL
1812–1888
m.
1858

Joséphine
m.
AY

Adèle
m.
Antoine
LOURDE

Charles   Hippolyte   Cami

Honorine
? –1939

Ernest

François

GENEALOGICAL TREE OF THE RASPAIL FAMILY

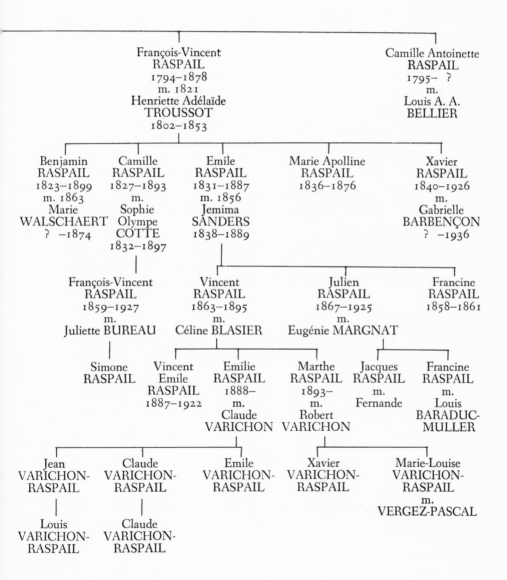

years later they were to pay half of Raspail's scholarship at the seminary. The young widow continued for a while to run the small restaurant. "François-Vincent's childhood was spent in great poverty," writes his grandson, who knew him well. "He was a courageous and devoted son and made commendable efforts to help his mother as far as he was able." [7] As a very old man, Raspail himself recalled those "very cruel winters . . . [when] we would gather wood in the forest to warm our poor little bodies in the evening before going to bed." [8] His mother soon noticed how strikingly alert her youngest son was, how observant, inquisitive, and quick to learn. A hard-pressed pious widow's resolve was predictable under the circumstances: she destined her son for a career in the Catholic Church.

Madame Raspail no doubt planned to send François-Vincent to school in the fall of 1799 when he was five-and-a-half years old. But primary schools were scarce at the time: until the French Revolution, most of them had been owned and staffed by clerics. But the religious orders were disbanded in 1792, and soon thereafter Church property was confiscated. Lay teachers had not yet been trained. In fact, not only the educational but the whole political scene was chaotic. Joseph Fouché, the Minister of Police, wrote about conditions in the Bouches-du-Rhône Department in a report of 1799:

Highway robbery is on the rise . . . ; each day there are more murders, thefts, and stagecoach plunders. The police commissioner attributes all these disorders to royalism. . . . [The neighboring Vaucluse Department] presents similar symptoms . . . Despite the vigilance of the authorities the brigands continue their criminal activities and easily elude their pursuers by running deep into the woods or into a neighboring department.[9]

The government of the Directory had been playing Right against Left for the previous four years, causing continued political stale-

---

[7] F. Raspail, *Biographie de F.-V. Raspail* . . . , 4.
[8] F.-V. Raspail, *Histoire de ma vie* . . . , 29.
[9] A. Aulard, *L'état de la France en l'An VIII et en l'An IX* (Paris, 1897), 27–29.

mate where intrigue flourished. Soon young General Bonaparte would return from his expedition to Egypt and, within a matter of months, create order as he saw fit out of the shambles of three revolutionary governments. In education the revolutionary régimes had destroyed much more than they had constructed, and primary schooling, Raspail's immediate need, was the subject of much talk but little action.[10] French primary education could not be reformed by itself, for it was too closely interwoven with religion and politics. Only after 1802, when Napoleon Bonaparte solved the conflict between France and the pope, could the role of the clergy in education be determined. Raspail's early childhood thus coincided with an educational interregnum. His mother would have to choose between an illegal or a makeshift school and an illiterate child.

The sweeping measures of the Revolution had indeed left French education in disarray. When the National Assembly, aiming at the abolition of all privilege, dissolved all medieval corporations, the religious orders became favorite targets because they were often wealthy and were resented for imposing Catholic values and law. Thus at the beginning of the first year of the "new era" (September 22, 1792), France had no primary schools.

Nothing was done for fifteen months. This is not surprising, for the republican government then faced the gravest national emergency France had experienced in two hundred years. The country was invaded by allied foreign armies; most French officers—being nobles—had emigrated; the king was known to be a traitor to the new régime and was being held a prisoner; subversion and danger lurked everywhere.

The need for public education was evident, but its fulfilment impossible. The government passed the necessary laws just before Raspail's birth. On December 20, 1793 (29 Frimaire, Year II), the Convention legislated that each commune create a compulsory, free, lay, primary school. With idealistic confidence it provided that teachers were to be chosen by the municipalities and paid partly by the state. The Committee of Public Safety even proposed to furnish the textbooks.

[10] For the best general treatment of this question, see A. Duruy, *L'instruction publique et la révolution* (Paris, 1882); see also R. J. Vignery, *The French Revolution and the Schools* (Madison, 1965), which has a good bibliography.

After the fall of Robespierre, however, the legislators were less anxious to educate all Frenchmen and thus promote equality. Georges Lefèbvre, in his authoritative *Révolution française,* comments that "many [legislators] . . . thought it unwise to help the growth of an ambitious and parasitic minority of literate poor." [11] The government then refrained from any constructive action, with the result that the report on public education in Vaucluse, sent to Bonaparte late in 1799, when Raspail was ready for school, reads: "Not one tenth of the population knows how to read. The former priests and vicars are teaching the children their letters. The former nuns teach in the girls' schools, so that the old state of things has returned. . . ." [12]

[11] G. Lefèbvre, *La Révolution française* (Paris, 1951), 444.

[12] F. Rocquain, *L'état de la France au 18 brumaire d'après les rapports des conseillers d'état chargés d'une enquête sur la situation de la république* (Paris, 1874), 28.

The reversal to "the old state of things" in the educational field began, interestingly enough, in the nursing profession. Since all nurses were either nuns or lay sisters, the dissolution orders of 1792 had struck them too. By the fall of that year patients, doctors, and hospital administrators were in acute distress, especially since France was at war and casualties were high. Where to find lay nurses? The local authorities gradually had to yield and hire former nuns, many of whom were in hiding or had emigrated.

Once the nuns were re-admitted as nurses, they might also serve as teachers. Bonaparte, as First Consul, merely legalized the existing situation when he decreed that "the citoyenne Deleau, formerly Mother Superior of the Sisters of Charity, is authorized to train student nurses" (Decree of 22 December 1800 [1 Nivôse, Year IX]); and a few weeks later authorized the Ladies of Saint Thomas de Villeneuve to undertake "the care of patients and the teaching of children" (Decree of 4 February 1801 [13 Pluviôse, Year IX]).

The resumption of the nursing, teaching, and charitable work of these monastic orders for women also furthered Napoleon's personal aims as the establishment of the Empire approached. Charitable efforts had traditionally been undertaken by great ladies. It pleased Napoleon eventually to put all these endeavors under the patronage of his own mother, Letitia. Thus in December 1807, when thirty-four orders of religious nurses were represented at a general meeting held in Paris, Madame Mère presided and the Emperor contributed 182,000 francs to their expenses from the budget earmarked for religion. The bonapartist dynasty had taken another small step toward establishing its own legitimacy. See L. Deries, *Les congrégations religieuses au temps de Napoléon* (Paris, 1929), and J. Boussoulade, *Moniales et hospitalières dans la tourmente révolutionnaire* (Paris, 1962).

The re-establishment of monastic orders for men, with their strong international and legitimist connections and their role as teachers and confessors, held more danger for Napoleon than the women's orders. Nevertheless he had to

The "old state of things" was certainly returning, and the First Consul was not long in recognizing the need for a general settlement with the Catholic Church. As soon as the Concordat was under negotiation, its implications for primary education in France became apparent. Defending the project before the Legislative Body on April 8, 1802, Portalis, Councillor of State for Public Worship, said:

. . . primary instruction must be restored. Education is a human need and especially a social need. . . . Religious institutions are the channels through which ideas of order, duty, humanity and justice flow into all social classes. Learned men will always be few; but with the help of religion one can be wise without much formal education.[13]

Two weeks later, Fourcroy, Councillor of State for Education, presented to the same body the government's primary school bill.

The Government feels that a reorganization of primary education is urgently needed. It is at present almost nil. A great part of the young generation is so ignorant that communication with its elders, and soon with its own children, becomes impossible. . . . Primary education must be entrusted to the local governments.[14]

This last statement meant that the national government would make no effort at all, nor contribute in any way to the organization or financing of primary teaching. Answering the few objections that were voiced, Fourcroy said:

Let each commune make its own arrangements with a teacher. Let them choose a man of learning and good character. . . . Be confident

---

yield, once again, to the strong forces of the past and authorize the return of the Brothers of the Christian Schools. These Brothers had been founded in 1684 by Jean Baptiste de La Salle (1651–1719) and consisted of laymen who took a vow of obedience for one year at a time only, who depended on charity for their support and dedicated themselves entirely to the education of poor boys. These Brothers had won the affection, gratitude, and trust of the French population, much like the Sisters of Charity who, since their founding of 1633 by Saint Vincent de Paul, had educated many a poor French girl.

For details on the re-establishment of primary education under the Consulate, see A. Chevalier, *Les Frères des écoles chrétiennes et l'enseignement primaire après la révolution* (1797–1830) (Paris, 1887). For matters of education pertaining to the Concordat, see also J. E. M. Portalis, *Discours, rapports, et travaux inédits sur le Concordat de 1801* (Paris, 1845).

[13] A. Chevalier, *Les Frères des écoles chrétiennes* . . . , 52.

[14] *Ibid.*, 55.

that, as in former times, a part of these establishments will be financed by charitable contributions. You know how much has already been achieved in eighteen months of domestic peace and firmly re-established principles.[15]

The hope that the Church and the faithful would defray a large part of the cost of primary education proved so strong that the bill was adopted. The Law of May 1, 1802 (11 Floréal, Year X), opened the door for re-hiring the Brothers of the Christian Schools as teachers of young boys throughout the land. The Brothers were well-known and beloved by the people; they were available and eager to resume their work; they were inexpensive and good teachers. They would teach morality and religion, together with the three R's . . . just as under the old régime.[16]

The clock was thus gradually turned back in the ten years during which Raspail received his basic schooling. As far as can be ascertained he first studied in the grade school of M. Bernard Dutrain. Raspail remembered these painful years in a letter ad-

[15] *Ibid.*, 56.

[16] In many municipal schools throughout France, and in uncounted private schools of course, the Brothers of the Christian Schools now resumed their duties. In December of 1803 the First Consul approved the establishment of a "society for the free education of the young" (3 December 1803; 11 Frimaire, Year XII), thus officially re-establishing the Brothers. Napoleon was to remain much more wary of other religious orders for men, continuing to fear their politically subversive connections with Rome. The Brothers of the Christian Schools remained an exception; they contributed powerfully to teaching the lower class their duties and their place in Napoleon's Empire. The General Inspectors' report in April 1809 praised them:

"There is unanimity as to their conduct and the success of their teaching. The children of the people who attend their schools acquire excellent religious principles and impress by their good manners, obedience and mastery of the three R's. . . . Supervision [of the schools] is entrusted to the religious and municipal authorities. The priest holds the children to a punctual fulfillment of their religious obligations and to the study of the imperial catechism. The municipal authority consists of the mayor and a board whose members are the most distinguished and the wealthiest men in town. They supervise all the administrative details. Two inspectors visit the schools often, see to it that the children are properly dressed, question them about their work, praise those who are good and encourage them with little presents. At the end of each year, the good students of every school are rewarded. They take part in a competitive examination; the winner and the runner-up get their apprenticeships paid for. The children are thus encouraged to work hard and be good." Cited in A. Aulard, *Napoléon Ier et le monopole universitaire* (Paris, 1911), 243–44.

dressed in 1856 to the painter Denis Bonnet who had been a schoolmate:

I remember well all you say . . . about my first school and about my first efforts at teaching. Half of the building was used for the storage of salt.[17] Behind the entrance door, to the right, was the cursed staircase that led to the bedroom. There, our jesuitical master condemned us, in turn, to rock his offspring to sleep. This horrid black room ranks first on the long list of my prisons. The white shirts hanging from clotheshooks seemed like so many ghosts, and only by shutting my eyes could I banish them.

As for the little grey dwarf whom you mention, he had wit, but his heart was full of venom. I have forgotten his poetry, but I well remember his stinginess. He shivered in front of his fireplace, as he pushed away the glowing coals which his spouse kept pushing closer, once, twice, until Mademoiselle Courtois, his hefty wife, raised her fist and insulted him. Then the professor would keep very quiet, like a schoolboy threatened with extra work. Of all the flowery rhetoric which her "little grey man" was teaching, the worthy lady alone knew the argument *ad hominem,* and she used it with as much energy as purpose. . . .[18]

Eventually Raspail escaped from M. Dutrain's establishment to the small private school of a Madame Anselme, from whom he learned his letters, and then to a M. de Raoulx, who had only three students. Raspail yearned for a good education. At long last, he wrote,

my mother yielded to my entreaties and, despite her anti-revolutionary convictions, she consented to place me with the wise and noble Abbé Esseyric who taught his young students many subjects, with informal, almost playful methods. . . . During the Revolution, he had given up all paid religious employment and devoted himself to the education of the poor children of his native town. The very modest income from this teaching [four francs a month from each student] was enough for him to live on.[19]

---

[17] A "grenier à sel," such as the one here referred to, is not easy to define for the 1790s. Under the old régime, it could have been used as a storage depot for salt under the official state monopoly, a collection office for the salt tax, and a jurisdictional unit for the trial of accused offenders against the tax. See F. L. Ford, *Robe and Sword* (New York, 1965), 35.

[18] Autogr. ms. letter, No. 2120, Folios 32–33, Bibliothèque Inguimbertine, Carpentras, Vaucluse.

[19] F.-V. Raspail, *Histoire de ma vie . . .* , 40. (In 1814 Esseyric's school was one of seventeen in Carpentras and had forty students.)

The Abbé François-Siffrein Esseyric was without doubt the key figure in the adolescent Raspail's religious, moral, and intellectual life. Poor, proud, and very learned, the abbé taught Raspail Greek, Latin, and apparently also some Syriac.[20]

In a very short time I learned to read French, Latin, Greek, and even Hebrew. At the age of twelve I knew Virgil and almost all of Horace by heart.

Eventually I adopted the frugal and studious habits of this holy man; the Abbé Esseyric became my oracle; I knew him by heart like my Horace; our life was one long conversation, our walks one long lesson. . . .

Seeing my indefatigable passion for learning . . . he suggested to my mother . . . that I come to live in his little house near our town; he installed me in his library. . . .[21]

Thus the child lived among books, under the eye of a revered teacher.

Even more important for Raspail's future than Esseyric's passion for scholarship was his interest in the sciences. And the deepest impression Esseyric left on Raspail was his devotion to Jansenism. This sect, with which the "classical" writers Pascal and Racine were associated, had suffered proudly when the bigoted, aged Louis XIV persecuted and exiled them. They were considered the champions of Gallicanism against the Jesuits, whose international connections and supra-national allegiance had long made them suspect. Raspail espoused Esseyric's hatred of "Loyola"; he found lifelong inspiration in his teacher's commitment to a martyred, exiled, scholarly, puritanical French minority. In his memoirs Raspail even called himself a "Jansenist." [22] He adopted strict and frugal habits.

[20] The assertion that he knew Syriac seems to stem from Xavier Raspail's "Notice sur F.-V. Raspail," in *Catalogue de livres anciens ayant fait partie de la bibliothèque de F.-V. Raspail* (Paris, 1912), VIII. I have seen no evidence to substantiate this claim. Raspail's biographers faithfully repeat it; Jules Wogue, the most fanciful among them, writes: "At the age of twelve, François-Vincent speaks Latin, Greek, and Syriac. . . . Pico de la Mirandola has come back to life." J. Wogue, *Raspail*, 7.

[21] F.-V. Raspail, *Histoire de ma vie* . . . , 43–44. From 1808 to 1810 Raspail also studied and helped teach at the school of his second cousin, the Abbé Fortunet. He loathed every moment of his association with this man. *Ibid.,* 51 ff., *passim.*

[22] *Ibid.,* 86.

Throughout his life he would rise at six o'clock to work until eleven, joining his family for a first meal at noon. There is no record of his ever attending the theatre, and if he had a sense of humor it was well under control.

In politics Esseyric was a "constitutional" or "juring" priest, who had sworn allegiance to the Civil Constitution of the Clergy which the pope condemned in 1791. Raspail admired his teacher's independence of mind, and dedicated to him his first major scientific book, the *Nouveau système de chimie organique* of 1833, with words that read in part:

> To the memory of an upright man,
> my poor master the
> Abbé Esseyric.

To you who combined truly Christian qualities with scientific culture. To you who . . . never wished to cease teaching the poor in my village! To you, immensely erudite philologist . . . I offer the homage of this book. . . .

The end of Esseyric's life was tragic—as could be expected in legitimist Provence:

When Jesuitism returned triumphant with the Restoration, it brought persecution against the Abbé Esseyric. . . . Without regard for the advanced age of this venerable priest [who was then seventy-five years old] nor for his infirmities, these vagabond priests judged him unworthy of receiving the sacraments. . . . But the enlightened members of the clergy in Carpentras protested against this systematic harassment of a man whose whole life had been an admirable example of kindness, of enlightened belief, of truly Christian charity. . . . They collected money to provide their colleague with some financial resources during the last days of his long life.[23]

Esseyric thus paid dearly for his political sympathies. In spite of his pro-revolutionary orientation, the primary education he dispensed was modern only in its interest for science; otherwise it followed the time-honored classical tradition.

French secondary education in the modern sense was the creation of the Jesuits. Most educated Frenchmen of the seventeenth

[23] *Ibid.,* 40–41.

and eighteenth centuries had studied with them, or with the short-lived Jansenists, or with the Oratorians founded in 1611 by Father Bérulle. But the Jesuits were expelled and their colleges confiscated. Their place could not be filled. Secondary education was a major need confronting the revolutionary assemblies after 1792.

A remarkable creative effort was made by the Convention in 1795. The secondary "central schools" were founded, with a modern curriculum that emphasized French literature, science, geography, and history. Provisions were also made in each school for a library, a physics and chemistry laboratory, a natural history collection, and a botanical garden.[24] Unfortunately the salaries were to be paid from local sources. One of the four central schools in Vaucluse was located in Carpentras. It lasted from 1796 until 1803. The official report on Vaucluse for 1799 stated: "The four central schools . . . have, among them, less than two hundred students. . . . The chairs of grammar, history, literature, and legislation stand empty. Mathematics, chemistry, Latin, and drawing are faring a little better since the sciences lead to remunerative careers." [25] Aulard, in his excellent monograph on the subject, blames the slow growth of the central schools on the absence of religious instruction, the lack of facilities for room and board, and the neglect of Latin: "The opponents [of the central schools] included the advocates of routine and the Catholics, the Catholic bourgeoisie—they were the cause of eventual failure." [26]

The deliberations of the town council of Carpentras on this subject are revealing. Little was done until Bonaparte, as First Consul, took matters in hand. By a law of May 1, 1802 (11 Floréal, Year X), he abolished the central schools, transforming many into "lycées" of which he created about forty (but not in a town as small as Carpentras, which had only 9,000 inhabitants), and, beyond this, left the matter of secondary education—as well as primary education—entirely in the hands of the municipalities. Anyone could now open a secondary school provided the government ap-

<hr>

[24] On the teaching of science in the central schools, see L. P. Williams, "Science, Education and the French Revolution," *Isis*, XLIV (1953), 311–30.

[25] F. Rocquain, *L'état de la France* . . . , 28–29.

[26] A. Aulard, *Napoléon Ier et le monopole universitaire*, 32.

proved of him. Priesthood or monastic vows no longer precluded a
teaching career.

In May 1803 the town council of Carpentras finally grappled
with its educational problem:

It is important [the minutes read], that this discussion be not again deferred. Public education has been almost nil for many years. Parents as
well as the government would be keenly disappointed should there
again be a delay in setting up an institution which is urgently needed
to end the prevailing educational chaos.[27]

The city fathers then asked that the former Jesuit college be returned to them. They drew up a list of suitable candidates for
principal and teachers—a list that allows a revealing glimpse of
their state of mind: *all* the candidates were priests, several former
teachers or principals. No one questioned a secondary school faculty made up entirely of clerics. When left to their own devices,
the city fathers of Raspail's town wished to return to the *status quo*
of prerevolutionary days.

As for Raspail, he need not have gone to a Church-sponsored institution for his secondary schooling. He might have tried for a
scholarship to a lycée. It is tempting to speculate about the influence that a lay education with a strong emphasis on science might
have had on him.[28] He could have entered one of the "great"
schools or the graduate department at a university and emerged as
a well-trained scientist. Of course the draft would have made him
a soldier, and in the years 1813–1815 many Frenchmen his age
lost their lives. Perhaps it is simply too much to ask that a youngster living in the early nineteenth century be able to escape from
the state of mind adhered to by his ultraconservative surroundings,
including his mother and his teacher, both of whom foresaw a brilliant career in the Church. Also, such speculations overlook the
Abbé Esseyric's personal connection with Bishop Périer of Avignon, a major factor in directing Raspail to the Seminary of Saint
Charles. Yet there is no question that French secondary education

---

[27] *Séances du conseil municipal de la ville de Carpentras,* 3 Prairial, An XI.
Ms. in Bibliothèque Inguimbertine, Carpentras, Vaucluse.

[28] On the teaching of science under Napoleon, see L. P. Williams, "Science,
Education and Napoleon I," *Isis,* XLVII (1956), 369–82.

had by 1810 been sufficiently reconstructed to make lay schooling a possible alternative for a boy of sixteen.

On October 28, 1810, Raspail, "carrying four shirts, six handkerchiefs, and wearing my cassock," [29] arrived in Avignon at the seminary, which is run by the Order of Saint Sulpice whose major concern is the education of future French priests and seminary teachers. Raspail set to work with ardor and remained steadfast in his intention to become a priest. He had been tonsured at Avignon on September 9, 1807, and he took minor orders on May 25, 1812.[30] Being very poor, he was one of the students to whom Mgr. Périer referred in a letter to the Grand Master of the Imperial University written April 1, 1811: "There are in this seminary fourteen students with a full scholarship and twenty-eight with a half-scholarship. They are all so poor that the ones with the half-scholarships need to rely on the charity of the faithful to help pay for their room and board." [31] Similarly, the most recent historian of French Catholicism wrote in 1962 that "the seminarists belong to the poorest part of the population and, if we believe certain prefects, are often led to take holy orders to escape from poverty and from the draft." [32]

Among the manuscripts at the Bibliothèque Inguimbertine in Carpentras only six shed light on Raspail's frame of mind during this period:[33] a translation of Anacreon with the original Greek in Raspail's hand, dated 1811; a translation of three Odes of Horace into French verse, possibly composed as early as 1807; a poem of five quatrains *In Honor of the Holy Virgin*, dated 1812, full of conventional images and feelings of piety; and a long poem of twenty-eight pages, *The Students' Remedy*, dedicated to Monsieur Sollier, the director of the seminary, filled with affectionate respect

[29] F.-V. Raspail, *Histoire de ma vie* . . . , 60.

[30] These dates are recorded on the registers of the Order of Saint Sulpice, according to a letter addressed to the author, on May 17, 1964, by M. l'Abbé Noye, Chief Archivist of the Order of Saint Sulpice in Paris.

[31] Mgr. J.-F. Périer, *Correspondance avec le ministre des cultes et les préfets de Vaucluse et du Gard.* Ms. in Musée Calvet, Avignon, Vaucluse.

[32] A. Latreille, *Histoire du catholicisme en France*, vol. III, *La période contemporaine* (Paris, 1962), 194.

[33] The library of the Seminary Saint Charles at Avignon revealed no traces of Raspail's presence there between 1810 and 1813, despite a protracted search.

and composed in honor of summer vacations. In a letter to his friend Monier, written in 1815, Raspail offers good advice to budding seminarists:

The condition of the Carpentrassians at the seminary is that of the disciples of Jesus Christ. The world did not love them [*sic*]. Therefore, conduct yourself so as not to incur the least reproach with regard to your studies. Work hard in philosophy, so as not to have to repeat it next year. Concentrate on your reading; don't try to read fast, but rather with care. Be sure to choose good books. To guide your feelings, you have the excellent translation of the Cassianus' Conferences: they are free from error. Read the Imitation often [Thomas à Kempis' *Imitation of Christ*] even if you only read two sections a day it would add up to lot by the end of the year. During walks and when you wish to relax, you can get the poem on religion by M. Racine and the sacred odes by Rousseau.[34] Learn by heart the selections you prefer. For history, concentrate on Anacharsis. During vacation you can read Church history; this will serve as preparation for your course in theology. I am speaking to you as a friend: *Disce quod doceas.*

Well, I think the food is still bad; that's life in the seminary . . . where one never says what one thinks . . . .[35]

He was trying to keep his thoughts to himself. That was essential for his success at the seminary, especially since he soon became embroiled in the struggle of rival Catholic factions and personalities in Avignon. Recruits for the priesthood were rare in those days, and the Bishop of Avignon himself was to take a keen interest in the Abbé Esseyric's brilliant pupil.

This bishop, Jean-François Périer (1740–1823), was among "the constitutional bishops whom the French government forced the pope to accept,"[36]—even though the "refractory" clergy, faithful to the pope, had the most numerous following in the former Papal States. Périer occupied his episcopal see from 1802 until 1821, when he was forced to resign. A biographer gives this picture of his activities:

He re-organized worship, re-districted the parishes, re-opened many churches, appointed priests most of whom were excellent men despite

[34] He is, of course, referring to the poets Louis Racine (1692–1763) and Jean-Baptiste Rousseau (1671–1741).

[35] Ms. 2405, Bibliothèque Inguimbertine, Carpentras, Vaucluse.

[36] Mgr. Baunard, *L'Episcopat français: 1802–1905* (Paris, 1907), 90–91.

his unquestionable preference for former constitutional priests. He re-established the Great Seminary (in Avignon), founded a "Little Seminary," actively recruited for the clergy, visited his vast diocese, issued wise rules, proved himself a skilfull administrator, and worked with real zeal to make religion flourish anew. Despite all this, he never managed to defeat the prejudice which, from the first day, his priests and the faithful felt against him, so deeply attached were they to the ultramontane doctrines. To the end, they questioned the purity of his faith and the sincerity of his attachment to the Holy See, and to the end he showed himself an impenitent Gallican.

Under the Restoration, he was even more suspect because of his well-known sympathies for the Empire to which he had remained deeply attached even at the time of its gravest difficulties with the papacy. . . .

Until he drew his dying breath, on March 30, 1824, he refused, despite all the insistence of his successor, to retract his adherence to the constitutional schism.[37]

It may well have been the initiative of Monseigneur Périer that led Raspail to the Avignon seminary in 1810. Périer had indeed felt a rising concern as he surveyed the thinning ranks of the clergy. In 1807 he had written to the archbishop at Aix-en-Provence: "The dearth of priests is alarming; in the past fourteen months, fifty-eight have died in my diocese. Most of the others are old and will soon have to retire." [38] The extended travels that Monseigneur Périer undertook in his diocese must have led him repeatedly to the relatively important town of Carpentras. His recruiting efforts were gladly furthered by the Abbé Esseyric, especially since their constitutional convictions were a bond of sympathy between them. The following passage from Périer's biography may thus well relate to Raspail:

The appeal of the bishop was heeded by a goodly number of priests: here and there, in the shadow of the sanctuary, some of the most pious children and adolescents would be taught Latin by some aged priest. Sometimes, at the end of their literary studies, these young men would be sent to the seminary. . . .[39]

[37] *Ibid.*

[38] A. Durand, *Un prélat constitutionnel: Jean-François Périer (1740–1824)* (Paris, 1902), 479.

[39] *Ibid.*, 473.

In 1810, just in time for Raspail, Monseigneur Périer had finally managed to reopen the seminary at Avignon to students. The building—confiscated in 1792—had been returned to the Sulpicians in 1808. In the intervening two years Monseigneur Périer had to fight for funds to accomplish urgent repairs; the Prefect of Vaucluse had been in no hurry to grant them.

The choice of a director for the seminary proved to be a thorny problem, considering the ultramontanist allegiance of Périer's constituents. "Public opinion designated M. Sollier as Superior; Monseigneur Périer resigned himself to accept this nomination." [40] Henri-Anne Sollier (1761–1838) was then Superior at the College of Apt, near Carpentras. He had been a student at the Seminary Saint Charles before the Revolution, when the Sulpicians still owned it. [41] Though a priest, he disliked all orders and never belonged to any. At Saint Charles he had studied not only philosophy and theology but mathematics and physics as well. Refusing the oath of allegiance to the Civil Constitution of 1790, he had traveled abroad for ten years, learning Spanish and Italian. When he returned in 1802 and re-opened the College of Apt, he taught modern languages, algebra, geometry, geography, and mythology. Sollier personified the new curriculum. This must have attracted Monseigneur Périer who was also a modern, although on religious matters, of course, the two men held antithetical views.

Was there not a danger [asks Périer's biographer], that the bishop would interfere in questions of curriculum and other academic matters? Was it not his right? If he made use of his prerogative, would it not be in order to impose doctrines of suspect orthodoxy, or constitutional and even Jansenist priests? [42]

In the case of Raspail, the suspicion that Périer intervened seems justified.

[40] Abbé Granget, *Histoire du diocèse d'Avignon et des anciens diocèses dont il est formé* (Avignon, 1862), 2 vols., II, 549.

[41] The author gratefully acknowledges the help of M. l'Abbé Noye in tracing the relationship of the Order of Saint Sulpice with the Great Seminary Saint Charles at Avignon during the Revolution and in locating its present Superior, M. l'Abbé Druilhe. M. l'Abbé Noye also helped find the books by Barrat, Boissard [M. Boissard (Supérieur Général), *Trois siècles d'histoire*, 3 vols. (Paris, 1962)], Constantin, and Durand which have proved invaluable in writing this chapter.

[42] A. Durand, *Un prélat constitutionnel . . .* , 491.

During his three years at the seminary Raspail worked mainly with M. Sollier, of whom he later drew this unflattering portrait:

. . . he was a temperamental old man, dry, tall, pale-faced and snub-nosed; his last two remaining teeth in the upper jaw, the canines, moved when he spoke like those of a viper; his head was a veritable skull with two eyes sparkling like carbuncles. . . . When we went for walks, the holy man took on a seraphic air that one would have had to draw then and there, for, once back at the seminary, he resumed his despotic and resolute countenance.[43]

Besides M. Sollier, Raspail was taught by professors of dogma, moral theology, and philosophy. He was an excellent student, winning a first prize in philosophy in 1811, and in theology the following year.[44] Since the seminary could neither find nor afford more faculty members, the best students were pressed into service as teachers. During his third year, eighteen-year-old Raspail was asked to teach philosophy. He also helped with the music for religious services.[45] A short biography of his intimate friend and fellow student, the Abbé Antoine-Anthime Frizet, sheds additional light on their seminary days. Frizet was one year younger than Raspail, but they entered the seminary together.

[Frizet] was a quiet boy who loved the complete silence, interrupted only during recess, and the devotional services when the directors fortified the students' souls with sound teaching. . . .

It is current usage in the seminaries of St. Sulpice to choose the most intelligent and able students and make them assistant teachers. They are called lecturers. After class they take the chair and answer questions regarding the subject matter. This is a great honor for the seminarist; it implies the recognition of his real talents, and his firm grasp of philosophy and sacred theology.

The Abbé Frizet's close companion was Raspail. They were rivals; their talents had led to a close friendship.[46] They were the glory and

[43] F.-V. Raspail, *Histoire de ma vie* . . . , 78–79.

[44] *Ibid.,* 60.

[45] "During the week I sang in the choir and helped the others rehearse their parts by playing the violin." *Ibid.,* 80.

[46] Frizet came from Pernes where Raspail's mother was born, at a distance of four miles from Carpentras. During vacations the two boys visited each other every day. They would start out from home at the same time and walk toward each other, and whoever was closer to home when they met would take the friend to his house for the afternoon.

honor of the seminary. But Raspail lacked the faith and modesty which characterized Frizet. He was ruled by vain pride. He imitated the hypocritical wisdom of a Jansenist uncle [?]. But God disbarred him from His sanctuary. Raspail soon left the seminary and adopted all the doctrines which tend to subvert Christian society. The Abbé Frizet used all the powers of his friendship to try to restrain him and to prevent him from falling into the abyss, but all his efforts were in vain. Perversity is difficult to correct, says the Holy Spirit.[47]

What the Abbé Constantin called perversity was of course Raspail's growing skepticism. This is glaringly evident in a manuscript of sixteen pages that Raspail entitled *On the Non-Infallibility of the Pope*. He drafted it in preparation for one of the verbal duels that Bishop Périer delighted to hold and to which visiting Church dignitaries were often invited. Périer's biographer writes:

He liked to preside over their examinations as often as his age and his ill health allowed. Sometimes . . . the best seminary students presented theses of philosophy and theology. To add to the brilliance and solemnity of these occasions, the bishop . . . sometimes chose the episcopal palace as the lists where the combatants should joust. The victor would receive the bishop's congratulations and encouragements. . . .[48]

Raspail presented his case against papal infallibility on such an occasion,[49] displaying his detailed knowledge of Church history, scriptural exegesis, and theological argument. His examples, both in Greek and in Latin, were taken from the Church Fathers and were supplemented with quotations from the Gospels. His tone conveyed astonishment that anyone could accept the tortuous legalistic proofs that theologians proffered to assert papal infallibility. Mgr. Périer must have enjoyed Raspail's skill and liked his turn of mind. But not so Monsieur Sollier whose biographer writes:

Obviously such a student attracted Mgr. Périer who wished him well.

[47] J.-M.-J. Constantin, *Vie de Monsieur l'Abbé Antoine-Anthime Frizet, ancien directeur du Grand Séminaire de St. Charles à Avignon* (Carpentras, n.d.), 8 and 12–13.

[48] A. Durand, *Un prélat constitutionnel* . . . , 97–98.

[49] The untrustworthy Gabrielle Raspail comments: "He spoke with such success that the papal legate [who was present] wanted to take him along to Rome since he believed that Raspail would attain the highest ecclesiastical posts. But the young man refused, unwilling to leave his mother, whom he adored." G. Raspail, *La Vie et l'oeuvre* . . . , 10.

Portrait of H.-A. Sollier, Superior of the Seminary
St. Charles (Courtesy Musée Calvet, Avignon)
". . . his head was a veritable skull, with two
eyes sparkling like carbuncles."

And indeed, when Raspail finished his studies, the bishop chose him
for one of the professorial chairs at the seminary. But M. Sollier, the
wise and pious Superior, knew the young seminarist too well to accept
him as a collaborator, however considerable his talents. He even refused to ordain him. One knows what has since become of Raspail.[50]

The tug of war over the recruiting of Raspail into the ranks of
the constitutional, nationalistic French clergy, led in Provence by
Mgr. Périer, was only one instance in the struggle for power between the Bishop of Avignon and the Director of the Seminary.

Several other attempts were made to impose on the Director collaborators whose past and whose ideas rendered them suspect to the clergy.
M. Sollier . . . considered himself the incorruptible guardian of the
Church's interests and thus felt bold enough to reject any candidate he
considered either unpleasant or dangerous and to give the authorities
to understand that, if any professor of doubtful orthodoxy entered the
seminary, he would feel obliged to leave. . . . The bishop, for his part,

[50] Abbé Barret, *Vie de l'Abbé Sollier, vicaire général du diocèse d'Avignon*
(Avignon, 1843), 103, n.

Miniature showing Raspail at the age of fifteen, at the Seminary St. Charles at Avignon (From G. Raspail, *La vie et l'oeuvre scientifique de François-Vincent Raspail*)

disregarding his own tastes and preferences, resisted the pressures around him, and gave the Director of his seminary a free hand in the choice of his faculty and the orientation of the curriculum. He yielded to Sollier's arguments and to his firmness. Any public conflict would have impaired the bishop's prestige and compromised the true interests of the diocese and of clerical education.[51]

To what extent Raspail was aware of this struggle over his soul and his career we can only surmise. Nor is it clear whether he left the seminary because M. Sollier would not permit him to join the faculty, or on the advice of Bishop Périer, or of his own free will. According to Raspail's autobiography, Sollier made life impossible for him at the seminary: ". . . he pointed me out to everyone else . . . as tainted with heresy, guilty of schismatic ideas, a dangerous acquaintance." [52] When Raspail fell violently ill, he says that no one cared for him until his sister, Madame Bourges, and her husband forcibly carried him to their home, nursed him back to health,

[51] A. Durand, *Un prélat constitutionnel* . . . , 494–95.
[52] F.-V. Raspail, *Histoire de ma vie* . . . , 74.

and prevailed upon him not to return to the seminary.[53] In the summer of 1813 he sought employment in Carpentras. He was hired as sixth grade teacher and assistant librarian at the secondary school.[54]

If Raspail had not been so poor, he would not at this point have returned to his narrow home town:

Oh! if I had had a little money, enough to enter a law or a medical school, how my soul would have grown with new knowledge and what good work I would have undertaken ten years earlier! But my family was so poor and persecuted [55] and almost entirely dependent on my small teacher's salary [of twelve hundred francs a year], so I continued to teach . . .[56]

Soon the pitfalls of politics would open before him. Late that autumn, the town council of Carpentras was faced with the task, burdensome for a royalist community, of organizing a public celebration for December 2, the anniversary of the battle of Austerlitz and of Napoleon's coronation. Raspail was chosen to deliver the sermon in the Cathedral of St. Siffrein. He had preached there before, winning from an admiring crowd the title of "young Bossuet." The assignment was dangerous for Raspail: December 1813 also marked the first anniversary of the days when the starved,

[53] At eighty Raspail wrote: "I told my bishop that I had ceased believing in the [Catholic] religion. He said: 'Then, my friend, you must leave us.' And I quit the seminary." X. Raspail, *Procès de l'almanach Raspail* (Paris, 1874), 133.

In his autobiography, in 1871, he exclaimed: "Be blessed . . . my poor and noble sister, to whom I owe my life, even though, since my departure as an outlaw, you stopped writing to a poor brother whom you had loved so well for fear of impairing your husband's advancement!" F.-V. Raspail, *Histoire de ma vie . . .* , 78.

François Raspail comments: "Doubt had entered his mind and he loyally spoke of it to his bishop who realized that, under these circumstances, ordination was out of the question." *Biographie de F.-V. Raspail . . .* , 4.

Gabrielle Raspail writes: "Sick, ill at ease, feeling that he was not made for the Church, Raspail returned home." *La Vie et l'oeuvre . . .* , 10.

[54] Though only a sub-deacon, he seems to have heard confession: Simone Raspail reports having seen *billets de confession* signed "Abbé Raspail."

[55] There is no evidence of persecution toward the Raspail family at that time.

[56] F.-V. Raspail, *Histoire de ma vie . . .* , 120.

freezing remnants of the Grand Army fled westward from snow-covered Russia. And the disaster of Leipzig was but six weeks past. The young cleric knew that his audience was devoted to the pope and the Bourbons. To profess his bonapartism from the pulpit would be a grave risk.

As a public servant I could not refuse the task. I would lock myself into my room in order to measure the danger from every angle. For this danger was growing daily in my poor province. I jotted down some notes, and decided to rely on my imagination to guide me through this labyrinth. I would carefully register the impressions I could gain from my audience and would try to convince without offending anyone's feelings and lead my hearers on, once I was sure that I had impressed them.[57]

Danger apart, Raspail welcomed the opportunity of publicizing his admiration for Napoleon, in whom, like so many young men of this first generation of Romanticists, he worshiped the hero who had tamed and harnessed the Great Revolution. He acquitted himself brilliantly: taking patriotism as his theme, he stressed the need to rally around the Emperor in an hour of national danger. In fact the speech was so successful that it evidently induced the inhabitants to pay long overdue taxes. "The civil and military authorities sent the judge, the mayor and his assistants, and the police commissioner to congratulate my mother," Raspail wrote.[58] The local authorities wanted to forward the speech to the Emperor. But Raspail had spoken without notes; only with the help of some attentive listeners could the content be reconstructed. Napoleon did read the resulting text, and jotted in the margin: "Watch this young man, he will go far." [59]

The fall of the Emperor was a heavy blow to young Raspail. During the eleven months of Bourbon rule, while Napoleon was confined to Elba, Raspail subjected his own past to critical exami-

---

[57] *Ibid.,* 89–90.

[58] *Ibid.,* 93; see also G. Raspail, *La Vie et l'oeuvre* . . . , 12.

[59] F. Martin-Ginouvier, "Raspail et Napoléon Ier," *Revue mondiale,* CXLVI (Jan.–Feb. 1922), 63–74. See also F.-V. Raspail, *Histoire de ma vie* . . . , 95–96. Despite many attempts, this document linking Raspail with Napoleon could not be located.

nation. He had acquired the method at the seminary: ". . . in those three years . . . I had learned, at the expense of my health and of my first trusting illusions, to examine all my acts and thoughts critically; to believe nothing but the demonstrable; to act only on rational grounds; I had thus reduced all of theology to the formula: *God and Humanity.*" [60] Like another young Descartes, "I began by doubting everything, and then I subjected everything to the compass of reason and demonstration." [61] Once he had left the seminary, the scope of his critique widened: "All I had professed at the seminary was now judged by this criterion; and good God! what an abyss was thus dug . . . What remained of those three years of brilliant studies? What chaos in place of the eight volumes of theology which I knew by heart. . . ." [62]

From the shambles of his past Raspail's future emerged unharmed. He mentions in his autobiography "an insatiable desire to fathom the depths of Science . . . ," [63] and "studies of astronomy and natural history for which I had a strong liking." [64] His revolt against theology had been motivated by rationalism. He had followed the critical, empirical method which was also to guide his scientific work. But he was not to remain a lifelong convert to the method of Sir Francis Bacon. His belief in "infinitely small" parasites as the agents of contagious disease was to be based on deductive reasoning, not observation and experiment. Emotional factors would eventually guide his activities in science. He would, toward the end of his life, urge, advocate—yes, preach—social medicine to his thousands of followers. The clerical upbringing left its mark.

In 1814 Raspail felt more and more hemmed in by the limited resources of Carpentras:

. . . how incomplete my studies were, in a province deprived of all intellectual resources, without a law or medical school, without a museum or botanical garden, without the books of the past twenty years! I looked around everywhere: at the library I found an armillary sphere, at the college a celestial globe which the Jesuits had forgotten. At night, when all were asleep in town, I studied the heavens from the top of the college tower; and the peasants, seeing a light in this dungeon,

[60] *Ibid.,* 82–83.   [61] *Ibid.,* 85.   [62] *Ibid.,* 112.   [63] *Ibid.,* 83.   [64] *Ibid.,* 105.

crossed themselves as before a bad omen and inquired the next day, in town, about their nocturnal vision.[65]

All this time, he was very poor, and worried about the future. Napoleon's brief return only aggravated his insecurity. Raspail's high hopes and soaring joy found expression in a "bacchic poem," welcoming Bonaparte home from Elba—especially because he would reduce to silence all the clerics who had become too clamorous, thinking that the Empire was at an end. Raspail composed the poem for a friend, Eydoux, after exacting the promise that his authorship would not be revealed. The promise was broken. Raspail, still wearing the cassock, was now a marked man. Soon after the fall of Napoleon he was asked to submit his resignation from the college faculty. The need to escape, if he wished to lead a free and fruitful life, became increasingly clear.

After Waterloo, the "White Terror" struck in Provence. Private feuds were settled with a fierceness that only members of a resistance movement can feel toward collaborators. The records confirm that it was months before the government restored order. "Brigands" and "assassins" abounded; murder, pillage, and rape were common.

Provence was seething with revolt during the Hundred Days [wrote Ernest Daudet]. The royalist volunteers . . . had returned home but refused to give up their weapons. Free and armed, they awaited the hour of vengeance. . . . The region of Marseilles was full of deserters who spurned all ordinances and laws. . . . Discharged veterans and papists had retired into the villages where they could not be caught for want of regular troops. They were threatening Marseilles, eager for pillage.[66]

In August 1815 Raspail witnessed the ghastly murder of Marshal Brune in Avignon. The marshal, accused of having been the queen's jailer, was cornered by the milling populace. With shouts of "Kill him! Into the Rhône! Murderer!" they stoned and stopped his carriage, shot him, and threw his body into the river.[67] "Similar

[65] *Ibid.*, 106–7.

[66] E. Daudet, *La terreur blanche: épisodes et souvenirs* (Paris, 1906), 151–52.

[67] P. Vermeil de Conchard, *L'assassinat du maréchal Brune, épisode de la terreur blanche* (Paris, 1887), *passim*.

scenes," commented Daudet, "kept occurring outside Avignon." [68]

Another commentator, Albert Maurin, added: "Led by Cadillac, Pointu, Magnand, Nadaud, all of them porters or boatmen on the Rhône, . . . the murderers fanned out into the communes to kill all the officials who had served the 'usurper.' When they did not find the intended victims, they wrecked and burnt their houses." [69] Special criminal tribunals (*cours prévôtales*) were set up in each department, according to a law of December 20, 1815. They judged without appeal. Although it is unlikely that the murderers who roamed the countryside were formally employed by the government, these special tribunals were not unhappy to hear that bonapartists and republicans whom they had condemned *in absentia* had been murdered by "brigands." [70] "Later, the tribunals were filled with the murders committed in July and August [1815] in Roussillon, Point-des-Trois-Evèques, Loriol, Roquemaure, Carpentras." If an assassin was indicted, the judge acquitted him out of fear. [71]

When he was a very old man, Raspail told the story of those heroic days to his wide-eyed young grandson, François:

Trestaillon and Pointu were in power then, and perpetrated countless illegal and atrocious deeds. I was singled out as a dangerous imperialist. Soon I was condemned. [72] Not a day would pass when I did not have to defend myself ten times against hired royalist murderers. Sometimes they were supposed to kill me on my way to school, but I walked past them looking so unconcerned, with my hands in my pockets, that

[68] E. Daudet, *La terreur blanche* . . . , 182.

[69] A. Maurin, *La terreur blanche* (Paris, 1850), 18.

[70] Some information can be gathered from A. Paillet, "Les cours prévôtales, 1816–1818," *Revue des Deux mondes*, IV, Year LXXXI, 6ème période (July 1, 1911), 123–49.

[71] E. Daudet, *La terreur blanche* . . . , 182–83. See also D. P. Resnick, *The White Terror and the Political Reaction after Waterloo* (Cambridge, Mass., 1966.)

[72] Raspail was convinced—and repeatedly asserted throughout his life—that he and his brothers were inscribed on the lists of the *cours prévôtales* and marked for assassination. A search in the departmental archives of Vaucluse in Avignon (especially in Series M) did not yield any confirming evidence. A report sent to the Minister of Justice, on March 18, 1817, by the district attorney in charge of the *cour prévôtale* for Vaucluse—a court which had been sitting in Carpentras—contains the official summary of the court's work since December 1815. Raspail's name does not appear on its list. (Archives nationales, Series BB³, 125, dossier "Vaucluse".)

la maison de Raspail
a Carpentras

Raspail's birthplace at Carpentras   (Courtesy Archives du Département de la Seine)

the hirelings dared not attack me. . . . I remember one day when they wanted to burn us all alive in our house. The rabble were already piling up kindling in front of the door, when I appeared on the balcony to play a wild dancing tune on my violin. Soon the cries of hatred turned into shouts of joy.[73] But I witnessed so many crimes! The memory of these butcheries is so vivid that I have never revisited my home town.[74]

Life in Provence had become unbearable. The citizens of Carpentras were returning to the state of mind and to the way of life they had known under the old régime. While they did accept the French king as their sovereign instead of the pope, they still remained deeply loyal to Catholicism for many years. The past won out. But Raspail was already a man of the nineteenth century; his head was filled with ideas and his heart with passions that would soon be crucial to French life: social justice, economic equality, representative government, liberty of speech and conscience, a lay state, the progress of science. For him, Carpentras had become a prison. On April 10, 1816, he left for Paris.

---

[73] In memory of this event, the house where Raspail was born was willed by his children to the city of Carpentras, on the condition that it become a music school. But it stands empty.

[74] F. Raspail, *Biographie de F.-V. Raspail* . . . , 5–6.

*. . . these fifteen years of earnest,
conscientious conspiracy which gradually
ruined all my youthful illusions and all
my hopes for the future. . . .*

François-Vincent Raspail

III

PARIS AFTER NAPOLEON: THE SCIENTIFIC SCENE

THE CAPITAL LOOKED quite different then from what it is today [wrote Father Bertier de Sauvigny in 1955], even including the air which was not yet dirtied by industrial soot and the smoke of coal-stoves. An English traveler, in 1814, marveled at "the special transparency which makes objects stand out with amazing clarity," at the limpid waters of the Seine "of crystalline green," at the whiteness of the quais and monuments. The paintings of the era confirm this impression.[1]

By 1814 the monuments of Paris included the Bourse, the Madeleine, and the Triumphal Arch of the Etoile, all still unfinished but already joined by broad avenues.

In this beautiful city, a newly arrived provincial could see and sense the dilemma of France, still caught, in 1816, in the grip of

[1] G. de Bertier de Sauvigny, *La restauration* (Paris, 1955), 348.

53

her royalist past but already within the grasp of her democratic future. Paris, for centuries the vital core of France, offered striking evidence of the strains, pressures, and antagonisms to which Frenchmen were then subject. France was a country that needed to redefine its identity in terms of politics, social and economic structure, intellectual outlook, artistic production, and scientific orientation.

An occupation force of Russians, Scandinavians, and Germans were quartered in the Paris region until 1818. Their leaders hob-nobbed with the returned émigrés who preferred the company of titled foreigners to the nobility Napoleon had created. The émi-grés exerted constant and largely successful pressure on the king to help them recover their past power and wealth. Whenever they succeeded they faced competition from a newly rich group of merchants, bankers, and entrepreneurs of all kinds—some whose fortunes were made before 1789, some grown rich by profiteering, like Balzac's Père Goriot who married his daughters to a count and to a banker. Money was gradually becoming the chief ladder to power and the main yardstick of social importance.

The search for fortune and fame brought thousands of young men from the provinces to Paris—like so many Julien Sorels or Eugène de Rastignacs. Paris grew from 713,000 inhabitants in 1817 to 785,000 in 1831, an expansion largely due to the influx of young provincials. In fact, only one of every two persons who died in Paris in 1833 had been born there. The capital was filled with youths who had never known the Revolution, who tended to ignore the past and become intensely involved in nineteenth-century problems.[2]

Although the Industrial Revolution had not yet transformed France, competition for cheap labor was already keen. Women and children were widely employed.[3] In 1816, coming to Paris without money meant facing not only crowded lodgings, high rents, and unsteady employment, but also strict police supervision. Freedom of speech, press, religion, artistic expression, and academic life, al-though guaranteed by the Charter of 1814, were gradually re-stricted to the point of extinction. The bourgeois society and the

[2] *Ibid.*, 317–20.   [3] *Ibid.*, 343.

monarchist régime of Restoration France distrusted the working classes, whom they knew to be malcontent, as well as the liberal intellectual community, whom they knew to be restless. "I was anxious to reach Paris," Raspail wrote, "to find a small room and look for an occupation that would enable me to attend to my new studies of law and medicine. . . ." [4] An "old cousin" in Paris offered him lodgings.

Thus I was settled in Paris. I set out to search, left and right, in rain or shine, for a modest position in a college or boarding school, even as a substitute teacher, so as to attend my medical and legal courses. But bad luck followed me around, and I returned to my cell [!] each day as I had left it. And yet I carried in my pocket ten diplomas of good behavior and of outstanding achievement, two prizes of philosophy and theology, the offer of a chair of rhetoric which I had refused in order to retain a young class at the college of Carpentras. But each day nothing, and again nothing.[5]

The obvious employment for Raspail to seek was a teaching position, since he had served as a student teacher at the Seminary of Saint Charles at Avignon and had held a teaching post at the secondary school of Carpentras for almost a year. He knew Greek and Latin, had excellent training in philosophy, rhetoric, and literature and, most important, he was a teacher by temperament.

But in Paris in 1816 ability was not enough. An applicant's politics also had to be acceptable. The social and cultural temper of Restoration society was anti-bonapartist and anti-republican. Raspail's enthusiasm for the Emperor was already a matter of record; moreover, he was gradually being drawn into republican circles. Somehow his mother heard about it, for he received a letter from his brother-in-law, Joseph Bourges, which read in part: ". . . we heard that you are seen far too often among men considered as revolutionaries. . . . Mother Laty is very upset by this and she is always worried about you. . . . Permit me to urge you always to be careful, in politics as in love." [6] Raspail was not being careful at all. He found congenial political friends among the carbonari,

[4] F.-V. Raspail, *Histoire de ma vie et de mon siècle,* 191.

[5] *Ibid.,* 204.

[6] Autogr. ms. letter dated 27 July 1821, in the possession of M. Jacques Raspail.

whom he joined in 1821 or 1822 (that is, immediately after their establishment in France), and also among the freemasons.[7] In the company of these republicans his bonapartism gradually waned. This change of opinion was hastened by Napoleon's death in 1821 which left the Emperor's admirers aimless. Many of them, especially the young ones such as Adolphe Thiers (1797–1877), Armand Carrel (1800–1836), or Stendhal (1783–1842), had always combined their hero-worship with an ardent love of liberty. Raspail's transition from bonapartism to republicanism did not require a conversion, but simply an adjustment.

This change of mind was speeded by his growing sympathy for socialist ideas—a natural interest for a poor young man with a strong sense of justice. In discussion and political-action groups, such as the carbonari, students like Raspail who had formed the initial contingent soon met an ever-growing number of workers. Idealistic young intellectuals and provincials from farming country, such as Raspail's Vaucluse, became acquainted with the human problems that increasing urbanization was creating in France and with the restrictions and inequities imposed upon the working class. As soon as he was able, and throughout his life, Raspail would champion the workers' rights and call attention to their needs: in his newspapers in the 1830s and in 1848, and as a deputy to the National Assembly in 1869 and in the 1870s.

Between 1816 and 1821, when he was in his mid-twenties, Raspail gradually found his bearings and his identity. While the choice was easy in politics, his decisions were painful and slow concerning a profession, his religion, and his place in society. The choice of a profession was his most complex problem. If he had been rich enough to study law or medicine for three or four years, his whole life would have been changed—provided he could have hidden his political thoughts until he had earned a degree. Would he have been capable of so much self-restraint? This is questionable, for he lost several teaching and tutoring jobs because of his intransigence and his need to flaunt his political convictions.

[7] Raspail's membership in a masonic lodge is often referred to by him and others. I have not been able to find documentary evidence beyond the fact that in many of his letters of the 1820s and 1830s his signature is followed by the famous three dots of masonry (.˙.). There is no need to question his membership, which seems to fit his life and thought in the twenties.

Two teaching jobs in boarding schools were short-lived, the first at the Institution Stadler, an annex of the Collège Stanislas.[8] He lost it, according to Gabrielle Raspail, when his authorship of anonymously published newspaper articles became known.[9] The students protested, for he was a popular teacher. Many years later, when Raspail arrived in Belgium as an unwelcome refugee, one of his former students would demonstrate the enduring loyalty Raspail had inspired: Count Vilain XIV, then President of the Belgian Chamber of Deputies, would prevail upon his king to grant political asylum to the exiled democrat.[10]

Raspail was similarly dismissed, after a year, from the Collège Sainte-Barbe, an old and well-known Paris secondary school.[11] During testimony in a lawsuit many years later, Raspail confessed that, as a science student at the University of Paris after 1820, he was expelled on three consecutive occasions as "suspect of liberal opinions." [12] He worked for a lawyer for a while, but "soon gave up a profession so little to his taste." [13] In his memoirs he makes it quite clear that he felt drawn to that group of university students "largely composed of the young remnants of our armies who tried to rebuild a solid future for themselves in the honorable professions of the law and the sciences. . . . I belonged of necessity to this noble part of the young generation and, whenever danger threatened, I tried to risk my frail body and my modest means." [14]

He was eager to publicize his convictions in deed and in print. As early as 1820 he contributed articles to the liberal newspaper

[8] For a survey of the educational situation at this time see P. Gerbod, "La vie universitaire à Paris sous la restauration de 1820 à 1830," *Revue d'histoire moderne et contemporaine*, XIII (1966), 5–48, and the same author's highly suggestive book *La condition universitaire en France au dix-neuvième siècle* (Paris, 1965); see also F. Ponteil, *Histoire de l'enseignement en France 1789–1964* (Paris, 1966). For a study of reactionary Catholic power in education at this time, see A. Garnier, *Mgr. Frayssinous, son rôle dans l'université sous la restauration* (Paris, 1925).

[9] G. Raspail, *La vie et l'oeuvre scientifique de F.-V. Raspail*, 15.

[10] See *infra*, pp. 238–40.

[11] See J. Quicherat, *Histoire de Sainte-Barbe: collège, communauté, institution* (Paris, 1864), 3 vols., III, 191–92.

[12] F.-V. Raspail, *Nouvelle défense et nouvelle condamnation de F.-V. Raspail à 15,000 francs de dommages-intérêts . . .* (Paris, 1848), 5, n. 2.

[13] G. Raspail, *La vie et l'oeuvre . . .* , 17–19.

[14] F.-V. Raspail, *Histoire de ma vie . . .* , 228.

Minerve. Under the pseudonym of "Lutrin" he penned an anti-Catholic booklet entitled *Missionaries, the Enemies of Morality and Religious Law*.[15] These were minor provocative writings which one might dismiss as student pranks or bravado, were they not written by a man of twenty-five who needed to be concerned about his career. Raspail seemed eager to be known as a member of the political opposition.

Amicable relations with institutions, indeed with authority, were difficult for him; so he resorted, quite logically, to tutoring. On April 26, 1817, he wrote to his brother Joseph: "My big news is that, beginning May 1, I shall be the tutor of a well-born young man. May God help me earn the esteem of the family." [16] Within the subsequent four years he held several tutoring posts, in the families of the Marquis de Tholozan, the Marquis d'Argens, and Admiral de Sugny. The admiral's wife apparently wanted to present Raspail to the king. "But," Raspail reminisced years later at a trial for political subversion, "I could not admit to these ladies that I was an outlaw; I stopped seeing them." [17] In a different account he wrote that he felt "the constant fear of being recognized in their magnificent country estate at Bezons, which princes visited. I sank into nostalgia. . . ." He climbed over the wall and ran away, "delivered from a weight heavy as the world, delighted with my freedom and rid of my golden chains." [18]

His relationship to the aristocracy remained complex and pertained to the search for his own identity. He was attracted by these exclusive circles—as he was later attracted by the academies—feeling himself to be exceptional also. Much too mistrustful and

---

[15] F.-V. Raspail, *Les missionnaires en opposition avec les bonnes moeurs et avec les lois de la religion* (Paris, 1815). At the Bibliothèque nationale a booklet called *Secrets de la cour de Louis XVIII. Recueil de pièces authentiques* (Paris, 1815) is attributed to Raspail. The publication date seems to me to make his authorship extremely doubtful.

[16] Autogr. ms. letter in the possession of M. François Ay of Gigondas, Vaucluse, and communicated by Mademoiselle Simone Raspail.

[17] X. Raspail, *Procès de l'almanach Raspail . . .* (Paris, 1874), 119–20. He evidently also spent some time at the Château de Guermantes in 1822, perhaps in the capacity of tutor. (See F.-V. Raspail, *Nouvelle défense . . .* , 5.) There he knew Mme. de Dampierre and the Comte de Pontcarré, both of them later his patients.

[18] F.-V. Raspail, *Histoire de ma vie . . .* , 205.

proud to bend in the slightest degree, he would do nothing politic or ingratiating merely to further his career. Also, he was convinced of the government's persistent vindictiveness, although, at this time of his life, there is no evidence of official ostracism or persecution. "My life was a constant struggle between my insatiable desire to learn and the impossibility to find a moment to satisfy this passion." [19]

While struggling to find his place in a profession and in society, Raspail was also taking the final step in leaving the Church. He had come to Paris in the seminarist's garb, which he did not abandon until 1818 when he wrote to his brother Joseph: "I have finally taken off that cursed cassock which caused me to waste the best years of my youth." [20] To defrock himself was evidently not his initial intention: the Abbé Guérin of Carpentras recalled how Raspail approached him in Paris in the early years of the Restoration and asked for help in securing admission to the Paris Seminary of Saint Sulpice: "M. Duclaux [the Superior] would have admitted Raspail if M. Sollier had recommended him favorably. But that he did not do. . . ." [21]

Raspail's troubles had a result which is not entirely surprising. In his twenty-seventh year he experienced "a year of dissipation, and what dissipation! It was rather idleness, discouragement, and pain for which I have neither to blush nor repent." [22] He was rescued by marriage and by a professional commitment. Despite his unsettled life and lack of a steady income, he married Henriette Adelaïde Troussot (1802–1853), in a civil ceremony, late in 1821. Little is known about Madame Raspail, whose family lived in the Rue de Picpus. In one of his rare references to her, shortly after her tragic death, Raspail wrote to a friend:

Although she was ill-favored by nature and lacked good looks, social standing, and education, imagine that I have never ceased to be jealous

[19] *Ibid.,* 207.
[20] Autogr. ms. letter dated October 6, 1818, in the possession of M. Ay of Gigondas and communicated by Mademoiselle Simone Raspail.
[21] Letter from the Abbé Redon, Vicar General of Avignon, dated 22 February 1895, communicated by M. l'Abbé Noye.
[22] F.-V. Raspail, *Histoire de ma vie . . . ,* 257.

of her just as in my youth, jealous to the death, jealous for thrity-five years; it is hard to believe but true. . . .

and, somewhat indignantly:

She was not a little dressmaker [as someone had insinuated], but the daughter of rich artisans. At the age of eighteen she gave up her parents' inheritance to share forever the life of an outlaw. . . . She was very pretty when she was young; the smallpox had disfigured her without depriving her face of its candor and kindness. She suffered everything with a stoicism worthy of antiquity. Her apparent simplicity hid a stalwart soul.[23]

Her feelings toward him we can only infer. She devoted her whole life to his well-being, the success of his work, and the welfare of their five children. Given Raspail's unshakable convictions about ethical and political values, given his need to be in the forefront of the fight for civil rights, one can hardly imagine Madame Raspail making her wishes heard as to where she might like to live, whether they could have a vacation, or where the children should go to school. Her happiness can have lain only in complete dedication, just as he could never have lived with anyone but a totally submissive wife. The malicious Eugène de Mirecourt commented:

Madame Raspail was very ugly, but she had a warm heart and a will of truly superhuman strength. She followed her husband everywhere. No one else ever prepared the prisoner's food. In the last years of her life, she looked like a ghost and one can truly say that she died from exhaustion.[24]

Hers was indeed to be a long-suffering existence. When she married the handsome, intelligent young teacher and budding scientist, could she foresee that he would never settle down to steady work, that he would soon get deeply embroiled with the government and spend eight-and-a-half years in jail and nine in exile? She would have to move from poor lodgings to even more straitened quarters, live in a rented room near his prison, and come, with her small children, to bring him food and solace.

[23] To Marceline Desbordes-Valmore, from the Citadelle de Doullens, 10 March 1853. Ms. No. 2405, Folios 442–46, Bibliothèque Inguimbertine, Carpentras, Vaucluse.

[24] E. de Mirecourt, *Raspail*, 75, n. 1.

Raspail was convinced that she died of arsenic poisoning resulting from a meal that was prepared in the prison kitchen and was meant for him.

Their first two years together were blissful. Life was hard, but "thanks to the devoted help of the woman who consented to become my companion we steadfastly endured everything. I made a living by tutoring baccalaureate candidates, and thus I financed my studies of natural history." [25] By 1821, therefore, law and medicine had eluded the grasp of so poor a man. In the field of natural history, however, one could be self-taught and successful. Specimens for observation were plentiful and, decisive for Raspail, one could work alone. Every Sunday the two young lovers would undertake long field trips:

Departure, on foot, at dawn, and return, also on foot, after walking ten or twelve leagues through fields and woods, with a botany box on the back and deep thoughts in the soul. . . . When fatigue overcame us in summer, we would stop near a source of clear water, spread a clean handkerchief on our knees and unpack a piece of bread and some Gruyère cheese which we ate with an appetite the Gods might envy. In winter, which I devoted especially to research on mosses, lichens, and mushrooms, when hunger and cold grew strong, I would wrap my companion into my coat and, while warming ourselves, leaning against a tree, we would devour the piece of cheese and its colleague, the piece of bread, and wash them down with water from the stream that ran under the ice; . . . I believe that my books must show the reflection of these philosophic walks for two, who were but one in their tastes and in their hearts.[26]

"These walks were interrupted by the appearance of a child. This was sad for both of us." [27] Between 1823 and 1840 there were to be five children: four boys and a girl, Marie Apolline (1836–1876). Marie was seventeen at the time of Madame Raspail's untimely death; with truly stoic simplicity she stepped into her mother's place, sustained and nurtured her father, and shared his prison when he was eighty years old. When she contracted tuberculosis and died, he wept bitterly. For the second time he had

[25] F.-V. Raspail, *Histoire de ma vie* . . . , 253.
[26] *Ibid.*, 254.
[27] *Ibid.*

lost an "angel." A codicil to his will asked his four sons to have Marie Apolline's full-size portrait painted and her bust sculptured by an excellent artist. Only the latter wish was fulfilled. Raspail must have anticipated trouble among his sons, for the codicil also reads: "I recommend resignation and harmony to my children. My ghost would rebel at the idea of the slightest dispute over my inheritance. Let it be divided with as much dignity as I showed in earning it." [28] Had he died poor they might have respected his wishes. But the inheritance was sizable, and led to litigation that would indeed have made him turn in his grave. [29] The focal points of the dispute were money, politics, and religion.

Raspail's civil marriage in 1821 was the beginning of a family life from which the Church was strictly excluded. Profound impressions in childhood and adolescence account for his intransigence. He was, at the same time, no atheist. He often professed his belief in God, sometimes in Nature, sometimes in transcendent ethical principles that unite all humanity.

As for God [he wrote in a private letter in 1832], I believe in Him, but I do not deck Him out as you do. Jesus Christ was the son of God, just like you and I, or rather, more so than you and I, for he was better than we are. His sublime morality is also inherent in me—only his conduct and his actions expressed it best. Death means the return of the thinking part of ourselves to that great reservoir of thought of which it is an emanation. [30]

He spoke in the same vein at the grave of Ludwig Börne (1786–1837) on February 15, 1837, when he declared that the poet's soul had now returned to its source, "the great reservoir of universal intelligence." [31] He professed his tolerance when he said: "Börne was Jewish by birth, but through his writings he belongs to my religion, to our religion, to that of enlightened men everywhere." [32] Years later he wrote: ". . . atheism is a nonsense repugnant to

---

[28] Raspail's Last Will and Testament. Ms. No. 2405, Folio 554, Bibliothèque Inguimbertine, Carpentras, Vaucluse.

[29] See *infra*, pp. 249–52.

[30] F.-V. Raspail, "Lettre au citoyen Victor Delaunay," Ms. No. 2405, Folio 292, Bibliothèque Inguimbertine, Carpentras, Vaucluse.

[31] F.-V. Raspail, *Discours prononcé par M. Raspail sur la tombe de Ludwig Börne le 15 février 1837* (Paris, 1837), 3.

[32] *Ibid.*, 2.

our consciences, for it turns chance into a god. . . ."[33] In his will he expressed his wishes as follows:

. . . at my grave, no speech shall be given. No religion shall preside over my funeral procession or burial. My own cult is above sects; it spans the universe. Its temple is boundless, its code of ethics is the human conscience; life is one of its countless forms; death is one of its transformations.[34]

Certainly he led a life of dedication and sobriety. He transmitted his convictions to his children and grandchildren, all of whom were married by a civil magistrate. His great-grandchildren are divided into church-going Raspails and unbelievers.

The first years of his marriage were the sunniest moments of Raspail's life. Poverty he was used to.[35] His young wife was close to him. His days and nights were filled with study, with absorbing all the knowledge that Paris offered. His timid curiosity about science, encouraged by the Abbé Esseyric and nurtured by M. Sollier, grew into a strongly motivated purpose. He felt the attraction of firm truths to replace those of religion which he had discarded. (He also knew that science could be useful in forging ideological weapons against the entrenched power groups.) The challenge of research tempted him, and he dreamt of a brilliant career. He needed to work hard for he was almost thirty and had so much to learn. He launched into the study of science: botany, zoology, anatomy, physiology, chemistry, physics—every accessible avenue toward the mastery of science he now yearned to explore. He read profusely, attended lectures, and began to experiment. The eventual results of these years of study are found in fifty scientific papers published before 1830, and in the elaboration of a method of personal hygiene, home nursing, medical care, and public health known as the "Raspail system of medicine." The im-

[33] F.-V. Raspail, "Open letter to the citizens of Carpentras," April 28, 1870. Fonds Raspail, Archives du Département de la Seine, Paris, LXXXVII.

[34] Raspail's Last Will and Testament. Ms. No. 2405, Folio 554, Bibliothèque Inguimbertine, Carpentras, Vaucluse.

[35] Madame Raspail may have been skilfull enough a seamstress to earn some money by doing alterations. His mother occasionally sent money, but he often returned it, knowing that she deprived herself for his sake. (See J. Saint-Martin, *F.-V. Raspail,* 13, n. 1.). His letters to his brother Joseph testify to his constant money troubles. (The few letters dating from these years are in the possession of M. Ay of Gigondas and were communicated by Mademoiselle Simone Raspail).

portance of this system, and Raspail's contributions to biology and chemistry, hygienic practices, and sanitation must be evaluated within the context of contemporary French medicine and science.

French doctors and scientists under the Restoration needed— like all Frenchmen and indeed all Europeans—to recover from the tempests of the preceding twenty-five years, to find their bearings, and to chart their future course. This course was to be greatly influenced by French politics, because politics controlled medicine and science in multiple ways.[36] Ever since Napoleon had incorporated all professors and teachers into the national "Université de France," they had all become civil servants.[37] The government thus controlled every professorial appointment—to the Faculties of Liberal Arts and Sciences, the Medical Faculties, the famous independent research and teaching institute, the Collège de France, the many excellent "Great Schools," and the Museum of Natural History with its large botanical garden and zoo. In short, all teaching positions, amphitheatres, laboratories, and research facilities were the government's to award, withhold, or withdraw. Any remaining illusions about the king's adherence to the Charter were shattered in 1822, when the Paris Medical Faculty was closed for four months, eleven professors were dismissed, and only supporters of throne and altar were appointed or reinstated.[38]

The medical and scientific academies and independent societies fared somewhat better than the schools. The Institut de France emerged in 1816 with four sections.[39] The Academy of Medicine was not reopened until 1820 when, in contrast to its parent organizations under the old régime, it included not only doctors but surgeons and pharmacists as well. The Restoration attempted not

[36] On medical education at this time, see J. Léonard, "Les études médicales en France entre 1815 et 1848." *Revue d'histoire moderne et contemporaine,* XIII (1966), 87–94.

[37] Napoleon was of course less of an innovator than would appear at first sight, and the historic beginnings of this centralization and of political control over education can be traced to the late Middle Ages.

[38] See P. Ménétrier, "Le centenaire de la suppression de la faculté de médecine de Paris," *Bulletin de la société française d'histoire de la médecine,* XVI (1922), 440–45.

[39] The Académie des sciences morales et politiques was only reopened in 1832, on the proposal of François Guizot.

only to preserve the equality between surgery and medicine which the Revolution had nurtured, but to raise even pharmacy to the same level of prestige. After the initial nominations to the new Academy of Medicine had been made, membership was obtained by co-option. But all nominations remained subject to governmental confirmation. The political temper of the Restoration would have made the choice of a well-known anti-royalist a gesture of calculated defiance.[40]

The interested public had access to the meetings of the great academies. A number of professional, more or less independent societies could be joined by qualified persons, and Raspail, whose knowledge of botany and zoology was increasing daily, was elected to membership in the Philomatic Society[41] and in the Society for Natural History.[42] The latter accepted several of his papers for publication in its *Memoirs,* and one of his earliest investigations was reported on at length by Adrien de Jussieu in the January 1826 *Bulletin* of the Philomatic Society.[43] Although we lack spe-

[40] For a general picture of educational institutions at the time, see F. Picavet, *Les Idéologues: Essai sur l'histoire des idées et des théories scientifiques, philosophiques, religieuses, etc., en France depuis 1789* (Paris, 1891), especially Chapter I, section II "Les écoles normales, centrales, spéciales," and section III "L'Institut, les sociétés savantes." For an excellent account of scientific activity at this time, see M. Crosland, *The Society of Arcueil—A View of French Science at the Time of Napoleon I* (London, 1967).

[41] Founded in 1788, the Philomatic Society had members belonging to many scientific specialties. A considerable number of well-known scientists had joined after the dissolution of the Academy of Sciences in 1793, among them Berthollet, Fourcroy, Monge, Lamarck, and Lavoisier. See M. Berthelot, "Origines et histoire de la société philomathique," *Mémoires publiés par la société philomathique à l'occasion du centenaire de sa fondation, 1788–1888* (Paris, 1888), 1–15.

[42] He was elected to full membership in the Botany section on June 23, 1826. This Society had existed briefly in 1788 and became genuinely active after 1793. It was frequented by professors from the *Muséum d'histoire naturelle* such as Lamarck, Cuvier, Lacépède, and it published significant papers in its *Mémoires* from 1795 on. See H. Guerlac, "Science as a Social and Historical Phenomenon: Some Aspects of Science during the French Revolution," *The Scientific Monthly,* LXXX (1955), 98.

[43] A. Saint-Hilaire, "Extrait textuel d'un rapport de M. Adrien de Jussieu sur un Mémoire de M. Raspail avant pour titre: 'Sur le développement de la fécule dans les graines céréales et sur l'analyse microscopique de la fécule'," *Société philomathique de Paris. Nouveau bulletin,* XII–XIII (1825–26), 11–14. This excellent critical—but interested and favorable—résumé was based not only on Raspail's paper but also on experiments he performed especially for Adrien de Jussieu. See *infra,* pp. 86 ff.

cific information about the courses Raspail attended during this
time, it is not difficult to picture him as a student in Paris in the
early 1820s.[44] Much can be inferred from the papers he published
and from the acquaintances he made. One educational center, the
Athénée (formerly the Lycée des sciences et des arts) is described
in a letter of C.-A. Sainte-Beuve (1804–1869), the famous critic
and Raspail's slightly younger contemporary who was "very much
interested in medicine" in 1820. He attended lectures at the
Athénée every night from seven to ten, and reported that "one
could hear Biot, Cuvier, Thénard, Richerand, Roederer, Auguste
Comte, Armand Marrast, Adolphe Blanqui, Geoffroy Saint-
Hilaire, Jean Baptiste Say, Raspail,[45] and many others. . . ."[46]
Paris was then becoming the scientific capital of the world.

The prestige of French science [writes a historian], was unchallenged
for its scope and excellence. Students from all parts of the Continent
flocked to the scientific schools of Paris where they learned the methods of classification, calculation, and measurement that French scientists and educators had systematized and applied to the study of all aspects of nature.[47]

Thus a discussion of the main medical and scientific issues that
were being debated, and a thumb-nail sketch of the most brilliant
teaching will give a picture of what was available to the voracious
Raspail. His circle of acquaintances, revealed by some hitherto unpublished correspondence, will also help elucidate this period of
his life.

In French medical thought at the turn of the nineteenth century the rationalist and empiricist philosophy of P.-J.-G. Cabanis

[44] For a general picture of scientific education at the time, see C. C. Gillispie, "Science in the French Revolution," *Behavioral Science*, IV (1959), 67–73; H. Guerlac, "Science as a Social and Historical Phenomenon . . . ," *The Scientific Monthly*, LXXX, 98; L. P. Williams, "Science, Education and the French Revolution," *Isis*, XLIV, 311–30, and "Science, Education and Napoleon I," *Isis*, XLVII, 369–82; R. E. Cameron, *France and the Economic Development of Europe* (Princeton, 1961), ch. III, Section I "Science, Technology, and Indus-try," and Section II "The Work of the Schools."

[45] This sounds as if Raspail had lectured there, which seems unlikely.

[46] A. Billy, *Sainte-Beuve, sa vie et son temps* (Paris, 1952), 2 vols., I, 45.

[47] R. E. Cameron, *France and the Economic Development* . . . , 43.

(1757–1808) and his fellow "ideologues" set the tone.[48] The Cartesian dualism of mind and matter was finally being rejected in favor of a philosophy that traced ideas to sensations and experience. In 1795, Cabanis acceded to the chair of medicine at the new "Paris Health School"—the revolutionary reincarnation of the Medical Faculty—and later exchanged it for the chair of legal medicine and medical history. He wrote the extremely influential *Relationship Between the Physical and Moral Natures of Man* (1802) and the revealing *Survey of Revolutions and Reform in Medicine* (1804). His influence on medical thought was "tremendous—down to the middle of the nineteenth century." [49]

Of the older generation of medical "ideologues," only Philippe Pinel (1745–1826) was still actively teaching when Raspail arrived in Paris. Pinel had held the chair of pathology at the Paris Health School since 1795, had been teaching at the Salpêtrière Hospital, and in 1798 published his epoch-making *Philosophic Nosography,* "the charter of French medicine [for a generation]." [50] His famous *Treatise on Mental Alienation* was published in 1800. Many brilliant, often younger men had in the meantime helped make the "Paris Clinical School" famous.[51] Foremost among them were J.-N. Corvisart (1755–1821), the well-known personal physician and friend of Napoleon and professor of clinical medicine since 1795; R.-T.-H. Laënnec (1781–1826), the inventor of the stethoscope; and P.-C.-A. Louis (1787–1872), the great systematizer of observation and popularizer of medical statistics.

Physiology became increasingly attractive to scientists as the Romantic movement began to stir. Collecting and classifying—the passion of eighteenth-century science—no longer satisfied early

[48] See F. Picavet, *Les Idéologues* . . . , especially ch. VII "Les auxiliaires, les disciples, les continuateurs de Cabanis et de D. de Tracy."

[49] E. H. Ackerknecht, "Elisha Bartlett and the Paris Medical School," *Bulletin of the History of Medicine,* XXIV (1950), 45–60.

[50] These were the historian Mignet's words, quoted in Picavet, *Les Idéologues* . . . , 172.

[51] The term "Paris Clinical School" refers to a new way of teaching medical students which was initiated at the Paris Health School at the turn of the nineteenth century. Bedside teaching on the hospital wards, clinical conferences, and laboratory exercises were the crux of the new method. See also E. H. Ackernecht, *Medicine at the Paris Hospital, 1794–1848* (Baltimore, 1967).

nineteenth-century scientists. Questions of growth and decay, of life and death gradually took the center of the stage. The first great teacher of physiology was M.-F.-X. Bichat, whose *Treatise on Membranes* (1800) founded the science of histology. Soon the microscope would be sufficiently perfected to permit the detailed study of tissues and the cell. It would enable Raspail to achieve pioneer work in microscopy and in histochemistry. Another creative teacher of physiology, pathology, and experimental pharmacology was Bichat's colleague F. Magendie (1783–1855), attending physician at the Hôtel-Dieu and professor of physiology and general pathology at the Collège de France. From these two great professors Raspail may have learned much.

In the exact and natural sciences the turn of the nineteenth century also marked the beginning of a new era. The "naturalist," the "man of science" became increasingly rare, although one still spoke in these terms of philosophically inclined botanists, zoologists, or anatomists such as J.-B. de Lamarck (1744–1829) or Georges Cuvier (1769–1832). But specialization was growing, aided by the astounding advances in technology that put ever improved tools into the scientists' hands. Special fields in science began to be delineated, but few men as yet restricted themselves to one specialty. It was still common for a professor to teach astronomy and physics, like J.-B. Biot (1774–1862), or physics and chemistry like J.-L. Gay-Lussac (1778–1850), or chemistry and natural history like A.-L. Laugier (1770–1832), or legal medicine and chemistry like M.-J.-B. Orfila (1787–1853). The amount of knowledge available in any one sector of the physical or natural sciences was not yet so formidable as to preclude mastery of several specialties. More important, the age of laboratory science was only dawning. Raspail studied in this atmosphere of wide horizons for naturalists and scientists, of approval for informed curiosity which permitted one man to ask questions of nature in many fields.

In the exact sciences, chemistry had made spectacular strides since Antoine Lavoisier (1743–1794) had built for it a solid quantitative foundation. Electricity and magnetism, although long known as natural phenomena, were now being studied in physical and mathematical terms by J.-M. Ampère (1775–1836), professor of mathematics at the Ecole Polytechnique since 1809, among others. Electricity and magnetism were now used in experiments with animals, with chemical substances, and also in psychotherapy. François Magendie excelled in animal work, and his *Elementary Textbook of Physiology* (1816–1817) became a classic. With Ampère, electrochemistry advanced substantially. Both the Collège de France and the Academy of Sciences were astir over the theories and calculations of the Marquis P.-S. de Laplace (1749–1827), whose nebular hypothesis on the origin of the universe added another challenge to Genesis.

In the natural sciences, the great collections and compendia of the eighteenth century—the work of men like Carl von Linné (1707–1778) and G.-L.-L. Buffon (1707–1788)—were being put to use in the controversy over evolution. J.-B. de Lamarck's *Philosophie zoologique* had appeared in 1809, and he was in the process of publishing his *Natural History of Invertebrate Animals* (1815–1822) in which he posited the theory of the use and disuse of organs. Two younger protagonists in this controversy were even then teaching and writing in Paris: Etienne Geoffroy Saint-Hilaire (1772–1844) and Georges Cuvier.[52] Geoffroy Saint-Hilaire had been professor of zoology at the Faculty of Sciences since 1809. In 1818 he published his *Anatomic Philosophy*. He was impressed by the similarity in the structure of various groups of animals: this implied the possibility of evolution. Georges Cuvier taught comparative anatomy at the *Muséum* and, after 1800, at the Collège de France. In 1805 he published his *Lessons of Comparative Anatomy*, and in 1817 his *Animal Kingdom*. He did not find similarities between the species convincing enough to suggest evolution; rather he believed that groups of species descended from separately created ancestors. Though the famous debate over evolution between Geoffroy Saint-Hilaire and Cuvier would not take place at the Academy of Sciences until July 1830,[53] the controversy and their rivalry were already public knowledge when Raspail arrived in Paris and must have given a sense of importance to all workers in biology. Raspail was passionately partisan—per-

[52] On Cuvier's theory of evolution, see W. Coleman, *Georges Cuvier, Zoologist* (Cambridge, Mass., 1964).

[53] For Raspail's comments, see his ". . . Discussion entre MM. Cuvier et Geoffroy," *Nouveaux coups de fouet scientifiques* (Paris, 1831), 1–24.

haps because Geoffroy Saint-Hilaire's views implied an attack on
Genesis and surely because he agreed with those views; but also
because that famous scientist had expressed admiration for Raspail's work when, on November 2, 1824, as a trembling novice, he
read his first paper to the Academy of Sciences.

According to Raspail, Etienne Geoffroy Saint-Hilaire was the
only one among the academicians who listened to his paper "On
the Formation of the Embryo in Grasses" and later sought him out
to say: "Don't be discouraged, young man, you are twenty years
ahead of them." [54] Eleven years after that he would attempt to
obtain for Raspail the Academy's Montyon prize, and would fail,
owing to political pressures.[55]

The hitherto unpublished manuscript correspondence between
these two men—which is now at the *Muséum d'histoire naturelle*
—reveals Raspail's feelings of admiration and gratitude and also
Geoffroy Saint-Hilaire's high esteem for Raspail's work.[56] After
reading Raspail's book on plant physiology, the great naturalist
wrote to him on March 25, 1837:

I have just read the *New System of Plant Physiology*. It was conceived
and written by a philosopher. . . . I found perspectives and ideas in
the manner of Buffon. . . . They shall be incorporated into my brief
. . . Introduction for a new edition of [Buffon's] *General and Detailed
History of Nature*. I feel impelled to do this by my deep convictions and
high regard for you which I shall explicitly mention in the piece I am
writing. [Raspail, however, is not mentioned in E. Geoffroy Saint-Hilaire's *Notice sur Buffon* (Paris, 1837).] I remember [the letter con-
tinues] hearing you read your first paper to the Academy. Its nature
was clear to me from your first sentences; I rose in order to escape from
a talkative neighbor and took a seat next to you.

One day, in an election at the Academy, I was the only one to put
the name of Gall [57] into the ballot-box. I might do the same for you
when the occasion arises. . . . One has a right . . . to speak out

[54] F.-V. Raspail, *Nouveau système de chimie organique*, 2nd ed., "Avertissement historique," XXII–III.

[55] See *infra*, pp. 126–28.

[56] The author wishes to thank Dr. Jean Théodoridès of Paris for drawing her
attention to the Fonds Raspail at the *Muséum* and M. Yves Laissus, the librarian,
for permitting its use.

[57] Franz Joseph Gall (1758–1828), the controversial neuro-anatomist and phre-
nologist.

when the number of conformists crushes the few men of genius who will not and cannot be understood until fifty years or more have passed. . . .[58]

Raspail was deeply touched by this tribute. "The letter with which you honored me yesterday is like a title one bequeaths to one's family as an heirloom," he wrote.[59] The warm relationship with Raspail was continued by Etienne Geoffroy Saint-Hilaire's son Isidore (1805–1861), also a distinguished scientist and member of the Academy of Sciences. For his part, Raspail espoused the father's hostility toward Georges Cuvier:

. . . he is not worth one millionth of his reputation [Raspail wrote to his eminent friend on March 26, 1837]; he was a fact-collector, but far from a genius; I am convinced that you are tempted to think so too. . . . His descriptions were great, but his mind was narrow; he was a scholar with a prodigious memory but a limited horizon; his political fortune was a curse for learning and academic life. Posterity will judge him harshly.[60]

Raspail was convinced that, when he applied for a position at the *Muséum* in 1830, he was rejected by the all-powerful Cuvier because of his loyalty to the elder Geoffroy Saint-Hilaire.

The correspondence at the *Muséum* shows that Raspail had many other friends among the naturalists, and also some eminent foes. Among his friends were P. L. A. Cordier (1777–1861), the mineralogist,[61] J. Decaisne (1807–1882), who worked at the Botanical Garden from 1824 on,[62] and V. Jacquemont (1801–

[58] Ms. No. 2388, Fonds Raspail, *Muséum d'historie naturelle*, Paris. Henceforth referred to as "Fonds Raspail, *Muséum*."

[59] *Ibid.*

[60] *Ibid.* Cuvier, who died in 1832, had successively been made a member, then Perpetual Secretary of the Academy of Sciences; a Councillor of State; Chancellor of the University; a peer; a member of the French Academy and the Academies of Inscriptions and of Medicine; a baron; and a Grand Officer of the Legion of Honor.

[61] Professor of geology at the *Muséum* since 1819 and a member ofa the Academy of Sciences since 1822.

[62] He was elected to the Academy of Sciences in 1847. He taught agricultural statistics at the Collège de France after 1848, and horticulture and agriculture [*culture*] at the *Muséum* after 1850.

1832), the naturalist and traveler.[63] Possibly the two friends with whom Raspail had most in common were J. B. Robineau-Devoidy (1799–1862) and A. C. M. Le Baillif (1764–1831). Robineau-Devoidy combined his professional knowledge of medicine with a competence in botany, geology, and paleontology. He was a liberal in politics and a prolific writer. In a letter of 1828 he urged Raspail:

Take good care of yourself for the sake of all your friends and also for the sake of science which you serve so well. You have aptitudes and knowledge lacking in almost all our botanists who wield the magnifying glass but have no competence in chemistry. . . . You will found a school of microscopic chemistry which is needed in science and which the authorities with their leaden sceptre will be *forced to adopt.* . . .[64]

Le Baillif was a physicist who constructed or perfected many a precision instrument helpful to physicists and chemists, including some that made use of electric current. He perfected the microscope invented by Charles,[65] and constructed excellent micrometers mounted on plate glass, batteries, an electrometer, and a galvanometer. He was also a good enough chemist to detect the danger of artificial colors in candy and was public-spirited enough to draw attention to it. Raspail too was to denounce this source of poisoning, once public health became his main concern.[66]

The letters from these correspondents are filled with friendly shoptalk, acknowledgments of rare specimens exchanged, offers to lend books, thanks for information, references, and referrals. The general tone reveals that Raspail was accepted as an equal by a wide and varied circle of acquaintances in the scientific community.

[63] He studied chemistry with L. J. Thénard and later explored North America and India.

[64] Fonds Raspail, *Muséum.*

[65] J. A. C. Charles (1746–1823), physicist, experimenter, known as an admirer and French popularizer of Benjamin Franklin.

[66] It may have been through Le Baillif that Raspail made many scientific acquaintances. Indeed, a student of Le Baillif wrote: "The office of this philosopher, which many compared to the study of Dr. Faustus, was a meeting place for scientists and artists, among them . . . Brongniart, . . . Biot, . . . Bory de St. Vincent, de Cassini, . . . Gaultier de Claubry, Lassaigne, . . . Orfila, Payen, Raspail, . . . Turpin. . . ." [Ch. Chevalier, *Des microscopes et de leur usage* (Paris, 1839), 261.]

His experiments were watched with considerable interest, his articles were widely read.

But there were exceptions. On January 16, 1827, for example, Raspail wished to attend an open meeting of the Academy of Sciences. The president, A.-T. Brongniart (1770–1847), the eminent geologist, refused him permission to enter the auditorium. In Raspail's mind the exclusion was a reprisal for his antagonism toward Brongniart's son Adolphe-Théodore (1801–1876), a botanist. Yet, according to a letter from the elder Brongniart, he simply applied the rule that no one could enter while papers were being read. "After the presentation I sent for you, but you were gone." [67] Concluding his letter, A.-T. Brongniart pleaded: ". . . do discuss scientific matters graciously; . . . scientists wish to be approached in a considerate manner. They have the right to expect it." [68] Raspail would not forget. In the Preface of his *New System of Organic Chemistry,* published in April 1833, he commented bitterly on the recent election of the younger Brongniart to the Academy of Sciences, writing that "academic chairs are becoming family property." In a private letter to Etienne Geoffroy Saint-Hilaire he added: "I blush to think that by birth the sons and sons-in-law of M.B. . . . should fill vacant posts, and that an as— should sit in the chair of Daubenton next to Geoffroy Saint-Hilaire." [69]

Raspail often suspected plagiarism of his work. Jules Decaisne, for example, working at the *Muséum,* kept sending him leaves, flowers, plants for his experiments. In 1834 or 1835 Decaisne wrote to ask Raspail's opinion about the change of color he had observed in madder roots exposed to the air. The letter carries this annotation in the handwriting of Raspail, who had worked on the same plant: "Espionage Jussieu-Gasparin. Later elected to the Academy of Sciences for his good and loyal services." [70] P. J. F. Turpin (1775–1840), the botanist, protested in August 1826 against Raspail's accusation of plagiarism and wrote:

What evil demon constantly impels certain [persons] to complain without cause, slander everyone, attack everything respectable and shout "Stop thief!"? One pities these men since . . . they make new enemies

[67] Fonds Raspail, *Muséum.*
[68] *Ibid.*　[69] *Ibid.*　[70] *Ibid.*

daily, and they will end by being completely isolated and considered as wicked people whom it is best to shun.

You do not lack enemies, sir; if you do not know it, let me tell you so with my usual frankness. And you justify your nickname of "wasp" when you call me a thief. . . .[71]

Raspail jotted in the margin, "Plagiarist who protests against a priority claim: this plagiarism opened the door of the Institute to him."

A similar tone pervades Raspail's correspondence with J.-J. Coste (1807–1873), the embryologist and professor at the *Muséum*, and later at the Collège de France. Raspail had wrongly contested the scientist's embryological findings.

Science is not an arena where antagonists fight and snatch at victory [Coste wrote to Raspail in 1835], but a sanctuary accessible to dedicated scholars whose collaboration multiplies their powers. . . . It is high time to . . . end this polemic in which quarrels have replaced discussion and where responsible men have gone so far as to suspect the sincerity of their colleagues without bothering first clearly to define the meaning of their own words or to circumscribe the topic under investigation.[72]

Raspail had evidently become so convinced of his own scientific eminence that he was much too quick to accuse others of plagiarism. He was excessively prone to feeling slighted by professors and academicians.[73]

Raspail's professional relationships in the medical world followed the pattern suggested by his correspondence with scientists and naturalists, except that in medicine he lacked a famous friend such as Etienne Geoffroy St.-Hilaire. There are, however, notes from J.-F. Malgaigne (1806–1865), the noted surgeon, and from Emile Littré (1801–1881), the translator of Hippocrates and

[71] *Ibid.*

[72] F.-V. Raspail, *Lettre à M. Coste* (Paris, 1835), 8.

[73] It is difficult to know what to make of four letters from the botanist Viscount Henri Cassini (1784–1832), one of a committee of three appointed by the Academy of Sciences to check the facts in Raspail's "Recherches sur les tissus organiques" which had been sent to the Academy on October 11, 1827. Raspail failed to keep several appointments with the committee. He wrote to Cassini who replied on April 24, 1828, inviting Raspail to pick up his manuscript at the secretariat of the Institute. Fonds Raspail, *Muséum.*

author of the renowned dictionary. An amicable prolonged correspondence survives between Raspail and Gilbert Breschet (1784–
1845), editor of the *General Repertory of Anatomic and Physiologic Pathology and Clinical Surgery*.[74] Breschet was at the time
chief prosector at the Paris Medical School, and later professor of
anatomy and a member of the Academy of Medicine. Some of
their communications deal with the microscopic study of the
chorion of the egg which Raspail had undertaken. On April 16,
1828, Breschet wrote:

You refer . . . to the research on the structure of the placenta that
we were going to do together. If you are still so disposed I shall be
delighted to collaborate with you in studying this interesting and little
known organ. Should you prefer to undertake it alone, I shall make it
my duty to supply you with everything needful in your research. . . .
   If you have anatomic or physiologic papers you wish to publish in
the *Repertory* they will always be welcome.[75]

Breschet kept his promise most generously; on October 29, 1828,
he asked Raspail if he would like to come and examine the uterus,
placenta, and fetus of a woman who had died in the eight month
of pregnancy. On February 25, 1829, he provided Raspail with
sheep and cow ovaries, and promised rabbit and rat ovaries, injected and ready to work on. He also lent him books over many
years. On July 24, 1830, he sent "corpuscles" from a tumor, writing
that Guillaume Dupuytren (1777–1835), the famous pathologist
and surgeon, would like to know what the naturalist thought of
them. This letter, of course, did not find Raspail at home, but
rather among the revolutionary crowd, preparing to defend his
political beliefs.
   The correspondence with men in the medical profession thus
again suggests that Raspail was regarded as a serious student and
researcher. The content of his published papers makes it evident
that he must have read voraciously in his student days, and attended many lectures and conferences by eminent scientists,
clinicians, and exponents of modern methodology and medical
theory. Despite his unorthodox training and the lack of an official
position, Raspail found that his scientific papers were readily ac-

[74] Paris, 1826–1829, 8 vols.
[75] Fonds Raspail, *Muséum*.

cepted for publication. The *Memoirs* of the *Muséum* and those of the Society for Natural History of Paris each printed several of his articles. So did the highly regarded *Annals of Natural Sciences,* although after his quarrel with the editor, Adolphe Brongniart, in 1827, Raspail stopped contributing. The *General Repertory of Anatomy* of his friend Gilbert Breschet contains several of Raspail's pieces, as does the *New Journal of Medicine, Surgery and Pharmacy.*

In 1826 Raspail became an editor of the *Universal Bulletin of Sciences and Industry.* In a friendly letter dated October 8, 1825, the editor-in-chief Baron A. E. F. de Férussac (1786–1836) offered Raspail six hundred francs a year to come in every Tuesday and edit the botany section. Raspail accepted with alacrity. His correspondence with a fellow editor, Colonel Bory de St. Vincent (1780–1846), the naturalist, traveler, and professional soldier, also shows friendly collaboration on equal terms. But then Baron de Férussac accepted for his *Bulletin* the sponsorship of the dauphin, the Duc d'Angoulême. Raspail and his colleague Jacques Frédéric Saigey (1797–1871), a well-known mathematician and formerly a secretary to Victor Cousin, immediately resigned. The two young men then founded a review of their own, the *Annals of the Sciences of Observation.*[76] Seventeen of Raspail's papers appeared in this journal,[77] which labored under great financial difficulties until it ceased publication in 1830. "That whole year of 1829," Raspail wrote later, "was but one hard and cruel fight in which two men without resources or protection had to struggle alone against the combined tricks of fanaticism and scientific ambition."[78] Once again Raspail the scientist paid dearly to uphold the purity of his political ideal.

As one pauses to survey this period of Raspail's student life in

[76] *Annales des sciences d'observation comprenant l'astronomie, la physique, la chimie, la minéralogie, la géologie, la physiologie, et l'anatomie des deux règnes, la botanique, la zoologie, les théories mathématiques, et les principales applications de toutes ces sciences à la météorologie, à l'agriculture, aux arts et à la médecine.* (Paris, 1829–1830), 4 vols.

[77] In Section I: *Bulletin des sciences mathématiques, astronomiques, physiques, et chimiques,* and in Section II: *Bulletin des sciences naturelles et de géologie.*

[78] F.-V. Raspail, *Nouveau système de physiologie végétale et de botanique, fondé sur les méthodes d'observation qui ont été développées dans le Nouveau système de chimie organique accompagné d'un Atlas de 60 planches* (Bruxelles, 1837), 8.

Paris under the Restoration, one wishes that he had made better use of the educational opportunities the capital had to offer. He acquired much knowledge, it is true; but he lacked graduate diplomas that would silence hostile critics. Although he enrolled as a student at the Faculty of Sciences, he was never officially licensed to teach or practice any scientific subject matter. Not even his most violent detractors doubt that he was eminently qualified for graduate studies, and could have mastered them with ease. It is true that he was poor, but he could have found—like many a student then or since—a means of working his way through graduate or medical school.[79] Regular contact with his peers would perhaps have helped him to be more self-critical and to temper the exultant and sometimes aggressive feeling of being a lone explorer, indebted to no one.

The conclusion soon becomes inescapable that Raspail refused to pursue regular university studies because he decided to shun any association with the royal, Catholic government. He took pride in his political purity, to a degree that was excessive and no doubt offensive to some. Thereby did himself irreparable harm. The ensuing five years spent as club leader, newspaper editor, legal counsel, and political prisoner were to undermine his capacity to dissociate his thought from politics. It is possible that a more rigorous institutional scientific training would have strengthened his ability for unbiased empirical research. This might have enabled him—after militant republicanism was throttled by Louis Philippe in 1836—to return to scientific work without a thought for politics. But, then, Raspail was too emotional a man thus to compartmentalize his interests and to let his data speak for themselves without *ad hominem* polemics. The predominantly scientific phase of his life ended abruptly in July 1830. Fortunately by then he had written the more than four dozen articles on which rests his reputation as an original and creative scientist.

[79] This was done, e.g., by the slightly older R.-J.-H. Dutrochet (1776–1847) whose interests closely paralleled Raspail's and who obtained medical training in Paris in 1802–06, despite his crushing poverty. See A. R. Rich, "The Place of R.-H.-J. Dutrochet in the Development of the Cell Theory," *Bulletin of the Johns Hopkins Hospital*, XXXIX (1926), 330–65. Another impecunious adolescent who rose to eminence in medicine was J. E. D. Esquirol (1772–1840), the famous psychiatrist. The hospitality and generosity of the Comte de Molé's mother smoothened his path during the time of his medical training in Paris.

. . . nature . . . took me by the hand:
"Come," she said, "don't look back. . . . I
have treasures for your mind and for your
heart; . . . in this green blade of grass you
shall discover the formation of the embryo
and the origin of life . . . ; this round
drop of water shall . . . reveal a new
universe to you, . . . the enigma of how
organized beings combine. . . ."

The microscope finally won the battle and
became a reagent in its own right. The
pharmacists and chemists of the capital
were forced to adopt it and yield to public
opinion which rules the world.

F.-V. Raspail

IV

THE YOUNG

RESEARCHER,

1822–1830*

ONLY ONE OFFICIAL DOCUMENT actually proves that Raspail pursued academic studies of science: his student card at the Faculty of Sciences in Paris. It reads: "On December 2, 1820, the Dean of the Science Faculty issued to M. Raspail (François-Vincent), twenty-six, born in Carpentras, Vaucluse, living in Paris at 71, rue Saint Jacques, card number 1369, entitling him to attend lectures at this Faculty." But we do not know what courses he attended. He obtained no diploma. We do know that he was a frequent visitor at the *Muséum* of Natural History, its hothouses and

* WRITTEN BY SIMONE RASPAIL. TRANSLATED AND EDITED BY DORA WEINER.

78

botanical garden, and that he worked on the large herbal of Benjamin Delessert.[1] With characteristic drive, he had soon mastered the basic, classical training. The references he cites in his papers bear witness to his precocious erudition.

What Raspail thus acquired—largely on his own initiative—was the sparse knowledge that the young science of botany amounted to by 1820. The description and classification of plants, begun in modern times by Conrad Gessner of Zurich (1516–1565), first focused on the characteristics of flower and fruit, and on the idea of genus and species. After Andrea Cesalpini (1519–1603) had attempted a classification of some 840 plants into fifteen groups, an important step was taken by the Englishman John Ray (1628–1705) who noticed that the embryo of flowering plants offers a constant characteristic: one or two cotyledons. It was Carl von Linné who established the modern method of plant classification. Although his system was based, somewhat simply, on the number of stamens, its clarity, order, scope, and the use of two Latin names to designate each plant render his work exceptionally important. It is still in use and has been extended to animals, even to microbes. In the realm of morphology two Germans, Joseph Gärtner (1732–1791) and Joseph Köhlreuter (1733–1806), recorded acute observations and insights, and the ingenious Stephen Hales (1671–1761) had already progressed far on the way along which plant physiology would proceed.[2]

Frenchmen who had contributed to the progress of botany included Michel Adanson (1727–1806) and Bernard de Jussieu (1699–1777), who grouped genera into families, as well as his nephew Antoine-Laurent de Jussieu (1748–1816), a brilliant botanist trained by his uncle from an early age who further defined families, genera, and species. Although he did not emphasize anatomical characteristics, these have usually confirmed his classification. R.-L. Desfontaines (1750–1833), with whom Raspail was to have dealings, attempted to describe the internal as well

[1] Delessert (1773–1847), a famous financier and philanthropist, owned a collection of 86,000 species of plants, begun by his mother's friend, Jean-Jacques Rousseau.

[2] For a good survey in English of late eighteenth-century botany, see A. Wolf, *A History of Science, Technology, and Philosophy in the 18th Century* (New York, 1961), 2 vols., 2nd revised ed., II, ch. XVII.

as the external organs of plants and their physiologic functions. As early as 1799 he had shown by striking examples that the internal organization of plants could be related to their external form.

Botany was a lively field of study in France in the 1820s. Problems of physiology and classification were debated in and outside the Academy of Sciences. Reminiscing in 1837, Raspail recalled that as early as 1822 he had decided to study the laws governing the organic world: "Looking at a huge tree one thinks of the seed and wonders about the profoundly mysterious organic mechanism that produced this giant from so small a shell. The answer to this mystery would solve the problem . . . of plant physiology." [3] This passage points to the gist of Raspail's work, elaborated fifteen years later in his *New System of Plant Physiology*—a vast project inspired by the philosophic notions of the former seminarist. The young scientist hastened to adopt a strict method:

From the beginning of my studies I believed that nothing would be more damaging than to proceed by leaps and bounds. . . . I thought, on the contrary, that once I had obtained a just and reasonable idea of one family of plants or animals, this would be applicable to all of them. I decided to study the most neglected one, hitherto unappreciated by authors, deformed by draftsmen, and, so to speak, stepped on by common observers: the obscure grasses, those pariahs of vegetation which are mowed down with scythe or sickle, and barely included in herbals. [4]

Although his observations would focus on minute details, he would attempt to interpret his findings not as a specialist, but with an awareness of the multiple interrelationships that exist in nature. He wrote: "Nature is neither chemist, nor botanist, zoologist, mineralogist nor physiologist. She is not divided into scientific compartments, she does not proceed by classification or artificial systems. She is a single cause of varied combinations." [5]

The idea of beginning with the grasses was suggested by the

[3] F.-V. Raspail, *Nouveau système de physiologie végétale et de botanique, fondé sur les méthodes d'observation qui ont été développées dans le Nouveau système de chimie organique accompagné d'un Atlas de 60 planches*, 65.

[4] *Ibid.*, 67.

[5] F.-V. Raspail, *Nouveau système de chimie organique* (Paris, 1833), 31. [Unless otherwise indicated, all references are to this first edition.]

large number of species available, the confusion in their classification, the ease of finding them near Paris, and their humble, "proletarian" place in the kingdom of nature. He described the procedure he would follow:

> Observe much; read little. (One reads much better after observing; one observes more freely before reading.)
> Prejudge nothing; take note of everything.
> Draw much; describe little.
> Draw several different enlargements. Compare from every angle.
> Count, measure, and review often.[6]

For two years, bending eight hours a day over his small grasses, he did not deviate from this method.

I would not leave a grass, even the most trivial, until I had studied it exhaustively and until neither my eye nor my mind could extract any more from it. I was so little preoccupied with nomenclature and so much with analysis that I could have drawn the smallest detail of a plant from memory, before I could have named it. I do not think I exaggerate if I say that I devoted two consecutive days to establishing the shape of two tiny organs on the spikelets of a flower: I mean the two lodicules at the base of the stamens in *Agrostis spicaventi*. The point was to decide whether these small organs were bidentate. This observation, apparently so futile, determined a whole law of classification.[7]

In 1824 Raspail was to submit his first paper, "On the Formation of the Embryo in Grasses,"[8] to the Academy of Sciences. He intimates that the road, although long, would lead to new horizons:

I hope I shall not startle the reader if, in discussing the embryo, I begin with a bract (a small, scalelike leaf). Scientists are convinced

[6] F.-V. Raspail, *Nouveau système de physiologie végétale et de botanique* . . . , 68.

[7] *Ibid.*

[8] F.-V. Raspail, "Mémoire sur la formation de l'embryon dans les graminées," first appeared in *Annales des sciences naturelles*, IV (1824), 271–319, and was translated into German and published both in *Notizen aus dem Gebiet der Natur- und Heilkunde*, L. F. von Froriep, ed., No. 243 (October 1825) and *Bulletin de l'académie de Saint-Pétersbourg*, K. B. von Trinius, ed. [It has been impossible to verify this last reference, but von Trinius was indeed professor of botany at Saint Petersburg at the time.]

The great German naturalist L. Oken also announced Froriep's translation in *Isis*, VIII (1826), 780. (See *infra*, pp. 85–86 and 90.)

that any part of an organized being is related to all other parts and that organs which seem to be an enormous distance away in the functional hierarchy are often those which provide the closest analogy. . . .[9]

Faithful to his guiding principle of establishing a history of plant organization and evolution, Raspail analyzed plant ovaries. Before complete maturation, the pericarp of the ovary is detachable from the perisperm and has considerable consistency. If a young wheat ovary is sectioned lengthwise, one can observe the yellowish pericarp around the ovary, then a second, distinct and rather thick envelope in which the ovary is embedded. If one dissects ovaries of increasing age, one observes that the substance of this envelope is enlarged, first at the top, and comes closer to the pericarp. At the same time, the walls of the cavity surrounding the embryo close in on it, until they enclose it completely. If a trace of the cavity remains, it is always at the base of the embryo. This would not happen if the perisperm were a new organ developing between the embryo and a skin which one would be entitled to call a separate envelope (episperm).

The perisperm can therefore only be the tissue of an unsplit leaf whose parenchyma overflows with a sugary sap, not used in vegetation, and transforms this sap into a starchy substance through evaporation and through a chemical process proper to this organ. The upper part of the perisperm is never filled with starch.[10]

This quotation foretells the direction which Raspail's research would take. He then established the formation of the embryo:

Before fertilization the ovum adheres to the cavity that encloses it. Once fertilized, it is isolated and enclosed in a lower leaf whose cellular tissue, injected with starchy matter in the graminaea, will first be its "silo" and later its perisperm. The embryo is isolated from contact with air and thus preserved. . . . The seed falls, enclosing next year's hope.[11]

This first paper established a close relationship among the organs of grasses. It showed the capital importance of veins and the care with which they must be studied. By emphasizing the comparative

[9] F.-V. Raspail, "Mémoire sur la formation de l'embryon . . . ," *Annales des sciences naturelles,* IV, 272.

[10] *Ibid.,* 297.

[11] *Ibid.,* 304.

study of plant embryos at successive developmental stages Raspail pointed the way to experimental embryology. He proposed new criteria for the classification of grasses, emphasizing physiology and microscopic analysis, which permitted K. B. von Trinius' seventy-seven genera of grasses to be reduced to Raspail's fifty-eight. In criticizing his predecessors, Raspail pointed out that they had too often based their classification on dried samples, neglecting to moisten them before observation. In that way microscopic examination had taken place under poor conditions, with the sample held in the hand instead of fixed on the stage. Modern botany has profited from the stress on physiology and on microscopy that Raspail constantly emphasized in his work.

In fact, his daily use of the microscope was unorthodox in France.[12] True, botanists employed it extensively, but the influential Bichat had discouraged its use in biology, arguing that "when one looks in the dark, everyone sees what he can and wishes."[13] H. M. de Blainville (1777–1850), a prominent physiologist, echoed this verdict in 1829 when he wrote: "The microscope teaches nothing new about the anatomic structure of cell tissue . . ." and he condemned "mistaken theories which the microscope often supports with illusory data."[14] Blainville was but re-

[12] The microscope had, of course, been widely known for over a century and had even, for a time, been a social fad. [See M. H. Nicolson, "The Microscope and English Imagination," in *Science and Imagination* (Ithaca, 1956).] But the quality of the old-fashioned "spy-glasses" was quite inferior. Only in Raspail's day was the achromatic, compound microscope being perfected. [Notably by J. B. Amici (1784–1864), an Italian astronomer and optician.] In Germany, this new tool was widely used, but most Frenchmen thought little of it. [See M. Klein, *Histoire des origines de la théorie cellulaire* (Paris, 1936), 40–41; and R. H. Shryock, *The Development of Modern Medicine* (New York, 1947), 169.]

[13] Quoted in M. Klein, *Histoire des origines* . . . , 41.

[14] *Ibid.*, 43. A modern author explains: ". . . in the 1830s the microscope was still a very imperfect instrument. Techniques for preparing specimens were rudimentary. Plant material, with its relatively rigid walls, lent itself to freehand sectioning, but with softer material only spreads and squash preparations were available. Modern routine procedures, fixation, embedding, accurate sectioning and differential staining were not then known. . . .

"The delicate nature of the cell membrane, the similar refractive index of cell wall and cell contents, and the granular appearance which both might manifest, all intensified the difficulty. The great variety of cell forms also raised problems in recognition and identification. Furthermore, the use of water as the medium for examining fresh specimens induced cellular changes that complicated any interpretation." L. King, *The Growth of Medical Thought* (Chicago, 1963), 187–88.

peating the opinion of his friend Auguste Comte (1798–1857) whose Positivist philosophy exerted considerable influence on scientific conceptualization and methodology in France. To Comte, various tissues constituted the basic elements of physiology. He condemned scientists who speculated about smaller fundamental units. "The abuse of microscopic research and the excessive credit often granted to so deceptive a tool have helped give this fantastic theory [the cell theory] a specious certainty. . . ." [15] Raspail went ahead regardless of these reservations and possibly because he wished once again to oppose what the majority practiced.

When Raspail dared present his work to the Academy of Sciences he felt that he was contributing important new ideas. He gives a dramatic account of his state of mind when he took this important first step:

From a garret of Paris, a region where God feeds only the birds, I walked one day into town. . . . For two years an idea had been absorbing all my research and a hope had been consuming me. I had finally captured the idea and I thought that fortune was smiling. In those days, young men knew only one dream, a kind of glory, whose temple was the Academy of Sciences, guardian of truth. . . . Today it would be difficult to understand the religious aura surrounding the Academy of Sciences. . . . As for me, who knew no one, I venerated each member of this learned society like those Benedictines of St. Maur, always faithful to science, who welcomed all those who approached them with fatherly solicitude. I believed that their only ambition was study and service, and modesty their only striving. I remember how I trembled when I dared speak to one of them for the first time, in the courtyard of the Institute. It was the late Desfontaines, professor of botany at the *Muséum*. I wanted to ask for his help in reading my paper at a meeting of the Academy:

"What is your subject?"

"Botany." (I did not dare pronounce the word physiology; I did not think I was capable of such research.)

"Botany? Have you new and exotic species?"

"No, Sir, new organs and new analogies."

Hearing these words, Desfontaines turned his back as if I had insulted him and disdained answering me.

Mere schemers will laugh at me if I admit what a blow this cold reception was to my pride; I was not the kind of man who would now

[15] Quoted in M. Klein, *Histoire des originies* . . . , 50.

try to approach other academicians. But, eager as I was, I found out that one could obtain the right to read a paper simply by registering. So I did, and three months later I was called: it was on November 2, 1824.[16]

Amid general indifference, noise, and chatter, Raspail read his paper. It was when he was leaving the building, disappointed and discouraged, that Geoffroy Saint-Hilaire caught up with him in the courtyard of the Institute and spoke kind words of praise.[17] The paper was referred to a committee of two, composed of C. F. Brisseau de Mirbel (1776–1854) and A. A. Dupetit-Thouars (1758–1831). Only the latter showed any interest.[18] Raspail was curious to know Dupetit-Thouars' opinion and decided to pay him a visit.

I arrived at Dupetit-Thouars' study [Raspail wrote], through a whole forest of tree trunks, staves of wood, branches, bulbs, roots, and buds lying in the hall. The mantelpiece was loaded with grasses of all kinds over which the scientist was bending, magnifying glass and microscope in hand, a scarf wound around his head, and his body swathed in a costume quite different from the academician's embroidered cutaway. I must admit that the sight reassured me; nothing resembling arrogance, which I find ridiculous, nor pompousness, which horrifies me. "I have not yet found a single error," he said, "but I do not agree with all your opinions. Nevertheless I shall not hesitate to do you justice." [19]

A month later he read his report at two long meetings and concluded: "This paper deserves the encouragements of the Academy." No prize, no publication in any official bulletin. And yet the German scientist Trinius had deemed the paper worthy of a full-

---

[16] F.-V. Raspail, *Nouveau système de physiologie végétale et de botanique* . . . , 2–3.

[17] See *supra*, p. 70.

[18] He was something of an eccentric among the academicians, being neither a writer, nor an orator, nor a man of the world. But he had traveled widely, and observed rather than read and, Raspail says, he refused to adopt the manner of the Academy whose methods he attacked quite roughly, often in public. His colleagues thought Dupetit-Thouars rather ridiculous when he took up Linnaeus' ideas on the analogy of the bud with the flower and the seed, and on the common origin of leaves and flowers.

[19] F.-V. Raspail, *Nouveau système de physiologie végétale et de botanique* . . . , 4–5.

length translation in the *Bulletin of the Academy of Sciences of Saint Petersburg.*[20]

Raspail's second long paper, his "Memoir on the Development of Starch in the Reproductive Organs of Grasses," fared somewhat better. It was read on August 6, 1825, to the Philomatic Society of which Raspail was about to become a full-fledged member and was published in the *Annals of the Natural Sciences.*[21] Raspail's earlier work had broken new ground in botany. This second paper fully revealed the creative genius of the scientist. "It caused a scientific revolution," he wrote many years later.[22] In this paper Raspail wished to ascertain the exact position of the embryo, even in its rudimentary state. But the delicacy of unfertilized ovarian tissues hampered dissection. Samples were often distorted. Only two other authors had touched on the problem of the embryo: Mirbel in the *Journal de physique* of July 1802, and A. M. F. Palisot de Beauvois (1752–1820), in his *Esquisse d'une nouvelle agrostographie* (1812). Mirbel defined the embryo as that small turbinate body, usually of greenish color (although white in cereals), found in young ovaries. Palisot de Beauvois maintained that the small body was actually the perisperm, while its tiny point was the embryo. He asserted that the skin which surrounds the small body is formed by a viscous membrane that disappears entirely when the body fills the whole cavity.

Raspail's first thought was to verify Palisot's assertions by the use of iodine tincture which will color starch purple. What did Raspail find? That the integument (skin) turns to a beautiful purple or blue when iodine is added, showing it to be filled with starch, whereas the turbinate body is found not to contain any starch. Here, then, was the idea basic to Raspail's procedures in microscopic chemistry, histology, and histochemistry: to find out

[20] Trinius criticized certain of Raspail's classifications that differed from his own, but he accepted Raspail's theory of the formation of the embryo and the description of organs in the seed. See *supra*, p. 81, n. 8.

[21] F.-V. Raspail, "Développement de la fécule dans les organes de la fructification des céréales et analyse microscopique de la fécule, suivie d'expériences propres à en expliquer la conversion en gomme," *Annales des sciences naturelles,* VI (1825), 224–39, 384–427.

[22] F.-V. Raspail, *Histoire de ma vie et de mon siècle,* 265.

whether the small, white, turbinate body in grain seeds contained starch by adding a drop of iodine to a section of wheat ovary placed under a modest microscope. Ever since the work of J.-J. Colin (1784–1865) and H. F. Gaultier de Claubry (1792–1878) in 1814, it had been known that iodine colors starch blue. F. S. Stromeyer (1776–1835) confirmed this in 1815, but neither the Frenchmen nor the German nor anyone else had thought of using this test under the microscope. Nor had it occurred to anyone to study by this simple means the place and distribution of starch in seeds. Raspail's originality consisted in adapting known chemical tests to microscopic research, and in devising and developing new tests and new techniques for histochemistry.

The season was now too far advanced to permit further research. So Raspail planned his work for the coming year:

1. Acquire the habit, through a great number of tests, of dissecting unfertilized grain ovaries [no larger than a pinhead] in every direction and from every angle;
2. Always compare several ovaries which are at different developmental stages under the same microscope in order better to understand the transition from one form to the next in the progress of vegetation;
3. Use frozen mixtures in order to avoid disfiguring and flattening the tissues with the scalpel;
4. Lastly: use alcohol and iodine tincture: the first to render tissues firm for observation; the second to color organs that contain starch blue, so as to recognize them at all ages, even after they lose their initial shape and become confused with the layers of adjacent tissue.[23]

The third and fourth paragraphs are of considerable historic importance: with these few lines histochemistry was born. The frozen section technique, which Raspail could not use as fully as he had hoped because he was too poor or because his tools were too rudimentary, was revived at the end of the nineteenth century and constitutes today an often indispensable technique. Modern histochemists consider Raspail as the inventor of this procedure. Professor John R. Baker, a cytologist at Oxford, commented in 1950:

[23] F.-V. Raspail, "Développement de la fécule . . . ," *Annales des sciences naturelles,* VI, 228–29.

The freezing of tissues so as to harden them and make it possible to cut thin sections was introduced by that remarkable and much-over-looked Frenchman, F.-V. Raspail, who . . . was the founder of the science of histochemistry. The invention of frozen section technique has unfortunately always been accredited to Stilling [the German anatomist B. S. Stilling (1810–1879)], who rediscovered it in 1842 when a nerve-cord in his possession was accidentally frozen on a cold night. Seventeen years previously Raspail (1825) had announced that one of the four "resolutions" on which his work was founded was "to employ freezing mixtures. . . ." [24]

The use of a reagent which permits differential staining and renders possible the study of a single substance in the chemically heterogeneous cell constitutes the basic principle of histochemistry. We shall see that Raspail developed this method by testing and adopting other reagents. In his second paper, the use of tincture of iodine permitted him to describe the unfertilized wheat ovary with great precision: according to shape, structure, place of the veins, and shape of the embryo. The iodine colors the cells yellow, the alcohol in tincture of iodine renders them firm. [25] Raspail was able to observe that the ovule or seed never contains a cavity comparable to a uterus. Neither can one detect the presumed amniotic fluid that the imagination of physiologists looking through a microscope had placed into plant ovules. [26] The end of the paper offers a perspective on the history of cell life:

[24] J. R. Baker, *Cytological Technique* (London, 1950), 3rd ed., 104.

[25] That alcohol "fixes" tissues was well-known at the time.

[26] After fertilization, Raspail observed that the pericarp lengthens and thins out, and iodine stains it blue. Then the turbinate body also lengthens, the cells in the center swell out and form a kind of cavity. Sometime after fertilization the iodine begins to detect ever larger traces of starch, until this organ is completely filled and is then called perisperm. At every stage one can ascertain that it is the tissue that is infiltrated and not a vesicle that is being filled. As for the embryo, as soon as one can detect it, one finds it in the embryo sac. It takes shape, and one can see the cotelydon, the plumule, and the radicle.

The second part of the paper is devoted to the microscopic study of starch in the perisperm. The chemical or—as Raspail says—"macroscopic" [*"en grand"*] study of starch would have added nothing to what the books said in Raspail's day. He carefully described starch grains in oats, and their coloration with iodine. The existence of these grains of given dimension, separate within the cell, their smooth and rounded shape, the fact that they remain unchanged in water, are colored by iodine, discolored by the addition of an alkali, led him to think that starch is neither a crystal nor an element, as was then widely be-

Before fertilization, the pericarp was filled with starch, the perisperm had not trace of it. After fertilization, the pericarp gradually loses its starch, the perisperm is gradually filled with it. At maturity, the pericarp has no more trace of it, the perisperm abounds with starch. The embryo contains none, the nourishment of the seed is completed. . . .[27]

The importance of Raspail's research was recognized by some of his contemporaries. But after the early 1830s he was almost totally ignored by scientists. Some despised his politics and therefore overlooked his experiments. Others were put off by his manner: he thought nothing of pre-empting several consecutive meetings of learned societies with the reading of one of his papers, and spared his listeners not a single conjecture, aside, or digression. Could one blame them for attempting to prevent similar happenings?

Most important, after 1829 he no longer published in any well-known journal with a wide circulation such as the *Répertoire général d'anatomie,* the *Annales des sciences naturelles,* or the *Mémoires* of the *Muséum* or the Academy of Sciences. All Raspail's work published after 1829 appeared only in his own journals, which few bothered to read.

His influence, which might otherwise have been considerable, was therefore negligible. True, some scientists, for example, Jean-Baptiste Biot, the chemist, physicist, and astronomer, praised Raspail's microscopic analysis of sugar and starch when he presented two papers to the Paris Society of Natural History in 1833.[28] The

---

lieved. The starch grain is composed of two parts: a kind of shell, which Raspail called "the integument of starch," and the soluble substance it contains. This led him to consider the starch grain as a cell within a cell. Today we know that starch is a substance contained in the cell. We also know that the insoluble part, Raspail's "integument," is made of amylopectin, a polymer of maltose. The soluble part consists of amylose, another polymer of maltose.

"The integument of starch," Raspail said, "will become a cell destined to elaborate a substance it contains. This cell differs from the one which encloses it because that one is agglutinated to several others, whereas the starch grain, and others like it, remain free within the enclosing cell." F.-V. Raspail "Développement de la fécule . . . ," *Annales des sciences naturelles,* VI, 412.

[27] *Ibid.,* 414–15.

[28] J. B. Biot, "Sur un caractère optique, à l'aide duquel on reconnaît immédiatement les sucs végétaux qui peuvent donner du sucre analogue au sucre de canne, et ceux qui ne peuvent donner que du sucre semblable au sucre de raisin," *Nouvelles annales du Muséum d'histoire naturelle,* II (1833), 107;

previous year Raspail had received a letter from Lorenz Oken (1779–1851), the German naturalist and philosopher, which reflected the German's esteem for Raspail's work;[29] its critical second paragraph explains why Raspail did not accede to Oken's flattering request:

Munich, October 2, 1832

Dear Sir,

I am currently making abstracts for *Isis* from the *Mémoires de la société d'histoire naturelle de Paris*. I find it impossible to give an exact account of your numerous discoveries as concisely as *Isis* requires. Therefore I am writing to ask whether you might not undertake this work yourself. In a few hours, you could do what would take me days, and, furthermore, I might distort your ideas. You may also include illustrations, enough to fill one plate.

The newspapers inform me of your difficulties which I regret, especially seeing that they distract you from your scientific occupations, which are so important to the world, and much more fruitful than your political activities. I must admit that I am convinced the world will progress by itself, and that it is as impossible to push and pull it as it is to compel plants to grow. The world needs only water, heat, and light, just as plants do. To attempt more is to crush the world, or to be crushed oneself.

Yours,

Oken.

Before continuing the discussion of his work, let us hear Raspail explain his ideas and the genesis of his thought:

. . . what I see through a weak magnifying glass seems obviously identical to what I observe with the naked eye; we increase the enlargement: I shall see more, but shall I see differently? . . . If the microscope, instead of revealing a new world, only makes tiny par-

---

and J. B. Biot and J. F. Persoz, "Mémoire sur les modifications que la fécule et la gomme subissent sous l'influence des acides," *Ibid.*, 110.

While preparing these papers, Biot has asked Raspail's collaborator J.-F. Saigey to bring him all of Raspail's written work on starch. [Raspail was then in prison.] ". . . . Generally speaking," wrote Biot, "we find ourselves using M. Raspail's experiments much more often than I had anticipated. . . ." Fonds Raspail, Archives du Département de la Seine, X.

[29] Fonds Raspail, Archives du Département de la Seine, VIII.

ticles visible to the eye, if it only serves to distinguish very complex mixtures, if it permits us to advance further in our study of organs, let us make it a fertile source of discoveries by submitting the phenomena we can now observe to all the reagents and controls which we normally use in our research; let us use it to discover not *miracles* or ingenious hypotheses, but positive results. . . .

This was the initial idea that occurred to me when I took the first steps in my career as an observer. Seeing the micrographer content to draw and dissect organs, and the chemist alter, mix, or destroy them in order to have the pleasure of rediscovering and recomposing them, I seemed to see two men walking side by side without knowing it, on two roads that would never meet. And I decided to follow them no longer, but to merge their work. I would no longer be sometimes a chemist, or physicist, or botanist, or physiologist, but all of these at once, all the time. I therefore needed to abandon known methods and create new ones, establish new rules, for I was to work in a new kind of laboratory.[30]

New rules, new procedures. . . . This ingenuity, combined with his poverty, would result in the simplicity of Raspail's technique, based on rigor, patience, intellectual honesty, manual dexterity, and extreme precision. His chief tool was the microscope.

The optician Deleuil, 34, rue Dauphine in Paris, built a small simple microscope according to the young scientist's instructions,[31] which was known as "Raspail's microscope." There have been some protests against this name, which was given to an improvement of the microscope designed by Cuff,[32] even though Raspail himself acknowledged that he had merely perfected Cuff's instrument.[33]

[30] F.-V. Raspail, Introduction, "Essai de chimie microscopique appliquée à la physiologie, ou L'art de transporter le laboratoire sur le porte-objet dans l'étude des corps organisés," first published in *Annales des sciences d'observation*, II (1829), 430–45; III (1830), 65–82; 216–28; 368–86; IV (1830), 65–81; 225–251. This reference is to II (1830), 434–36, *passim*. The *Essai* was published as a separate booklet (Paris, 1830), and finally revised and appended to the *Nouveau système de chimie organique*, 3rd ed. (Paris, 1838).

[31] See *Ibid.*, 438, n. 1.

[32] It has been impossible further to identify this designer of microscopes.

[33] On the usefulness of these early microscopes, see *supra*, pp. 83–84.

Thanks to Madame Emilie Varichon-Raspail, a great-grand-daughter of the famous scientist, one of Raspail's earliest micro-scopes has been preserved. It carries Deleuil's label and the number 9. It is thus one of the first of more than one thousand microscopes to come from Deleuil's workshop. Its great simplicity and conven-ience are striking.[34] A polished wooden box, which measures 185 mm x 100 mm x 45 mm, contains a drawer for the lenses, optical system, and dissecting tools. (The box could slip into the pocket of the frock coat which was then in fashion.) The upper part of the base has a square copper casing into which the foot carrying the optical system can be set. This foot, 110 mm high, permits the insertation of an arm which ends in a grooved ring for the lenses. A screw then allows the lengthening and shortening of this arm, which can turn 180° horizontally.

Halfway up the foot, a small sliding tube permits the insertion of the stage—a brass disc 53 mm in diameter holding a plate glass disc. The stage is vertically movable, which renders adjustment easy and permits one to move it away from the lens in order to deposit the reagents. A mirror to focus light can be fitted into the base of the foot.

Raspail's lenses included:

1. A biconvex lens of six lines[35] focal length, permitting an enlarge-ment of about 20 (of excellent quality).

2. Three biconvex lenses of tourmaline of ½ line of focal length, per-mitting an enlargement of about 240. These lenses have a diameter of 2 mm and are fixed at the highest point of a flattened, cone-shaped brass support of 21 mm diameter. The light beams pass through an opening of about 1 mm. Tourmaline has the property of polarizing light and thus eliminates chromatic aberrations. These three lenses are excellent and give a very clear image, but result in extreme eyestrain.[36]

[34] Raspail wrote confidently in 1845: "The microscope will unmask all causes of disease and replace traditional jargon . . . with the positive language of scientific observation." F.-V. Raspail, *Manuel-annuaire de la santé* (Paris, 1845), 1st ed., 40. He was fully conscious of being an innovator. See A. Hughes, *A History of Cytology* (New York, 1959), ch. I, "The Development of Micro-scopical Observation."

[35] A "line" was one-twelfth of an inch.

[36] Deleuil manufactured these lenses which give a yellow light; this is prob-ably why they were not more widely used.

3. Two lenses of blue glass, similarly mounted, with a focal length of ½ line.
4. A double lens, giving an enlargement at about 50, consisting of two plane-convex lenses, giving very light and exact images.

The observational field of the lenses of ½ line is less than 1 mm in diameter. The mobility of the arm carrying the lens permits observation of an object's entire surface.

Curiosity and family loyalty induced this author[37] to repeat some of Raspail's experiments with his own microscope. Any modern observer, used to the comfort of compound binocular microscopes with ingenious and precise lighting, must stand amazed at the patience that the delicate adjustment of lenses of half a line demands on a microscope such as Raspail's, and by the great fatigue which prolonged observation entails. And yet Raspail worked eight hours a day on this small microscope and some of his observations rival those obtained with modern instruments.

Later on Raspail had a compound microscope built, one that permitted many kinds of observations, even in corroding liquids, or in liquids at the boiling point. A micrometric measuring apparatus was attached to it. The stage consisted of a small rectangular glass vessel in which all chemical reactions could be effected while maintaining visual control through the microscope. But the quality of the compound lenses was less than excellent, and Raspail always preferred the small, simple microscope, which gave more reliable images, although it was less comfortable for the observer.

His dissecting tools consisted of a small scalpel with a thin, curved, narrow blade; two plain very sharp pins, mounted on handles, used to lacerate tissues; and very small steel hooks attached to a wire ending in a lead weight, used to hold membranes in place or apart. If an acid or corroding substance was to be used, he substituted platinum wires. He arranged reagents on the platform with the help of thin glass tubes that he lengthened under a flame. These were the modest, inexpensive tools of the founder of histochemistry.

Between 1825 and 1829 Raspail further investigated living tissues. The chemical analysis of flour obtained from various cereals

---

[37] Simone Raspail.

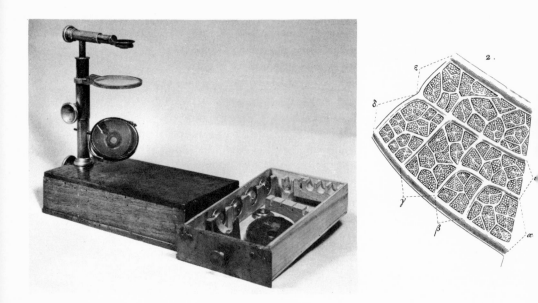

Above left, Raspail's microscope, made by Deleuil, ca. 1823 (Courtesy Mademoiselle Simone Raspail) Photo Bulloz

To its right, the development of the leaf, detail (From F.-V. Raspail, *Nouveau système de physiologie végétale et de botanique, Atlas.* Plate VI)

Facing page, upper left, the itch mite (From F.-V. Raspail, *Histoire naturelle de la santé* 3rd ed., Plate VI) This drawing, like all the others in this book, carries the legend: "F.-Benj. Raspail filius pinxit."

Far right, a working sketch (From F.-V. Raspail, *Revue complémentaire des sciences appliquées à la médecine et pharmacie, à l'agriculture, aux arts, et à l'industrie* [Paris, 1860], VI, 276)

Raspail was a careful draftsman. Witness this sketch of a strange carrot, drawn by Benjamin, a painter and engraver, corrected in Raspail's own writing. Raspail demanded absolute exactness and high artistic quality. His perfectionism can be observed in his critical remarks, jotted in the margin of the appended sketch which, to the uninitiate observer, looks accurate enough: "In this section we have *barely the right* texture; *you must be careful* trying to round out the shaded area, otherwise it will look square." "Try to soften these details." "I seem to see a double penstroke on this part of the contour. If so, take it off!"

Below, microscopic anatomy of the fibrils of the chorion (From F.-V. Raspail, *Nouveau système de chimie organique,* 1st ed., Plate VIII)

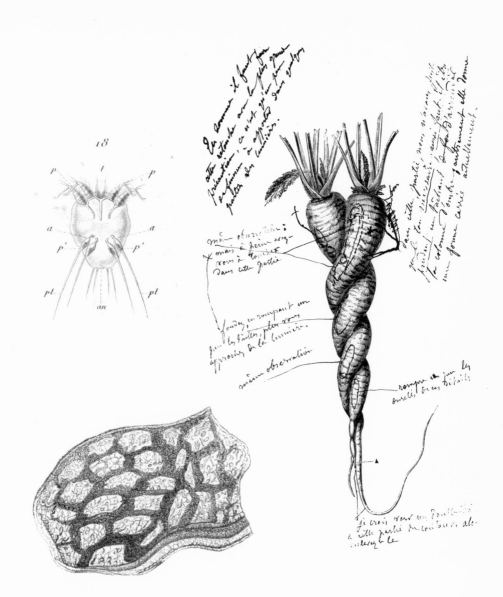

had been made by the end of the eighteenth century. Great pharmacists and chemists such as A. A. Parmentier (1737–1813), L.-J. Proust (1754–1826), L. J. Thénard (1777–1857), Sir Humphrey Davy (1778–1829) had separated starch from gluten and shown their proportions in flour. But where is the gluten in wheat? Where is the starch? What is their history? No one had asked these questions. Raspail would try to find out in which tissues of the seed these substances are to be found and how their evolution takes place.

In a paper read before the Society of Natural History in 1826, Raspail recounted his experiments with starch.[38] Having observed the transformations of starch granules within wheat seeds, he tried to reproduce in the laboratory, by physical or chemical means, the phenomena ascertained under the microscope. He also planted wheat seeds in moist earth and studied them a few days later. He reported on his findings:

Nature here exceeded her usual foresight: *the starch grains do not burst open within the seed* (as happens in starch subjected to boiling, acids, or concentrated alkalis), *but they empty slowly*. And owing to this mechanism, which I was unable to reproduce [in the laboratory] I discovered the internal organization of a starch grain. I should first point out that iodine colored these grains a less and less intense purple although the grain contains a free acid, so that the decreasing coloration could not be due to the presence of an alkali. Under the microscope the grains looked flat but not torn; in their center one could see a rounded mass of globules which were not isolated from one another (agitation of the liquid did not separate them). This round mass was obviously attached, at one point, to the integument for, upon rotation, it was never seen rolling around or changing its place within the integument; it seemed therefore likely that these globules were enclosed within another membrane which compressed them. . . . The existence of a large vesicle attached to the inner wall of the integument became evident.[39]

After many observations and measurements of cells he proclaimed: "Forgive my daring and mark my words: the day is near when this scientific challenge will no longer sound fantastic nor overconfident: GIVE ME A CELL WITHIN WHICH OTHER CELLS CAN BE FORMED

[38] F.-V. Raspail, "Recheches chimiques et physiologiques destinées à expliquer non seulement la structure et le développement de la feuille, du tronc, ainsi que les organes qui n'en sont qu'une transformation, mais encore la structure et le développement des tissus animaux," *Mémoires de la société d'histoire naturelle de Paris,* III (1827), 17–88, 209–313. (Read on July 21, 1826, to the Paris Society of Natural History of which Raspail had become a member on June 23, 1826.)

[39] *Ibid.,* 211–12.

BY ELABORATION AND INFILTRATION—AND I SHALL HAND YOU THE ORGANIZED WORLD."[40]

Speculation about the nature and role of the cell was related to the large questions of growth, change, and evolution that preoccupied contemporary naturalists such as J. B. de Lamarck, G. Cuvier, L. Oken, and J. W. von Goethe. Many distinguished scientists, for example, H. Milne-Edwards, R.-H.-J. Dutrochet,[41] and P.-J.-F. Turpin,[42] were even then speculating about basic similarities of plant and animal cells. This kind of speculation was encouraged by the vogue of *Naturphilosophie,* that child of Romanticism, originating in Germany with the philosopher F. W. v. Schelling (1775–1854), adopted by Fichte and well known to Hegel. As early as 1809 the German *Naturphilosoph* Oken had asserted: "The organic world has for its basis an infinity of little blebs [*Bläschen*]." [43] In the history of science, *Naturphilosophie* exerted its influence far into the nineteenth century. It encouraged vitalism, a theory that engendered the belief that each organ has its own specific energy and therefore its tissue is unique; muscles have contractility, nerves irritability. Even Pasteur would have to fight vitalism under the guise of the theory of spontaneous generation. Raspail's speculations on the identity of plant and animal cells resembled *Naturphilosophie,* but of course he did more than speculate.

[40] *Ibid.,* 305–6.

[41] This French scientist was also closely to approximate Schwann's work and has, in the opinion of a biographer, not received his due share of recognition. See A. R. Rich, "The Place of R.-H.-J. Dutrochet in the Development of the Cell Theory," *Bulletin of the Johns Hopkins Hospital,* XXXIX (1926), 330–65; and J. W. Wilson, "Dutrochet and the Cell Theory," *Isis.,* XXXVII (1947), 14–21.

[42] French workers in this field seem to have been well aware of each others' efforts: in a paper which Turpin read to the Academy of Sciences in Paris on June 12, 1826, e.g., he mentioned the work of Mirbel, Dutrochet, and Raspail, saying that the latter had found starch to be, indeed, "a mass of true vesicles born immediately from the mother-vesicles of the cellular tissue." P.-J.-F. Turpin, "Organographie végétale; Observations sur quelques végétaux microscopiques, et sur le rôle important que leurs analogues jouent dans la formation et l'accroissement du tissu cellulaire," *Mémoires du Muséum d'histoire naturelle,* XIV (1827), 47–48.

[43] L. Oken, *Lehrbuch der Naturphilosophie* (Jena, 1809), 26.

Much has been made of the motto *"Omnis cellula e cellula"* which Professor John R. Baker of Oxford calls "one of the grandest inductions of biology," [44] and which Baker, Long,[45] Singer,[46] and many others attribute to Rudolf Virchow rather than to Raspail. Baker concedes that "Raspail, Turpin, Schleiden, and Goodsir would perhaps have assented to it, if it had been put forward in their time. In fact, however, the phrase was *introduced solely* in reference to the origin of new cells by division." [47] And yet the motto appears as the epigraph of Raspail's study of starch, published in 1825, and was often repeated by him in subsequent years.

The study of cells profited more from empiricism than from such theorizing. But even observation and experiment were still far from any proof that each cell does indeed stem from a cell. Most progress had been made in the study of plant tissue where some cells had been accurately described as early as the seventeenth century by Robert Hooke in his *Micrographia* (1665). In the eighteenth century speculation abounded regarding a basic cellular unit in botany, variously called "vesicle," "bladder," "globule." A new note was sounded by Dutrochet in 1824,[48] and Raspail's work of 1825 closely parallels this new approach. Dutrochet inquired into the life cycle of cells, and he undertook the comparative study of plant and animal cells. Dutrochet's work re-

[44] J. R. Baker, "The Cell-theory: a Restatement, History, and Critique," *Quarterly Journal of Microscopical Science,* Pt. I, LXXXIX (1948), 103–25; Pt. II, XC (1949), 87–108; Pt. III, XCIII (1952), 157–90; Pt. IV, XCIV (1953), 407–40; Pt. V, XCVI (1955), 449–81. The above quotation is from 435.

[45] ". . . Schwann, following the lead of Schleiden, had proved the cellular character of organized beings . . . there remained but one step, but that the most important of all, the one that Virchow took, the recognition of the continuity of cellular life, as expressed in his immortal aphorism *"omnis cellula e cellula."* E. R. Long, *A History of Pathology* (Baltimore, 1928), 199–200.

[46] "In his *Cellular Pathology* (1858) Virchow says: 'Where a cell arises, there a cell must have been before, even as an animal can come from nothing but an animal, a plant from nothing but a plant. . . .' Virchow crystallized the matter in his famous aphorism *'omnis cellula a cellula.'* " C. Singer, *A History of Biology* (New York, 1931), 340–1.

[47] J. R. Baker, "The Cell-Theory: A Restatement . . . ," *Quarterly Journal of Microscopical Science,* 435. John Goodsir (1814–1867) was a Scottish anatomist.

[48] M. Klein, *Histoire des origines . . . ,* 28–29; see also J. W. Wilson, "Cellular Tissue and the Dawn of the Cell Theory," *Isis,* XXXV (1944), 168–73.

sembles that of his immediate French predecessor, H. Milne-Edwards,[49] who used an achromatic, compound microscope. The originality of Raspail in the study of plant tissue lies in his unequalled excellence as microscopist and chemist, and in the fact fact that he considered the cell as a laboratory.[50] He wrote: ". . . the simplest type of organized being is a vesicle whose solid wall can aspire and reject gases and liquids which the vesicle uses for its infinite development." [51] The worlds of plants and animals were formed, he thought, by similar, but not identical, processes. He formulated his idea as follows:

The essential difference between inorganic and organic substances is that gases and bases crystallize to form [inorganic substances] and organize to form [organic substances]. Thus organization is a crystallization within the cell. And when elementary substances combine in this way they acquire a distinct and special property which constitutes a new realm, that of life which is the law of development.[52]

In his *New System of Plant Physiology and Botany* (1837) Raspail even spelled out his notion of what was later called protoplasm. The cell, he wrote, consists of

1° an external vesicle. . . , 2° a colored, usually green vesicle . . . , 3° a liquid elaborated by the cell and contributing to its organization ["un liquide élaboré et organisateur"]. This liquid will only be replaced by air . . . when the organ stops developing.[53]

Klein, who cites this definition, comments:

This passage is remarkable. . . . It contains the description of cell content which was to render Hugo v. Mohl famous.[54] Raspail's vesicle

---

[49] F. K. Studnička, "Aus der Vorgeschichte der Zellentheorie. H. Milne-Edwards, H. Dutrochet, F. Raspail, J. E. Purkinje," *Anatomischer Anzeiger*, LXXIII (1931–1932), 390–416. This reference is to p. 393.

[50] He used the expression "la cellule laboratoire."

[51] F.-V. Raspail, *Nouveau système de chimie organique* . . . , 77.

[52] *Ibid.*, 2nd ed. (1838), I, 403.

[53] F.-V. Raspail, *Nouveau système de physiologie végétale et de botanique* . . . , par. 622, p. 150.

[54] Hugo von Mohl (1805–1875) who became professor of botany at Tübingen is usually acknowledged as the scientist who first defined protoplasm and observed cell division *accurately*. See his "Grundzüge der Anatomie und Physiologie der vegetabilischen Zelle," in R. Wagner, *Handwörterbuch der Physiologie* (Leipzig, 1851).

would become Mohl's nitrogenous utricle ["utricule azoté"]. The organizing liquid would become Mohl's protoplasm—the term protoplasm being meant to convey the generative potential of this liquid. Raspail is thus an eminent forerunner.[55]

The vexing question of priority of discovery can be elucidated most quickly and profitably in the context of the cell theory. Theodor Schwann (1810–1882) is generally acknowledged as the scientist who established by exact observation that all plant and animal cells have a nucleus, membrane, and protoplasm, and that a general law of cell formation applies to plant and animal tissues.[56] Both Schwann and his countryman and predecessor M. J. Schleiden (1804–1881) have been the object of controversy concerning their indebtedness to others.

As often happens in European history, nationalistic claims provided the spur to historical investigation. It was in order to vindicate the priority of his Czech countryman J. E. Purkinje (1787–1869) that F. K. Studnička reviewed the work of Milne-Edwards, Dutrochet, and Raspail in 1931.[57] And the Frenchmen L. Sassani and M. Klein—as well as the American A. R. Rich—wished to show how closely the Germans' work resembled that of their French predecessors.[58] In turning to Schleiden's paper of 1838 [59] one is indeed struck to read that he decided to dispense with a historical Introduction because "direct observations about the

[55] M. Klein, *Histoire des origines* . . . , 35.

[56] Th. Schwann, *Mikroskopische Untersuchungen über die Übereinstimmung in der Struktur und dem Wachstum der Thiere und der Pflanzen* (Berlin, 1839). See also, J. Henle, *Allgemeine Anatomie* (Leipzig, 1841), 128–30. G. Canguilhem, "La théorie cellulaire en biologie. Du sens et de la valeur des théories scientifiques," *Publications de la Faculté des Lettres de l'Université de Strasbourg. Mélanges 1945. IV. Etudes philosophiques* (Paris, 1946), 143–75; and M. Florkin, *Naissance et déviation de la théorie cellulaire dans l'oeuvre de Théodore Schwann* (Paris, 1960). See also F. Cathelin, "Les précurseurs des grands biologistes," *Le Progrès médical, Supplément illustré,* 6ème année, No. 9 (1929), 65–70.

[57] F. K. Studnička, "Aus der Vorgeschichte der Zellentheorie . . . ," *Anatomischer Anzeiger,* LXXIII, 390–416.

[58] L. Sassani, *Les précurseurs français de Schleiden et de Schwann,* Thèse de médecine (Paris, 1907). M. Klein, *Histoire des origines.* . . . A. R. Rich, "The Place of R.-H.-J. Dutrochet . . . ," *Bulletin of the Johns Hopkins Hospital,* XXXIX, 330–65.

[59] M. J. Schleiden, "Beiträge zur Phytogenesis," *Archiv für Anatomie, Physiologie, und wissentschaftliche Medizin,* Fr. J. Müller, ed., 1838, 137–76.

orgins of plant cells have not been made to date." [60] He then discussed the role of starch as a nutrient of the plant embryo, staining experiments of this starch with iodine, the location of the starch in the plant embryo,[61] without ever mentioning Raspail. But of course Schleiden had self-righteously stated in his opening remarks: "To discuss Raspail's work seems to me incompatible with the dignity of science. Whoever feels the urge to do so may read it for himself." [62] Had Schleiden felt that urge?

As for Schwann, Studnička writes: "It is strange that Schwann nowhere cites [Dutrochet's work]; of course it is well known that in the Introduction to his book [1839] he also forgot Purkinje, his immediate predecessor." [63] By comparing many passages in Schwann and Dutrochet, Rich strongly implies the possibility of borrowed French ingredients in Schwann's cell theory.[64]

If it is true, then, that significant contributions to the cell theory were made in France in the 1820s, in what way did Raspail break new ground? His original contribution consisted in considering the cell as a laboratory and in analyzing the contents of that laboratory with new reagents and new techniques. And by using animal as well as plant tissues he progressed along the road toward a unified cell theory, even though he was unaware of the nucleus and of cell multiplication by division. He subscribed to the erroneous theory of the endogenous multiplication of cells, "from small rudiments that appeared within pre-existing cells and gradually grew larger." [65] (Cell multiplication by division was not to be accurately described until the early 1850s.)[66]

[60] *Ibid.*, 138.

[61] *Ibid.*, 142–44.

[62] *Ibid.*, 138.

[63] F. K. Studnička, "Aus der Vorgeschichte der Zellentheorie . . . ," *Anatomischer Anzeiger*, LXXIII, 405. This judgment is not entirely fair: although neither Dutrochet nor Raspail are mentioned in Schwann's book, Purkinje's work is cited more than a dozen times in the text.

[64] A. R. Rich, "The Place of R.-H.-J. Dutrochet . . . ," *Bulletin of the Johns Hopkins Hospital*, XXXIX, 330–65.

[65] J. R. Baker, "The Cell-Theory: A Restatement . . . ," *Quarterly Journal of Microscopical Science*, IV, 407.

[66] *Ibid.* In this authoritative series of papers on the history of the cell-theory, Professor Baker assessed Raspail's work in the following terms: "From his study of the germination of cereals, Raspail concluded that new cells arose from starch-grains, which enlarged within the cell that produced them until they touched

Raspail knew his great predecessors' work and thought that "little remains to be done, unless news means of investigation can be found." [67] In 1826, he progressed in his study of cell content. He tested for the first time the acidity of cell parenchyma with litmus paper, and observed the formation of gluten and its disappearance during germination. In the spring of 1826 he found new reagents that permitted the detection of sugar, oil, and albumin within the cell.

Raspail's method of experimentation consisted in putting sulfuric acid in contact with all the substances whose existence he knew or suspected in grain ovaries.[68] He suspected the presence of sugar. Pure sulfuric acid on pure sugar colored it yellow and, after a long time, black.

I thought of trying to experiment with mixtures of sulfuric acid, albumin and gum, albumin and starch, starch and gum, but there was no coloration. But when I mixed the albumin of egg-white, cane sugar and sulfuric acid, I suddenly obtained the most intense purple coloration, quite similar to the color that only sulfuric acid gave to the sac of cereal ovaries.[69]

Thus both sugar and albumin existed in cereal ovaries.

When he repeated this experiment on the perisperm of corn,

---

one another, the mother-cell actually bursting. It is strange that the very man who discovered, by the iodine test, that these granules contain starch should have been so misled about their fate. He elaborated his views in further communications. He imagined that each starch-grain contained within itself one or more globules, and that there were other exceedingly minute ones inside these; this kind of emboîtement at the cellular level provided for repeated acts of cell-multiplication. He derived a whole leaf from a single cell, inside which two new cells arose endogenously and enlarged so as to fill all the space except what would become the midrib; globules arose within these two cells and enlarged to fill all the space except what would become the veins; and so on, till the final cellular structure of the mature leaf was achieved. He applied the same idea to the stems of plants and to the tissues of animals. He repeated his opinions on the endogenous origin of new cells in his book on biochemistry (*Nouveau système de chimie organique,* 85–86)." *Ibid.,* 414–15.

[67] F.-V. Raspail, "Essai de chimie microscopique . . . ," *Annales des sciences d'observation,* III, 66–67.

[68] F.-V. Raspail, "Nouveau réactif propre dans les expériences de chimie microscopique à faire distinguer le sucre, l'albumine et la résine," *Annales des sciences d'observation,* I (1829), 72–93.

[69] *Ibid.,* 76.

he saw small drops of oil escape from a fragment of the perisperm while the fragment itself turned purple. To check his results he put olive oil on cane sugar, added sulfuric acid, and he saw the strong purple color. In the perisperm of corn, sulfuric acid therefore detected the presence of both sugar and oil—the latter instead of albumin. On resin, sulfuric acid gave a color close to green. Consequently Raspail had found a reagent with the property of detecting four substances which it had been impossible to determine accurately until then.

He then pointed to the precautions with which these reagents should be prepared and how they should be applied to a certain number of plant and animal organs. Thus, cow's milk is found to contain sugar; but, Raspail noted, in this case the reaction is less intense.

Finally, oil, sugar, and albumin are present in all the ovaries, ovules, chorion, and membranes of the uterus of pregnant animals, in the membranes of the amnion, and in all the internal or external tissues of the fetus (observations made on trout, cow, sheep, and chicken). Raspail added: "This analogy between plant ovules and animal fetuses will doubtless seem odd. It proves that sugar plays an equally great part in nourishing the fetus in the animal as in the plant kingdom." [70] Thirty years later, Claude Bernard was to give a striking proof of Raspail's prediction.[71] In 1943 John R. Baker commented that Raspail had discovered a method which, in a modified form, is still one of our best tests for proteins, and added:

[Raspail] discovered that when concentrated sulfuric acid, sugar, and protein are present together, a purplish red color is produced. This reaction is due to the condensation of the indole radicle of tryptophane with an aldehyde—probably hydroxymethylfurfural—produced by the action of the sulfuric acid on the sugar. . . . It is strange that these tests are always said to have originated with Adamkiewicz (1875),

[70] *Ibid.*, 89.

[71] See C. Bernard, "Glycogénèse animale: évolution du glycogène dans l'oeuf des oiseaux," *Comptes-rendus hebdomadaires des séances de l'Académie des sciences* LXXV (1872), Pt. II, 55–60. There are earlier papers of Claude Bernard's on this problem, but this one parallels Raspail's experiments most closely. Bernard never mentioned Raspail's name: one may assume he did not know of his work.

who used acetic acid instead of sugar. . . . Raspail made his discovery forty-seven years before Adamkiewicz, and it is only just that the alde-hyde test for proteins—or rather for tryptophane—should be called modifications of Raspail's tests. It is convenient as well as accurate to associate the aldehyde tests with a pronounceable name. [!] *In my own experience Raspail's original method gives a more intense reaction in histochemical studies than the modern aldehyde test involving formal-dehyde and vanillin.*[72]

At the same time Raspail was also interested in crystal forma-tions, which had already intrigued other scientists. Louis Jurine (1751–1819), A. P. de Candolle (1778–1841), K. P. J. Sprengel (1766–1833), and R. E. G. Grant (1793–1874) had observed crystalline formations in the monocotyledons. But they did not suspect their true nature. Similarly, in the starch of *Phytollaca decandra,* one could see needles in the cells; J. A. Guillemin (1796–1842) had called them 'raphids.' The elegant method de-vised by Raspail bears mentioning:

I had left fragments of monocotyledon epidermis in water acidulated with hydrochloric acid. . . . I washed them well and incinerated them on a glass plate. When they had cooled, I put them under my microscope and I found hardly any change: the cells seemed as well defined after incineration as before. However, a diluted acid sufficed to dissolve this network. . . . and to prove that the incineration had been complete. What had taken place was mineral crystallization.[73]

He demonstrated the presence of silica in *Spongilla* and of calcium oxalate in the starch of monocotyledons. In 1829 he proved the presence of calcium oxalate in rhubarb and the similarity of calcium oxalate crystals in all plants.

In a long technical paper published in 1829 in the *Annales des sciences d'observation,* Raspail described the technique of micro-incineration which he had practiced and refined for years, and explained his microanalysis of the protoplasm of thirty cells burnt on a platinum spoon. He also reported his analysis of various salts

[72] [Italics mine.] J. R. Baker, "The Discovery of the Uses of Coloring Agents in Biological Microtechnique," *Journal of the Quekett Microscopical Club,* 4th series, I, Pt. 6 (Dec. 1943), 269.

[73] F.-V. Raspail, *Nouveaux coups de fouet scientifiques,* 27.

found in the dehydrated sap of *Chara hispada,* and of the acidity of protoplasm with the dye turnsole as an indicator. Reagents such as ammonia, nitric, sulfuric, and hydrochloric acids, tannin, silver nitrate, and alcohol had revealed to him the presence of iron, calcium, aluminum, and manganese in the cell protoplasm.[74]

Raspail was well aware that he helped inaugurate a new research technique. "We abandon not only the platinum crucible [he wrote], but the one-liter flask and the watch-glass, and we begin to use the stage with reagents, that is, we study chemical reactions on the scale of less than 1 mm." [75] The rules he established are still valid: the "microscopic" cleanliness of the stage, the use of reagents whose purity has been microscopically tested, and the chemical determination of impurities. Then comes micromanipulation. At a small distance from the object one deposits a droplet of the reagent, which must then be brought into contact with the object at the exact point to be examined. This is accomplished under the lens by moving a steel or platinum tip

until one's hand chances on the motion which puts the tip at the height of the object under observation without damaging it. One continues the curve until one meets the droplet of reagent into which one then dips the tip of the pin and, following the curve of the previous movement, one brings the droplet upon the object, since the reagent follows the metal wire on the glass plate.[76]

One can then watch the entire reaction.

Raspail knew that his microscopic techniques could render great service to other scientists, especially in France where the microscope was so neglected. His publication of a brief descriptive study of a "microscopic goniometer" [77] met with an encouraging reception, and led him to publish in 1829 the essay which, in the judgment of modern scientists, establishes him as the founder of chemical microscopy. This was his *Essay on Microscopic Chemistry Applied to Physiology or The Art of Observing and Manipulating Large*

[74] F.-V. Raspail, "Analyse microscopique du suc qui circule dans les tubes des Chara," *Annales des sciences d'observation,* I (1829), 396–429.

[75] F.-V. Raspail, *Nouveau système de chimie organique* (Paris, 1838) 3rd. ed., I, 309.

[76] *Ibid.*

[77] F.-V. Raspail, "Description d'un goniomètre microscopique," *Annales des sciences d'observation,* I (1829), 228–30.

TABLE SHOWING RASPAIL'S PRINCIPAL REAGENTS

Reagents	Reacting Substances	Organs Examined	Explanation of Reaction
Distilled water	Mucilage Sugar Liquid albumin (The cells look transparent)	Numerous plant organs	These bodies are dissolved in water.
Alcohol	Resin Essential oils (The cells look transparent)	Same	These bodies are dissolved in alcohol.
Tincture of iodine	Starch (purplish-blue coloration)	Wheat seeds Roots Pollen grains	Absorption of iodine at surface of starch grain. The color disappears when heat is applied or an alkali is added.
Nitric acid	Albumin (proteins) (yellow coloration)	Ovaries; ovules of plants and animals Animal tissues	Xanthoproteïc reaction; still in use.

and *Small Objects in the Laboratory and on the Stage of the Microscope.*[78] The accompanying table sums up the chief reagents and results as Raspail described them in his text. The reactions listed are perfectly valid from the point of view of modern organic chemistry. A modest conclusion ends Raspail's remarkable essay: "Scientists interested in studying the new method would do well to investigate staining techniques. Only a few have so far been de-

[78] F.-V. Raspail, "Essai de chimie microscopique . . . ," see *supra*, p. 91, n. 30.

Reagents	Reacting Substances	Organs Examined	Explanation of Reaction
Sulfuric acid and oil	Sugar (red coloration)	Same; also seeds before maturation	Reaction of aldehyde function of sugars on the tryptophane of albumins.
Sulfuric acid and sugar	Albumin or oil (red coloration)	Plant ovaries	Same.
Potassium hydroxide	Silica (dissolution of silica crystals)	Plants *Spongilla*	Formation of soluble potassium silicate.
Diluted hydrochloric or sulfuric acid	Carbonates (effervescence) Calcium oxalate dissolution	Certain plants Bones Crystals of monocotyledons	Forming of carbon dioxide bubbles. Calcium oxalate soluble in strong acids.
Silver nitrate	Chlorides (white precipitate)	Animal cells	White precipitate of silver chloride.
Potassium ferricyanide	Iron (blue coloration)	Microincineration Blood *Alcyonium*	Formation of blue iron ferricyanide.

veloped. Physiology and organic chemistry can derive the greatest advantages from these reactions." [79]

It was not long before Raspail extended his work to animal tissues. In November 1826 he undertook to refute the work of four scientists, Sir E. H. Home (1763–1832), J.-L. Prévost (1790–1850), J.-B. Dumas, and Milne-Edwards, who believed that animal tissues were composed of fibers that were identical either in

[79] F.-V. Raspail, *Nouveau système de chimie organique*, 3rd ed., I, 316.

shape or in the diameter of component globules—1/300 mm in all animals. Raspail, on the other hand, found that globules constituting elementary fibers vary in diameter. The elementary globules of earlier authors were simply young cells of varied sizes adhering to the walls of other cells.

The analysis of muscular tissue at that time had yielded a large number of substances whose chemical characteristics were somewhat confused. But microscopic chemistry revealed to Raspail the presence of albumin, oil, sugar, and sodium chloride. His results were conclusive because he worked on fresh muscular tissue, whereas other chemists put their tissue into retorts, distilled, and found the products thus decomposed by heat or reagents. The substances they obtained were then burnt and tarred.

Cellular tissue can be fatty, and its microscopic structure came to Raspail's attention by chance.

I had clumsily dropped human fat into nitric acid. I observed the lumps under the microscope and found the very result I had tried in vain to reproduce by more complicated means. Human fat, turned into soap by acid, had solidified and had caused the shrinkage of the cell contents and disclosed the cell wall. Thus, instead of a formless magma, the human fat showed me its well-defined, polygonal cells, and I could easily draw their shape and dimensions . . . fatty tissue [is] designed for supply and nutrition, analogous, in a word, to the tissue called perisperm in plants.[80]

[80] F.-V. Raspail, "Essai de chimie microscopique . . . ," *Annales des sciences d'observation,* IV, 240.

Raspail also observed bone and nerve tissue under the microscope. A. J. Bogros (1786–1823), by injecting mercury into nerve tissue under two atmospheres of pressure, had seen small canals in nerves, and Raspail had examined Bogros' best preparations. But, in his opinion, the mercury had infiltrated through the membranes. In order to learn about the composition of nerves, Raspail used a simple but exact procedure still used today in many experiments. Putting the large nerve of an ox on a slide, he cut a series of sections 1 mm thick. He immediately put them side by side and, under the microscope, he obtained an exact idea of the place of each fibre in a nerve bundle. But he never saw the little canals, whatever reagent he tried. He saw nerve fibres forming a large nerve, and on lengthwise sections, found they had a diameter of 1/50 mm in man. They are filled with a substance as refringent as the walls.

One should also include here Raspail's interesting research on fetal placenta in the cow undertaken with his friend Gilbert Breschet. (*Nouveau système de chimie organique,* 3rd. ed., II, 553, and Atlas, p. 13, fig. 4).

Despite the limited means at his disposal, it was logical that Raspail should try to understand the mechanism of cell life. The study of *Chara hispada* stalks revealed to him the possibility that the cell could, through its walls, select usable and reject harmful substances. Chara are aquatic plants with whorled branches and hollow, sectioned stalks. The liquid that fills the cavities between internodes is endowed with a turning movement that follows the direction of chloroplasts, which are arranged in oblique rows on the inner surface of the stalk. This curious phenomenon had already been observed by A.-C. Corti (1729–1813), and J. F. G. Gozzi (?–1852) whom Raspail cites. But Raspail also observed that the very walls of the stalk are the agents of this circulation. Because, if a fragment of stalk dries up, the internal movement stops; but a drop of distilled water on the outer surface is enough to restore circulation. The slightest discontinuity on the internal surface of the green cells interrupts the phenomenon. Raspail deduced that "the cell walls have the property of aspiring and expiring the . . . ambient fluids. . . ." [81] He inferred the analogy of the mechanism of vascular circulation in animals. He also formulated an idea taken up later by A. H. Becquerel (1852–1908): he attempted in 1837 to determine the influence of electricity on plant vitality.

All these varied observations and experiments produced a sum of knowledge which Raspail attempted to synthesize—a synthesis that would be included in his *Natural History of Health and Sickness* of 1843. [82] He had a rather accurate notion of the mechanism of cell life actually, although he did not suspect the function of the nucleus in cell division, as has already been pointed out. However, he did believe that organized cells absorb water charged with salts, carbon dioxide, hydrogen, oxygen, and nitrogen. He thought that the cell itself, and its products, are but combinations of two sub-

[81] F.-V. Raspail, "Analyse microscopique du suc . . . ," *Annales des sciences d'observation,* I, 405.

[82] F.-V. Raspail, *Histoire naturelle de la santé et de la maladie chez les végétaux et chez les animaux en général et en particulier chez l'homme, suivie du formulaire pour une nouvelle méthode de traitement hygiénique et curatif* (Paris, 1843), 2 vols. A second printing (Paris, 1845), 2 vols., repeats the original text. The "third edition" (Paris and Brussels, 1860), 3 vols., is a revised and much enlarged version. Many sections of the text were rewritten; additions were mainly made to the section on therapy. Unless otherwise indicated, all references are to the first edition.

stances: one organic (carbon, hydrogen, oxygen), the other mineral (calcium, sodium, potassium, iron). In this connection it is interesting to note that he was aware of the epoch-making synthesis of urea in 1828 by Friedrich Wöhler (1800–1882), which began a new era in organic chemistry.[83]

"A little more or less water, carbon, oxygen, or hydrogen, [Raspail wrote in 1843], a little more or less terrous salts or bases, in infinitely varying quantities, that is organized life, variety in unity, the infinite within the finite. . . ." [84] Nature can thus vary indefinitely the components of what we call organic chemistry. How does the tiny cell, this vital unit, operate?

Each cell selects from the surrounding milieu, taking in only what it needs. . . . Cells have varied means of choice, resulting in different proportions of water, carbon, and bases which enter into the composition of its walls. It is easy to imagine that certain walls permit the passage of certain molecules, others condense on their external walls. . . . You can see how varied the result can be, . . . according to the number of carbon and oxygen molecules—six, eight, twelve—surrounding the central carbon molecule. The modifications are infinite. . . . A cell is therefore a kind of laboratory within which cell tissues organize and grow.[85]

He understood the strict specificity of cells.

Gradually Raspail would be led to consider the results of possible malfunctioning of a cell. Thus he wrote in 1843: "Any liquid elaborated by a given living cell contributes, in turn, to the life of the organism. Any abnormal fermentation induces decomposition." [86] Still thinking in terms of microchemistry, he mused about the importance of studying this fermentation and its products under the lens:

We have long been saying that it is the microscopic study of organic salts that will sooner or later lead to the solution of the physiologic problems presented by the various liquids and transformations within tissues. This area, seemingly so minute, is the most fundamental of

---

[83] F.-V. Raspail, "Essai de chimie microscopique . . . ," *Annales des sciences d'observation,* III, 66–67.

[84] F.-V. Raspail, *Histoire naturelle de la santé . . . ,* I, 28.

[85] *Ibid.,* 35.

[86] *Ibid.,* 36–37.

all. The frontier between organic and inorganic chemistry is the spot where the organization of matter should be studied; there lies hidden the mystery of physiology.[87]

"It is difficult," concluded Baker, "to deny the name of genius to the man who not only founded [histochemistry] but also invented frozen section technique and microincineration, and was the first, or among the first, to test the reaction of the protoplasm of a single living cell." [88]

[87] F.-V. Raspail, *Nouveau système de chimie organique,* 2nd ed., III, 664.
[88] J. R. Baker, "The Discovery of the Uses of Coloring Agents . . . ," *Journal of the Quekett Microscopical Club,* 4th series, I, 270.

To Science, without which all is but madness,
To Science, the only religion of the future,
Whose goal is God,
Whose temple is the universe,
Whose cult is the study of Nature,
Whose practice is kindness to all
While being no one's dupe.
Its most fervent and disinterested believer,
François-Vincent Raspail

V

THE SCIENTIST

IT IS TEMPTING BUT VAIN to speculate about the creative and productive years that Raspail might have given to science, had not
the July Revolution torn from him his microscope and busy pen.
He fought on the barricades, and politics absorbed him completely
for a while. But he was soon afforded leisure of an unwelcome
kind. His involvement in subversion against the July Monarchy
resulted in twenty-seven months in jail.

What better way to use his days in prison than to survey and
summarize his experimental results and theoretical knowledge so
as to present his contribution to the scientific community? The
New System of Organic Chemistry (1833), and the *New System
of Plant Physiology and Botany* (1836) were the results of this
undertaking. But a new purpose also emerged: popularization. He
would write about science for the thousands of untutored citizens
who might profit from his knowledge. The aim of such work was
democratic and thus seemed to imply defiance of his jailers. A new
style, hortatory and didactic, now characterized his scientific prose.

The first book in the new vein was his *Elementary Course of*

112

Agriculture.[1] It was ideally suited for composition in prison: few instruments were needed, and a minimum of books sufficed. These could be brought by his wife, since political prisoners were granted such privileges under the July Monarchy. Madame Raspail's frequent visits were often enlivened by the presence of Benjamin and Camille, their eight- and four-year-old sons, and of Emile, the baby. Life in prison was thus bearable.

The *Elementary Course of Agriculture,* designed for use in primary schools, truly seems a work of leisure. It deals with farming, horticulture, arboriculture, and rural economy. Many examples are taken from the flora of Provence, and nostalgia for the farms and gardens of Raspail's youth pervades the book. No anger at his jailers is expressed; the tone remains calm and scholarly.

With this volume Raspail began a practice of publishing his work piecemeal, in the form of pamphlets, to make it accessible to the impecunious. The book is addressed to the intelligent farmer: Raspail urged that a corner of field or garden always be reserved for experiments.[2] He discussed the diseases of cattle and appended a farmer's almanac. (In future years, veterinary medicine and meteorology would help occupy him in prison and exile.) He advocated a wider cultivation of tobacco[3] and the care of silkworms in which the Abbé Esseyric had evidently excelled.[4] He urged regional cooperation and hoped for "a government friendly to agricultural interests." [5] The Bible and Lucullus provided quotations on the cultivation of grapes and on cherry trees.[6] "The *Course of Agriculture* proved unrewarding for the publisher: in 1838 the Royal Council on Public Education . . . refused to authorize [Raspail's] book for primary schools. Upon liquidation the publisher netted 301 francs. . . ." [7]

Even while composing this work on farming, Raspail was revising his chemical writings. The resulting book, his *New System of Organic Chemistry,* established his fame as a scientist. This volume

---

[1] F.-V. Raspail, *Cours élémentaire d'agriculture et d'économie rurale à l'usage des écoles primaires* (Paris, 1832).

[2] *Ibid.,* 159.   [3] *Ibid.,* 93.   [4] *Ibid.,* 101–2.   [5] *Ibid.,* 6.   [6] *Ibid.,* 111, n. 1.

[7] J. Mistler, *La librairie Hachette de 1826 à nos jours* (Paris, 1964). The author reproduces a receipt indicating that Louis Hachette forwarded Raspail's royalties to Versailles prison. [Reference communicated by Professor Robert Mandrou.]

begins with long excerpts from the "Essay on Microchemistry," in which Raspail had explained observation and experiment under the microscope in great detail. He then gave his classification of organic matter in plant and animal tissues, dividing it into "organized" and "organizing" substances. A favorable review in the *Journal des Débats* in May 1833 welcomed the released prisoner:

There is unquestionable merit in M. Raspail's approach to the chemical study of organized beings [the unsigned review stated]; substantial results will be derived from the idea of analyzing all their parts under the microscope and subjecting them separately to chemical agents. This is preferable to confusing them all under the pestle, as has hitherto been usual. The new method is the key to organic chemistry . . . this idea belongs exclusively to M. Raspail. . . .[8]

The book underwent three editions, with the second and third expanded to three volumes. It was translated almost immediately into German and English and, Raspail says, into Arabic.[9] Soon it appeared on the *Index of Prohibited Books.* The Catholic Church was evidently still keeping an eye on Raspail, scrutinizing even his books on science. It is not easy to fathom the reason for this condemnation,[10] but the two passages most likely to have provoked the Church's censure were the loving dedication to the late Abbé Esseyric—the Jansenist and "juring" priest[11]—or Raspail's quotation of the remark, which he first made at the meeting of the Academy of Sciences in 1827, when he prophesied that the whole living universe would be found to have originated in a single cell.[12]

The third book largely written in prison, the *New System of Plant Physiology and Botany,* was based on ten years of plant-collecting field trips, on intensive study of specimens under the microscope, and on an attempt to classify individual plants according

[8] May 13, 1833.

[9] F.-V. Raspail, *Nouveau système de chimie organique,* 2nd ed. (Paris, 1838), 3 vols., I, XXVIII.

[10] A request to the Vatican Library to permit access to the relevant documents has remained unanswered; the archives of the Congregation of the Index are closed to researchers.

It may be relevant to recall that in this same year (1833) the French government prevented the Academy of Sciences from awarding Raspail a Montyon prize. See *infra,* pp. 126–28.

[11] See *supra,* p. 35.

[12] See *supra,* pp. 96–97.

to their organs and functions. Raspail also collected information from correspondents throughout the country, witness his letter of April 27, 1834, addressed to a M. Auguste Pelleport, agronomist, in Toulouse:

Dear Sir:

I am much touched by your promise to answer my questions. I attach great importance to the empirical results of southern farmers.— My book is not yet in press, and will not be for another four to five months.[13]

Raspail's nomenclature and groupings in this book differed significantly from the widely accepted Linnaean system, mainly because he tended to emphasize function rather than structure. Other French botanists had been making similar efforts, notably Michel Adanson and Adrien de Jussieu (1797–1853).[14] The second part of the book dealt with the development of various organs in the plant. Again he included "Practical Applications" (Part V)— relating to agriculture, industry, and animal husbandry—and even a section on experimental physiology. An atlas of beautiful engravings completed the work. The engravings were finished, along with some of the writing, after he had once more regained his liberty in January 1836.

The tone of these books written in prison was little affected by the conditions of his existence. But the orientation and quality of his scientific thought underwent a subtle yet profound change. In composing handbooks for unschooled men such as farmers, he knew that his language must be simple. To give his readers their money's worth, his survey of a subject must be all-inclusive. The result of this dual purpose was not only a paternal and sometimes patronizing tone, but also a discussion of topics of which he could not have acquired a thorough knowledge—such as the diseases of animals. This is an early instance of what latter became habitual to Raspail: that his desire to be useful impaired his faculties of self-criticism.

Another gradual change became evident by the mid-1830s: Ras-

[13] Autograph ms. letter, Manuscript Division, Série biographie, dossier Raspail, Bibliothèque historique de la Ville de Paris.
[14] A. Davy de Virville, *Histoire de la botanique en France* (Paris, 1954), 70 ff. and 146 ff.

pail's interests were shifting from microchemical research to the pathogenetic role of parasites, and to larger questions of pathology, health, and disease. Consciously or not, he now made a loose analogy between the body politic and the human body, between Society and Nature. After five years of painful struggle to conquer freedom for all members of French society, to rid France of unhealthy political restrictions and disturbances, speculative fevers and social and political parasites, he gradually came to see all of nature as the theatre of a vast struggle—a struggle where healthy conditions could be attained only at the price of constant vigilance and readiness to fight against corruption and disease. It may well be that the very tissues he examined now looked different to him: that instead of acids, salts, and bases interacting under determined conditions, he now saw healthy tissues attacked by foreign bodies or by internal toxic secretions.

Just as, in politics, Raspail had come to suspect the agents of the police, the courts, the Church, and the king as carriers of injustice and destruction to republicans like himself, so, in biology, he now became increasingly aware of what seemed to him the malevolent designs of parasitic animals. Upon observing some microscopic animals under the lens, for example, he asked:

Am I not looking at . . . the unknown cause that devours us, that gives us fevers and death? Are these not the animals that live within us, fatten on our blood, crawl in our living tissue, swarm in our dead bodies, appear in all our sustenance, our drink, food, and air; parasites of our body as we are parasites of other animals' bodies and of all nature? [15]

The pathogenetic role of microscopic creatures increasingly impressed him as a major problem. He abandoned biochemistry in order to focus on biology. Within this field, his interest soon shifted from animals to man. A nagging, restless social consciousness urged him to abandon biology for medicine. Neglecting observation and experiment, he soon practiced diagnosis and therapy. The scientist was turning into a physician.

The change came slowly. It speaks more for Raspail's impetuous wish to help, soothe, and cure, than for his self-critical faculties

[15] F.-V. Raspail, *Histoire naturelle de la santé* . . . , I, p. XXXVII–VIII.

which should have told him that learning is no substitute for a diploma. In the early 1830s, Raspail was still far from being a medical man, but he was less and less of a laboratory scientist. His writings were increasingly concerned with problems in which the transmission of disease (and therefore social factors) played a part.

These preoccupations were by no means new to Raspail. In fact, it was early in his scientific career that the observation of tiny parasitic animals anchored in his mind the concept of their responsibility for many diseases. In his *History of Health* he wrote:

In July 1823, my room on the fifth floor had a balcony which attracted burrowing flies. They would deposit their eggs on the leaves of my sweetpeas and sunflowers, and I was thus able to study their habits and their history with some care. After birth, the small larva pierces the epidermis of the upper surface of the leaf, and, burrowing incessantly, traces a sub-epidermic labyrinth which grows longer and longer, turning and twisting, avoiding obstacles. [Raspail then carefully described this diaphanous larva and its transformation into a nymph.] The cellular web of the leaf is thus destroyed. . . .

The small larva I have described (the flies are no larger than 4–5 mm) is not the smallest insect of its kind; its size may be gigantic compared to the dimensions of flies which man will some day discover.[16]

Raspail would himself contribute to the knowledge of the itch mite, and to theorizing about the pathogenetic role of "infinitely small" parasites.

The itch mite (*Sarcoptes scabiei*) was known to the ancient Chinese and to the Arabs. Western European doctors, in the Middle Ages, considered scabies as a humoral disturbance, and this notion remained unchanged despite the rediscovery of the itch mite in 1687 by Giovanni C. Bonomo (?–1696) and Diacinto Cestoni (1637–1718), and then again by Baron C. de Geer (1720–1778) and P. A. Latreille (1762–1833). In the nineteenth century the French physician J.-L. Alibert (1766–1837), working at the Hôpital St. Louis in Paris, wished to ascertain the cause of scabies. He and his colleagues were astounded when an assistant easily

[16] *Ibid.*, 3rd ed. (Paris, 1860), II, 225–27.

isolated the much-sought itch mite. But no one was able to repeat the feat; it appeared that the discovery was a fraud. (Indeed, the assistant had substituted the cheese mite.) It was partly
Raspail's achievement to expose this deception during a spectacular demonstration on September 3, 1829, and then to describe and
picture the itch mite with its correct properties and in its true proportions.[17]

This pioneer work in parasitology has been acknowledged by
American and French specialists. The American author of the de-
finitive history of scabies wrote, for example: "An important role
in the history of scabies was played in 1829 by the eminent naturalist F.-V. Raspail. Between 1829 and 1834 he published several
articles on scabies in the horse. . . . [He] was the first author to
make a separate delineation of the head of the Acarus." [18] Two
modern French authors confirm this view when they write that
Raspail

. . . was a keen observer and a pioneer of microscopic techniques as
proven by the excellent illustrations of his *History of Health*. . . .

. . . we underline Raspail's unquestionable role in parasitology
through his contribution to the rediscovery of the itch mite, and we
deplore the fact that this man, so gifted for biology and natural history,
did not devote himself more fully to these disciplines rather than to
politics and polemics.[19]

As Raspail reflected about the action of the itch mite upon the
healthy human body, questions of larger scope arose in his mind.
What was the pathogenetic role of parasites? Was a toxic substance
injected, or perhaps produced, by the action of the parasite on
healthy tissue? Were all persons equally susceptible to the same

[17] See F.-V. Raspail, "La gale humaine est-elle le produit d'un insecte?," *Annales des sciences d'observation*, II (1829), 446–58; "Recherches sur l'insecte parasite de la gale du cheval," *Lancette française*, V, No. 34 (August 15, 1831), 135;
Mémoire comparatif sur l'histoire naturelle de l'insecte de la gale (Paris, 1834).
    For critical comments, see J. Guiart, "Histoire de la gale," *Paris médical*, No.
24 (May 16, 1914), 1079–85, and "La vérité sur Raspail," *Le Fureteur*, 3ème
année, No. 7 (July 1944), 100–102; P. Huard and J. Théodoridès, "Raspail et
la parasitologie," *Cinq parasitologistes méconnus* (Paris, 1959). See also, Illustration, *supra*, p. 95.
    [18] R. Friedman, *The Story of Scabies* (New York, 1947), 238.
    [19] P. Huard and J. Théodoridès, "Raspail et la parasitologie," in *Cinq parasi-
tologistes méconnus*, LXXII.

pathogenetic agents? Could a toxic substance be transmitted by an insect from a sick person to a healthy one? The naturalist in Raspail thus examined wider implications of the facts that the observer and experimenter had gathered. Gradually he conceived the project of surveying the whole field of health and disease. The result was his 1843 *magnum opus: The Natural History of Health and Sickness in Plants, Animals, and Man.*[20]

This book opens with a review of the history of medicine and contemporary anatomy and is divided into three sections: thirty pages of preliminary principles or "Prolegomena"; a long disquisition on the etiology and nosology of disease (nine hundred pages in the third edition); and a section on therapy and materia medica (four hundred and ninety pages in the third edition). The historic Introductions impress the reader because of the author's scholarship. He had evidently read Hippocrates, Galen, and Paracelsus; he had little good to say of any of them. Certain writings of the Hippocratic corpus impressed him more than those attributed to Hippocrates himself. Galen he scorned because by codifying Hippocrates he had killed observation and experiment for over a thousand years. He deplored the neglect of Arabic contributions in the Middle Ages; and he admired Paracelsus only because he was a rebel. The Introduction is pervaded by Raspail's scorn for the medical profession as ignorant, venal, unkind, and vain. He even discounted the medical revolution of the early nineteenth century, since contradictory diagnoses were still proposed, and competing treatments were advocated, while many patients died of unknown causes.

In the Prolegomena, man is pictured not as the king of creation but as the most complex of living beings. He is subject to disease and death just like any other creature. Health is seen—in the manner of Hippocrates—as a state of internal equilibrium and of mutually beneficial interaction with the environment. Rather than describing health vaguely as a state of well-balanced humors, Raspail tended to localize it in well-functioning tissues, or rather, cells. Disturbing or disorganizing elements were seen as intrusions, and the function of the body, aided by the physician, was to eject the agent of sickness.

[20] See *supra*, p. 109, n. 82.

In etiology Raspail distinguished between physical and moral causes of disease. The physical causes he subdivided into causes of deprivation (such as asphyxia, unassimilated food, or unbearable temperatures); poisons (inhaled, ingested, or injected); amputations or wounds; and parasites. In discussing psychological factors as the causes of disease, Raspail insisted that ideas, impressions, hopes, and disappointments often determine our general physical condition. Mental suffering renders the organism vulnerable to somatic illness.[21]

As for parasites, Raspail examined them all in this book, from fleas and lice to leeches and tapeworms; of course he paid special attention to his "infinitely small insects or worms." Since he dealt with the parasites of plants and animals as well as those of man, this long section amounts to a treatise on comparative parasitology —fifty years before the material became academic subject matter.

In contrast to most of his learned contemporaries in France, Raspail believed in contagion. He imagined many varieties of "infinitely small" parasites to be the omnipresent carriers of disease. He only imagined this, because he never saw a microbe. Raspail's parasites were the creations of his prophetic fantasy. In the Preface to the *History of Health* he recalled his amazement when he first consciously observed some real microscopic animals:

With the help of this sixth sense [of microscopic sight] the observer perceived that all organic liquids exposed to air and light were crawling with worms. In our humors and tissues he discovered living beings whose structure was quite complex and which were so small that the tip of the scalpel hid them entirely.[22]

The presence of these parasites and their pathogenetic role from then on remained the central factor in Raspail's scientific and medical thought.

In his *Memoir on Scabies* of 1834 Raspail had also raised the question whether "the pustules caused by the itch might not be the abnormal products of the presence and suction of an insect which would disorganize the tissue by feeding on it." [23] He generalized on his notion of toxic substances produced in tissues or injected

[21] F.-V. Raspail, "Causes morales des maladies," in *Histoire naturelle de la santé* . . . , II, 286–94.

[22] *Ibid.*, I, XXXVII.

[23] F.-V. Raspail, *Mémoire comparatif sur* . . . *la gale,* 30.

into them, and he studied their action under the microscope. He also noted that patients were not equally receptive to diseases. ". . . not all skins will be in such a state as to incite the insect to work on them." [24] His notions of toxins and immunity thus dated back at least to 1834. It is tempting—albeit pointless—to ask how far Raspail could have pushed his inquiries if he had subjected his findings to thorough scientific testing.

He extended his concept of the cell as the smallest biological unit to pathology. In his *History of Health* he developed this idea, thus becoming a French precursor of Virchow's cellular pathology —at least as an hypothesis. In the Prolegomena to the *History of Health,* Raspail proposed:

Theorem XIV: In a dead cell, nourishing liquids ferment and become poisonous.

Theorem XV: The disorganization of a [cell] can be the cause of poisoning for congeneric cells and may thus gradually invade other organs.[25]

Pursuing this basic notion, he introduced his analysis of sickness with a sweeping sketch:

Give me a sick cell with disturbed functions, I declare it disorganized, threatened with death. If the damage stops there, the individual will hardly notice it, since he becomes conscious of a fatal agent only when serious symptoms appear. The underlying or contiguous cell replaces the disorganized one which eventually isolates itself as epidermis externally and as mucus on internal walls. The healthy cells so to speak merely close ranks, and life continues the interplay of its admirable circulation, inside that marvelous creation we call an organ.

But if, by one of those accidents that science can recognize but not predict, disorganization is gradually communicated from cell to cell; if the first becomes for its neighbor the dispenser and carrier of contagion; if it stops to produce organizing fluids and transmits nothing but the products of disorganization and asphyxia for absorption by its neighbor, then the invasion of sickness proceeds by contagion, with the speed of circulation proper to the organ to which the infecting cell belongs.

And if death is not to ensue from all these movements which cross, push, and collide in a way detrimental to health, then art, with the help of knife, fire, or medication, or what we call nature, that is, the

[24] *Ibid.*
[25] F.-V. Raspail, *Histoire naturelle de la santé* . . . , I, 36.

regular interplay of laws whose principles we do not grasp, must inter-
vene in time to sever the organic communications between the seat of
the invading internal infection and the adjacent portions of the body. If
not, the microscopic point, victim of the disorder, will become the start-
ing place of a general disorganization.[26]

These ideas on the pathology, no less than on the growth of cells,
anticipated Virchow's by twelve years.[27] On this point Virchow's
latest American biographer, Dr. Erwin H. Ackerknecht, has been
quite explicit:

Virchow was not the first to look for pathological changes in the cell.
He was the first to make this procedure a system. He was not the first,
either, to claim that cells descended only from cells. This opinion was
entertained in the "globule" period, for instance, by Raspail who in 1825,
after all, preceded his treatise "Développement de la fécule" with the
motto *Omnis cellula e cellula.*[28]

Raspail's notions about the mechanism of contagion were as
vague as those of his contemporaries. Various types of infection
were sometimes distinguished—but often confused: contagion from
one person to another by direct contact; and contagion through an
object such as food or through the air. In every case the agents of
sickness were thought to be inanimate or animate "contagia," ex-
halations or "miasmata." [29] The notion of an animal vector was not

[26] *Ibid.*, 43–44.

[27] The author of the best modern history of medicine is quite unaware of Raspail when he writes: "According to Virchow's theory . . . 'The essence of disease . . . is a modified part of the organism or rather a modified cell or aggre-
gation of cells (whether of tissue or of organs). . . . Actually every diseased
part of the body holds a parasitic relation to the rest of the healthy body to
which it belongs, and it lives at the expense of the organism.' This concept has
had to be considerably modified . . . by more recent studies in experimental
pathology, immunology, and endocrinology . . . It is no less true, however, that
Virchow's revolutionary contributions should be regarded as among the most significant in the history of medicine." A. Castiglioni, *A History of Medicine* (New
York, 1947), 696.

[28] E. H. Ackerknecht, *Rudolf Virchow, Doctor, Statesman, Anthropologist*
(Madison, Wisconsin, 1953), 83.

[29] See M. Greenwood, "Miasma and contagion," in *Science, Medicine, and
History: Essays on the Evolution of Scientific Thought and Medical Practice
written in Honor of Charles Singer* (London, 1953), II, 501–7; and L. Belloni,
Le 'contagium vivum' avant Pasteur, Conférence D 74, Palais de la Découverte
(Paris, 1961).

considered. No one seems to have suspected flies or mosquitoes. Only rats were associated with epidemics: experience had proved the connection. Raspail would talk in the same breath about miasmata and infinitely small live agents of disease, and would advocate preventive measures against both. He thus did not make the distinction—which divided "sanitarians" from "contagionists"—between cleanliness and isolation as the essential (but different) steps to prevent the transmission of contagious disease.

Confusion about these subtleties actually mattered less in Raspail's France than one might expect. The whole idea of contagion was then derided as old-fashioned. No doubt Economic Liberalism, with its dislike for quarantines, government regulations, and control indirectly inspired the adoption by the French Academy of Medicine in February 1828 of a report in which contagion was definitively condemned. The Academy of Sciences concurred; the Chamber cut its appropriations for quarantines. France went "anti-contagionist" and many other countries followed suit.[30]

At the centenary celebrations of the French Academy of Medicine in 1920, one speaker reported:

In 1849, one of our predecessors was still hailed by his colleagues when he declared: "If the opinion that cholera is contagious were to gain credence beyond these academic walls as a consequence of the present debates, it would be a greater tragedy than the epidemic itself. . . . Even if cholera were contagious, it would be our duty not to mention the fact."[31]

In urging anti-contagionist, hygienic, and "antiseptic" precautions,[32] Raspail was therefore fighting fashionable contemporary medical

[30] E. H. Ackerknecht, "Anti-contagionism between 1821 and 1867," *Bulletin of the History of Medicine*, XXII (1948), 572–73.

[31] L. Vaillard, "Le rôle de l'académie de médecine dans l'évolution de l'hygiène publique," *Bulletin de l'académie de médecine*, 3ème série, LXXXIV (1920), 405.

[32] Strictly speaking, it is anachronistic to use the terms "antisepsis" and "asepsis" before Lister and Pasteur. However, the precautions which Raspail and others—Oliver Wendell Holmes (1809–1894) and Ignaz Philip Semmelweis (1818–1865), e.g.—advocated from the 1840s on, exceeded mere cleanliness. These men inferred the existence of an invisible agent of infection and assumed that doctors and their instruments often transmitted communicable diseases. For want of a better term, "antisepsis" and "asepsis" are used in this book, but in quotation marks.

thought. At the same time he was in line with the most advanced, if unpopular, theories. These can be found in the pages of the *Annales d'hygiène et de médecine légale,* where French pioneers in public health and preventive medicine such as Villermé, Parent-Duchatelet, Leuret, and Ollivier investigated the problems that also concerned Raspail.[33] The year the *History of Health* appeared, Oliver Wendell Holmes published his celebrated essay on puerperal fever,[34] and it was then that Ignaz Philip Semmelweis began to combat the same disease in Vienna. At least a quarter of a century was to pass until Sir Joseph Lister's antiseptic practices were to become widely known.[35]

Raspail's work on contagious disease is both impressive and disappointing. While Raspail the naturalist surveyed the phenomenon of contagion in the realm of plant, animal, and human biology, and Raspail the reformer marshalled the resources of social action, what happened to the critical faculties of Raspail the exact scientist and empiricist? True, he did suspect, long before Pasteur, the mechanism and even the unseen carriers of contagious disease. But why was Raspail never tempted to isolate any one of these carriers and test the mechanism of contagion? One assumes that he had lost patience with minute, exacting laboratory experiment; that larger visions of science and social welfare lured him on; that he felt he had sufficient evidence to proceed. Thus, Raspail, potentially a great scientist, did not make full use of his native gifts nor of his acquired knowledge.

When the *History of Health* appeared, it was greeted with enthusiasm by C.-A. Sainte-Beuve, who published a review in the *Revue Suisse* of May 21, 1843:

[33] See *infra,* ch. X.

[34] *New England Quarterly Journal of Medicine,* I (1842–1843), 503 ff.

[35] See H. E. Sigerist, "Surgery at the Time of the Introduction of Antisepsis," *Journal of the Missouri State Medical Association,* XXXII, No. 5 (May 1935), 169–76.

It is relevant to recall that, as late as 1861–1864, over 1,200 out of almost 10,000 women who gave birth at the Maternité Hospital in Paris died of puerperal fever; and in the Franco-Prussian War, 10,000 of the 13,000 amputations performed on French soldiers proved fatal owing largely to the disregard of antiseptic precautions. See R. J. Dubos, *Pasteur, Free Lance of Science* (Boston, 1950), 300 and 303.

A very learned and important book by Raspail has just been published
[he wrote]. It is fascinating to read, systematic, philosophical, and full
of observations on physics and microscopy. It is one of those fundamental theoretical works which the School [of Medicine] has long stopped
producing, a courageous attempt to reform the whole science of life, and
thus the art of healing, a kind of social contract of physiology and
therapy, more in the manner of the Germans than the French. . . .
The work of Raspail will leave its mark on science, and should be noted
abroad. . . .[36]

Sainte-Beuve was alone in publishing his praise, at least during
Raspail's lifetime, but other great writers read the *History of
Health* when it appeared and definitely were influenced by it. The
famous historian Jules Michelet (1798–1874), working feverishly
on his book *Le peuple* in the fall of 1845, read it and thereupon
rewrote the whole section on the worker, the shopkeeper, and the
bourgeois.[37] In England, George Eliot (1819–1880) made Dr.
Lydgate, the innovating physician of *Middlemarch,* state: "They
will not drive me away, . . . I have a good opportunity here, for
the ends I care most about; . . . and I am more and more convinced that it will be possible to demonstrate the homogeneous
origin of all the tissues. Raspail and others are on the same track,
and I have been losing time." [38]

But in France, Raspail's important, original contributions to
science remained virtually unknown. He remained aloof from the
scientific and medical community. In fact he was reduced to seek-
ing the medical editorship of a small republican newspaper, *La
Commune*. But its publisher had to refuse: the paper was too
poor.[39] More affluent publications would not welcome his services.
The lack of a university degree, a recognized professional position,
membership in an academy, or friends in high places, as well as
Raspail's notorious participation in varied revolutionary activities,

[36] C.-A. Sainte-Beuve, *Chroniques parisiennes* (Paris, 1876), 47.

[37] G. Monod, *La vie et la pensée de Jules Michelet, 1798–1852* in *Bibliothèque de l'Ecole des hautes études* (Paris, 1923), 2 vols., II, 202.

[38] G. Eliot, *Middlemarch* (London, 1950), 435. [First published in 1871.]

[39] See a ms. autogr. letter from M. de Mortiller, publisher of *La Commune,*
dated 19 September 1845, which reads in part: "We should have been happy to
have you as our collaborator: a few articles from your pen, from time to time,
would have been a reflection on this journal of the popularity you so justly en-
joy." Fonds Raspail, Archives du Département de la Seine, LXXXV.

now took their toll. His occasional attempts to reach the academic public, and the rare efforts of his friends to arouse the scientific community in his favor, seem all the more pitiful. He evidently did give some lectures on the microscopic method at the Hôpital Saint Louis[40] and at the Faculty of Medicine.[41] He later asserted that the room was often "crowded with doctors; men who are now professors stood in a circle around me: they hoped to enhance their own popularity by assisting me in my unofficial professorship, and to attract the attention of the students who were listening to me." [42] But these occasional lectures, however interesting, did not reach many ears.

In 1833 his eminent friend Etienne Geoffroy St.-Hilaire, then President of the Academy of Sciences, proposed Raspail for the Montyon prize, an award of 10,000 francs granted by the Academy for fruitful research. In July of that year Raspail received from the great naturalist a letter which read in part:

Your microscopic research has revealed . . . certain molecular properties and you have brought new materials within the reach of science and thus amassed treasures of enormous potentialities . . .

Who has a better right to the plaudits of scientists than you, Sir, who have just opened a new avenue for research, discovered facts so full of promise, and formulated ideas that are both original and suggestive for further research.

One point I must make clear is that I am not acting at anyone's behest . . . ; I declare this on my honor. Quite on my own, I feel that the moment has come to be just toward you and to act accordingly. . . .

. . . I feel that a solemn reward from the fortune left to science by the philanthropist Montyon should be yours. . . .

If you could answer in a way which would help me convince certain recalcitrant minds, you would serve my purpose. . . .[43]

Geoffroy St.-Hilaire took pains to emphasize that the offer was not

[40] F.-V. Raspail, *Mémoire comparatif sur . . . la gale*, 5–8.

[41] J. Raspail, *Le rôle pathogène des helminthes en général et en particulier dans les maladies infectieuses* (Paris, 1906), 26. See also a poster advertising a "Free and public course on organic chemistry applied to physiology and natural history," n.d., Fonds Raspail, Archives du Département de la Seine, CXX; and *La France médicale*, No. 22, Nov. 26 and Dec. 6, 1836.

[42] F.-V. Raspail, *Procès et défense de F.-V. Raspail poursuivi le 19 mai 1846 en exercice illégal de la médecine . . .* (Paris, 1846), 32.

[43] Fonds Raspail, *Muséum.*

a bribe. Under these conditions, even the suspicious republican was ready to accept. "But I declare," he wrote, "that I am doing so without any strings attached to my consent, and that I shall not change my attitude nor my prose in matters concerning [the Academy]." [44]

Not long after this exchange of letters, Geoffroy St.-Hilaire was summoned by François Guizot, the Minister of Public Education. At the end of the interview, Guizot apparently said: "Let the Academy do its duty, I shall do mine." Or, in a less genteel version: "I forbid you to line the rioters' pockets." [45] Soon after, on August 23, 1833, at the conclusion of a meeting of the Republican Association for the Free Press, over which he had presided, Raspail was arrested. After three months in custody, a jury acquitted him. [46] He was never offered the prize. This was a pity, for as Eugène de Mirecourt wistfully comments: "Some little encouragement might have unreservedly attached this man to the realm of science, whereas he wasted the most productive years of his career on fomenting revolt." [47]

Rumors about Guizot's intervention must have generated much adverse publicity, for on November 21 the following unsigned disavowal appeared in the *Journal des Débats*:

According to several newspapers, the Ministry is said to have offered a certain position to M. Raspail, on condition that he devote himself exclusively to science. The Minister of Public Education is said to have *forbidden* M. Geoffroy St.-Hilaire, in his capacity as President of the Academy of Sciences, to award to M. Raspail one of the Montyon prizes for his *New System of Organic Chemistry*.

These assertions lack any factual basis; no position has been offered to M. Raspail, under any condition. M. Geoffroy St.-Hilaire indeed once mentioned to the Minister of Public Education that an award might be offered to M. Raspail. The Minister emphatically replied that the Academy alone was competent to decide on a purely scientific matter and that he had no intention either of opposing it or of intervening in any way. Since that day the Minister has heard no more about this matter.

[44] F.-V. Raspail, "Avertissement historique" (May 20, 1838), in *Nouveau système de chimie organique*, 2nd ed., I, XXIV.
[45] "grossir la caisse de l'émeute." E. de Mirecourt, *Raspail*, 61.
[46] See *infra*, p. 175.
[47] E. de Mirecourt, *Raspail*, 63.

Raspail's statue in Paris, Place Denfert-Rochereau, and bas-reliefs depicting him, above, at the Hôtel de Ville during the February 1848 Revolution and, below, at an indigent patient's bedside

Frenchmen were to hear almost nothing about Raspail the scientist for the rest of his life.

After his death in 1878 the official attitude toward Raspail changed. France was by then a republic and the government had at last defeated all attempts at a monarchist restoration. The republicans felt an acute need for a national mystique that would unite their followers and help them transcend their ideological and sectional divisions. For that purpose the republic needed heroes. Alive, Raspail had proved intractable, but dead he became an idol.

It was thus for political reasons that Frenchmen briefly paid tribute to the memory of Raspail the scientist.[48] During the centenary celebrations of the Great Revolution in Paris a huge statue was raised to Raspail—paid for by a national subscription.[49] (In 1940 it was melted down by the Germans together with many other memorials.) In 1888, on the tenth anniversary of Raspail's death, a workers' delegation of four thousand persons made the pilgrimage to the Père Lachaise cemetery.[50] In 1932 Carpentras dedicated to him a marble bust on the "Square Raspail," opposite his childhood home.[51] In 1913 Paris completed its wide, tree-lined "Boulevard Raspail," and at least thirty other French communities baptized avenues or squares for him.[52] During the ceremonies for the Boulevard Raspail in Paris, President Raymond Poincaré spoke, but without even mentioning Raspail's name.[53] This snub provoked ironic but indignant protests from an unexpected quarter, namely from the leader of the royalist Action Française, Charles Maurras:

The President of the Republic inaugurated two bridges yesterday, as well as four squares, twelve public gardens, and one boulevard. Each time he made a good speech, of course. But at the Boulevard Raspail he did not mention Raspail. I protest in the name of logic and tradition, in the name of science and in the name of France.

This Raspail, a '48er and supporter of the Commune, it is true, but a pharmacist of genius and the forerunner of Pasteur! From that point of view he is ours, like all that is French. In the name of his famous liqueur, of his sedative lotion, and his camphorated alcohol, I solemnly state that

[48] The French workers had long been unreservedly attached to Raspail. On January 7, 1879, the "Workers of France" placed a large commemorative wreath on his tomb at the Père Lachaise cemetery. Contributions of 25 to 50 centimes from Parisian workers and sums ranging from 3 to 30 francs from provincial committees had paid for the offering. See *Anniversaire de la mort de F.-V. Raspail, Jan. 7, 1879* [a bound volume with all the contributors' names and many letters], Série Biographie, dossier Raspail, Bibliothèque historique de la ville de Paris.

[49] The invitations to the inauguration of Raspail's statue, sent to members of the extreme Left, and written on Chamber of Deputies letterheads, read in part: "You are earnestly requested to attend this commemoration honoring one of the great soldiers of the democratic and social republic." Signed: Clémenceau. Archives du Département de la Seine, Fonds Raspail, XXXVII.

[50] *Ibid.,* XXXV.

[51] See P. Wertheimer, "Carpentras élève un monument à Raspail," *Le Miroir du monde,* July 23, 1932, 137.

[52] See G. Raspail, *La vie et l'oeuvre scientifique de F.-V. Raspail,* 116.

[53] Nor was Raspail's last surviving son invited to the ceremonies. X. Raspail, *Procès de l'almanach Raspail . . . ,* 489.

it is a blatant injustice to inaugurate the Boulevard Raspail without mentioning a man who is so well known and beloved of republican families and who contributed so much to the progress of our country. . . .[54]

French scientists were just as slow as the politicians in raising Raspail to his rightful place. J. Thoulet (1843–1882), the geologist, was the first Frenchman to discuss Raspail's contribution to microchemistry and microcrystallography:

It is certain [he wrote], that the first man to enunciate the principles of microscopic science and to provide enough examples clearly to indicate the line to follow is a Frenchman whose name, associated with a notoriety of an entirely different order, is now too much forgotten; I mean François-Vincent Raspail. . . .[55]

And Thoulet underlined the heroic circumstances of these discoveries and once again quoted Raspail's famous words: ". . . a cot has been my table, and my workroom is a cell which does not even offer the advantages of a dungeon, namely solitude and silence." [56]

When Dr. Jules Guiart was installed as professor of parasitology and medical natural history of the Medical and Pharmacy Faculty of Lyons in 1906, he referred to the "revolution" brought about by Raspail's *History of Health* of 1843.

This remarkable work is unfortunately little read by the present medical generation. . . . All the great conquests of modern medicine can be found in it: cellular pathology, parasitology including bacteriology, antisepsis and asepsis. . . .

My work during the past few years has confirmed my impression that Raspail was right. I am happy to contribute to his medical rehabilitation, a short distance from the square named for him, with its monument raised by the people of Lyons for their onetime deputy. Carved into its base there is proof that, here at least, the scientist was appreciated as well as the citizen.[57]

The scholar who labored most diligently to make Raspail's work

[54] *Action Française*, July 13, 1913.
[55] J. Thoulet, "La microchimie et la cristallographie dans les travaux de F.-V. Raspail," *Revue scientifique*, No. 17 (April 1887), 522–28.
[56] First printed in "Avertissement" in *Nouveau système de chimie organique*, 1st ed., 9–10.
[57] Quoted in X. Raspail, *Raspail et Pasteur* . . . , 368–69.

known was Raphaël Blanchard (1857–1919), professor of parasitology at the Medical Faculty in Paris, member of the Academy of Medicine, active member (and, for a time, president) of the French Society for the History of Medicine. He was also a lifelong friend of Raspail's youngest son Xavier. Blanchard published an excellent biographical note on Raspail in 1903.[58]

In his opening lecture at the Collège de France in January 1914, Professor Lucien Cayeux (1864–1944), the famous geologist, also paid tribute to his great forerunner:

According to the authors who have written on microchemistry [said Cayeux], this science was born abroad, either in 1876 with the work of Streng, or in 1877 with that of Boricky. Honesty as well as the wish to repair an injustice obliges me to say that microchemistry is more than three quarters of a century old, and that it is obviously of French origin. There is no doubt that Raspail was its real founder. . . . I am honored to begin my course . . . by proclaiming Raspail the founder of microchemistry.[59]

Cayeux' motive was twofold: he wished to honor Raspail, and also reclaim for France the glory of pioneer work that had been mistakenly credited to Germany. This nationalistic attitude was widespread among Frenchmen after their humiliating and totally unexpected defeat by Prussia in 1871. The French had despised the Germans for centuries. For a long time after 1871 it was unthinkable and unbearable for Frenchmen to regard the Germans as equal, let alone superior. Any claim for German scientific priority was therefore resisted, or answered with a counterclaim. Already in 1866 Paul Broca had written in his *Traité des tumeurs*:

It is generally believed that the cell theory is a German invention; this is a grave error. It was formulated neither in 1838, nor even in 1837; it is the child neither of Schwann nor of Schleiden. It is twelve years older than that: the cell is French and belongs to M. Raspail. . . .

---

[58] R. Blanchard, "Notice biographique: F.-V. Raspail," *Archives de parasitologie*, VIII (1903–1904), 5–87.

[59] L. Cayeux, "Raspail, inventeur de la microchimie," *Revue scientifique* (*Revue rose*), No. 25 (June 1914), 777–78. E. Boricky (1840–1881) was professor of mineralogy at the University of Prague, and J. A. Streng (1830–1897) was professor of the same discipline at the University of Giessen.

Never has the cell theory been formulated with more precision or daring and the men who, ten years later, pretended to invent it did not know how to present their thought in equally striking words.[60]

During the First World War this feeling was again made explicit. In 1916 Raphaël Blanchard exclaimed in a speech before the Academy of Medicine:

We have the sacred duty to defend our positions, that is, our glorious scientific patrimony. . . . We must know our own history and defend it against the insidious intrusions which falsify it to Germany's advantage. . . . Thus we shall act as good citizens and contribute successfully to the defense and to the triumph of French science.

I hope the Academy will join me in rendering a well-deserved homage to Raspail. This gesture would honor the Academy as well as a great Frenchman. The dates and contents of Raspail's publications make him the founder of the cell theory and of cellular pathology, and one of the first apostles of parasitology.[61]

Although Raspail benefited temporarily from this upsurge of nationalistic pride, the efforts of his admirers to change the official French attitude permanently were not successful. When the French Ministry of Education compiled a two-volume survey of "French Science" on the occasion of the International Exhibition at San Francisco in 1915, Raspail was mentioned only once in passing, in the chapter on "Zoological Paleontology," although profuse attention was paid to every minor French scientist.[62] The same is true of the two volumes on French science in Gabriel Hanotaux' *Histoire de la nation française*.[63] Similarly, in the chapter on "The History of Histology" in the *General History of Medicine* (1938), edited by M. Laignel-Lavastine, the "pharmacist Raspail (1828)" appears only as one of the first students of the cell.[64] In the classic

[60] P. Broca, *Traité des tumeurs* (Paris, 1866), 2 vols., I, 29–30.

[61] R. Blanchard, "Méconnaissance de la nomenclature zoologique et botanique et de l'histoire des sciences biologiques; son influence fâcheuse sur le langage médical," *Bulletin de l'académie de médecine*, LXXVI (1916), 387.

[62] Paris, Ministère de l'instruction publique, *La science française* (Paris, 1915), 2 vols., I, 298.

[63] E. Picard et al., *Histoire des sciences en France*, vols. XIV and XV of *Histoire de la nation française*, G. Hanotaux, ed. Raspail is mentioned in connection with the cell theory as "one of the precursors." XV, 189.

[64] M. Laignel-Lavastine, ed., *Histoire générale de la médecine, de la pharmacie, de l'art dentaire, et de l'art vétérinaire* (Paris, 1938), II, 348.

Histochimie animale of Lucien Lison (1936), Raspail's book on organic chemistry is cited, in passing and without date, among the works that paved the way for "physiological chemistry." [65] And Albert Policard, in *La méthode de la microincinération* (1938), wrote: "X. Raspail [sic] proved the value of this technique in 1833 in a little known book [no title]. He was a remarkable forerunner." [66]

Like the proverbial prophet, Raspail received the warmest recognition from foreigners, a recognition based largely on his contributions to microscopy. A growing number of modern American microchemists have paid tribute to Raspail's work. The author of a textbook on *The Technique of Inorganic Analysis* stated in his Introduction that "François-Vincent Raspail was probably the first to conceive and apply the principles of microanalysis. . . ." [67] Professors E. M. Chamot and C. W. Mason of Cornell University were more explicit when they wrote:

. . . this work [Raspail's *Nouveau système de chimie organique* to which was appended the *Essai de chimie microscopique*] is, we believe, the first attempt to present in a systematic manner microscopic information, methods, and tests, *for the chemist.* . . . [Raspail] was also one of the first to suggest the observation of crystal habits under the microscope as a means for the identification of chemical compounds. His drawings of crystals are remarkably well done . . . he was a pioneer in a new realm of chemistry, . . . he was destined to attract few followers, and his efforts did not bear fruit until almost half a century later. This book, partly didactic, partly polemical, can in no sense be regarded as a discussion of microchemical methods alone (such as were then possible), but covered substantially the whole field of what the writers believe should be entitled chemical microscopy. As an historical document relating to the early art of applied microscopy its importance cannot be overestimated.[68]

In accordance with J. R. Baker's convincing observations quoted

[65] L. Lison, *Histochimie animale* (Paris, 1936), 2–3.

[66] A. Policard, *La méthode de la microincinération* (Paris, 1938), 4.

[67] A. A. Benedetti-Pichler, *Introduction to the Microtechnique of Inorganic Analysis* (New York, 1942), 4.

[68] E. M. Chamot and C. W. Mason, "Chemical Microscopy. Its Value in the Training of Chemists," *Journal of Chemical Education*, V, No. 3 (March 1928), 260.

earlier,[69] A. G. E. Pearse, author of the recent authoritative treatise *Histochemistry, Theoretical and Applied,* accorded the place of honor in his volume to a photograph of Raspail and wrote in his Introduction: "[Raspail's] claim to the title [of founder of histochemistry] I regard as unassailable and his portrait therefore forms the frontispiece of this book. . . ."[70] At last in 1956, when the French Society of Histochemistry began to publish its *Annals,* the editor, Dr. R. Wegmann, placed the work of the Society under the aegis of Raspail.[71] And similarly, the First International Congress of Cytology and Histochemistry in Paris in August, 1960, was held under the sponsorship of Raspail—whose portrait appeared on the cover of the program. Raspail's place in the history of French science now seems secure.

[69] See *supra,* pp. 87–88, 103–4, and 111.
[70] A. G. E. Pearse, *Histochemistry, Theoretical and Applied* (Boston, 1953), 3.
[71] *Annales d'histochimie,* I, No. 1 (1956).

In this house
François-Vincent Raspail
Promoter of Universal Suffrage
born at Carpentras on
January 25, 1794,
died at Arcueil on
January 7, 1878,
gave free medical care to the sick
from 1840 to 1848 *

VI

POOR MAN'S

DOCTOR

IN MAY 1846 when François-Vincent Raspail stood trial in Paris
for the illegal practice of medicine, he was well known as a radical
orator and publicist who had been prosecuted repeatedly for revolutionary activity. He had achieved great popularity as a medical
practitioner. His books and pamphlets were selling by the thousands, and throngs of patients were coming to his dispensary for
free medicines and advice. "Are you a doctor?" the defendant was
asked at the trial. "I am the inventor of a new system of medicine,"
Raspail replied, "and therefore I profess not to be a doctor." [1] The

*Marble plaque, affixed on September 22, 1898, by order of the President of
the French Republic, to the building that had housed Raspail's dispensary in
Paris, 5 rue de Sévigné.

[1] F.-V. Raspail, *Procès et défense de F.-V. Raspail poursuivi le 19 mai 1846 en
exercice illégal de la médecine devant la 8ème chambre (police correctionnelle)
à la requête du ministère public, et sur la dénonciation formelle des sieurs Fouquier, médecin du roi, et Orfila, doyen de la Faculté de médecine de Paris, agissant comme vice-président et président d'une association anonyme de médecins*
(Paris, 1846), 12.

prosecutor thereupon explained to the court that the government was not so anxious to stop Raspail's medical practice as to make him acquire a degree. "The court is today confronted with an eminent scientist," he continued, "a man whom the medical profession would be honored to have as a member if he would deign join it and accept a diploma from the Medical Faculty which would be happy to welcome him." [2] But Raspail declined. He argued that a diploma would cost him the people's confidence. He preferred to pay the maximum fine of fifteen francs, and to resume his illegal practice.

It is startling to read the statement that Raspail owed popular confidence to the lack of a medical degree. But the people's trust in doctors was low a century and a quarter ago. Clinical knowledge was growing rapidly, but therapy could not keep pace with diagnosis. Cholera epidemics decimated Europeans, serious operations were fatal, contagion was unexplained. Debilitating treatments such as purging and bleeding were still in fashion, while doctors cloaked their ignorance in pomposity and Latin jargon.

In this period [writes Castiglioni], . . . we see the greatest contrasts in the history of therapy and pharmacology. On the one hand, the Viennese clinicians affirming that all treatment should be withheld in acute diseases, on the other, the disciples of Broussais[3] who continued to practice blood-letting on a vast scale. New therapeutic fantasies, such as magnetism and homeopathy, existed along with the return to ancient methods, such as hydrotherapy, dietetics, and other physiologic treatments.[4]

Many contemporary professors and researchers expressed their skepticism about therapy, and thus helped spread this feeling among the public. Bichat, for example, in his *Anatomie générale,* referred to the current materia medica as a "formless mixture of mistaken ideas, often childish observations, and illusory procedures." [5]

[2] *Ibid.,* 21.

[3] In the late 1830s, F. J. V. Broussais (1772–1838) still dictated medical fashion in Paris. He had been surgeon of the armies and was then physician-in-chief at the Val-de-Grâce Hospital and professor of pathology at the Paris Faculty of Medicine.

[4] A. Castiglioni, *A History of Medicine,* E. B. Krumbhaar, tr. (New York, 1947), 744.

[5] X. Bichat, *Anatomie générale* (Paris, 1830), I, p. XVIII.

Prevalent attitudes toward the medical profession contributed to the success of Raspail's medical "system" as much as his theories, medication, and therapy. The masses were ignorant of medicine, and diffident toward doctors. For centuries they had relied on the druggist for prescriptions, on the traveling barber-surgeon for bleeding, operations, and the extraction of teeth, and on the itinerant healer for patent medicines. The physician was still a frightening figure to the proletarian, and medical care was often made inaccessible by its cost. The peasant, or poor city dweller, would often prefer to consult a "health officer," one of the cut-rate physicians that Napoleon had created out of distrust of an élite and in the hope of supplying the country with doctors quickly. A profession that admitted to these many levels of competence filled its clientèle with reluctance rather than trust.

The French state had as yet contributed little to the medical welfare of the masses, and the Industrial Revolution had not progressed far enough in France to make state intervention in health care imperative. Before the French Revolution, city governments and the Catholic Church had provided the personnel to tend the sick and staff the hospitals. But the state had then impoverished the Church without taking over its charitable functions. Lastly, private initiative was not encouraged in France. The old habit of administrative, political, and cultural centralization had trained Frenchmen to expect state action, but this was not yet forthcoming. Therefore many problems in public and private medical care were left untouched.[6]

Medical care in private clinics proved far too expensive for the masses, who hesitated, at the same time, to request free medical service in public hospitals. These hospitals were all charitable institutions where patients lived on dole: charity in Europe had never distinguished between idle paupers and the medically indigent.[7] Apart from the humiliation implied, the danger of contracting a

[6] For new concepts introduced at the time of the French Revolution, see G. Rosen, "Hospitals, Medical Care, and Social Policy in the French Revolution," *Bulletin of the History of Medicine*, XXX, No. 2 (March–April 1956), 124–49.

[7] See M. Fosseyeux, "Histoire de l'hospitalisation des malades en France," in *Histoire de la médecine, de la pharmacie, de l'art dentaire, et de l'art vétérinaire*, M. Laignel-Lavastine, ed. (Paris, 1949), 3 vols., III, 681–93.

contagious disease in a hospital was considerable.[8] Furthermore, hospitals generally accommodated only acute cases; convalescents or chronically ill patients were sent home, unless they requested admission to public *hospices,* also supported by alms. In Paris, medical care as well as food, clothing, and money were distributed at the district *bureaux de charité.* But registration on a paupers' list was once more a precondition for this public generosity.

Raspail's medical services had the rare advantage of being neither expensive nor free to those who could afford to pay. No humiliation need be suffered. A further and even greater attraction was that Raspail prescribed medication with complete faith in its effectiveness: an attitude that contrasted with the skepticism of the best clinicians. Many of these proclaimed their impotence in the face of epidemics, sepsis, and pain, while Raspail's humanitarian urge to help the suffering poor did not permit such impassiveness. He felt it morally wrong to withhold medication; for to him the etiology and characteristics of many illnesses were no mystery. He believed that "microscopic worms," the main agents of communicable disease, were highly susceptible to camphor, and could not only be eliminated from the sick body but could also be prevented from attacking a healthy host—provided sanitary practices and camphorated medicines were used.

Raspail's success stemmed in no small part from his passionate striving to be a democrat as well as a doctor: to make himself available to all, and to train people to help themselves. These twin objectives reflected his deep philosophic convictions. Aware that salubrious living conditions, protection against contagion and preventable accidents, and free medical care were not provided for the masses, Raspail set an example by offering consultations and medicines to all who asked for his help. He thereby eventually defeated his own purpose as a medical practitioner whose art must deal with individuals, not with multitudes. Finally, the democrat in him overpowered the doctor. Personal consultations gave way to written therapeutic advice; concern with individual sickness yielded to action in public health and social medicine. Confronted with problems dating back to the first socially conscious doctor, Raspail attempted twentieth-century solutions. But neither the French gov-

[8] See L. Tanon, "Histoire de l'hygiène," in *Ibid.,* 475–504.

ernment nor society was ready to share in the work or the cost of public medical care.[9] His effort was isolated, but it had enough appeal and therapeutic (if not pharmacological) validity to outlast his death by almost one hundred years. The remnants of his "system" still survive in France, and the principle that inspired him— the citizen's right to medical care—is now being adopted by an increasing number of nations.

Raspail might have continued merely to write on medical matters and do laboratory research without two experiences which, in the early 1830s, brought him into contact with men in need of immediate medical help: first, the victims of the street fighting in July 1830 (when he himself sustained a slight head wound); and second, the men imprisoned with him during his twenty-seven months in jail, primarily in "preventive custody" under a system without *habeas corpus*. After these experiences Raspail's conscience would not permit him to restrict his medical activities to theorizing and writing. The year 1830 therefore marked a turning point for him, in medicine as well as in science. The change in his orientation was partly due to his discovery of a remedy that helped prevent sickness—or cured it after it occurred—and that had been highly effective for himself and his friends.

Camphor will preserve biological specimens; Raspail the naturalist had long known this fact.[10] He tells the story that one day in 1827, when he was out of breath from blowing glass utensils over a burner, he felt palpitations and acute chest pains. He rubbed himself with camphorated alcohol, chewed a little piece of camphor, and found instant relief. From then on "camphor became my panacea." [11] He used it for personal hygiene in prison; it saved him, he thought, from the cholera of 1832.[12] He emphasized the antiseptic qualities of camphor,[13] and recommended it, specifically,

[9] The short-lived Second Republic did create a national "public assistance" program. But its emphasis was on charity.

[10] This section on camphor (pp. 139–44) was written in collaboration with Mademoiselle Simone Raspail.

[11] F.-V. Raspail, *Nouveau système de chimie organique*, 2nd ed., II, 640.

[12] *Ibid.*, 642.

[13] *Ibid.*, 1st ed., 441.

against small insects, notably ants.[14] Furthermore, personal experience had taught him that if open wounds are cleansed with camphorated alcohol they will heal rapidly. (The camphor rather than the alcohol seemed to him the active agent.) He believed that even gangrene could be cured with the help of camphor. For his first lengthy advocacy of this drug he composed an open letter to the medical profession published in the fall of 1838 in *La Lancette française, L'Expérience,* and other journals.[15] It was modestly written, but full of conviction. He submitted his findings and his excellent therapeutic results to the judgment of doctors and urged them to test his data.

How does camphor dissolved in alcohol act? Raspail gave this explanation: "If alcohol is spread on an infected wound, it coagulates the infecting virus[16] and fixes it. The camphor then exerts its antiputrefactive action and destroys the living cause of infection." [17] Naturally, his unlimited reliance on camphor has been criticized as well as ridiculed. In fairness it should be mentioned that he wrote: "If I had encountered a more effective drug, from the point of view of combatting sepsis and putrefaction, I would not have based my medication on camphor." [18]

In 1839 he published *Camphor Cigarettes and Hygienic Camphor Kits.*[19] This pamphlet marks the beginning of his lifelong advocacy of camphor as a drug of great sanitary value and as a weapon in the fight against contagious disease. He considered it the best "vermifuge," that is, the best drug against the "infinitely small parasites." The pamphlet contained instructions for making camphor cigarettes [a forerunner of mentholated cigarettes] and small boxes for powdered camphor which he hoped would replace snuff.

[14] *Ibid.,* 2nd ed., II, 682.

[15] F.-V. Raspail, "Appareils pour l'emploi du camphre en poudre et des cigarettes de camphre," *La Lancette française: Gazette des hôpitaux civils et militaires,* November 17, 1838; also in *L'Expérience. Journal de médecine et de chirurgie;* and in the *Journal général de médecine, de chirurgie, et de pharmacie,* II (November 22, 1938), 489–91.

[16] Raspail used "virus" interchangeably with "the infinitely small parasites" and with "microscopic agents of sickness."

[17] F.-V. Raspail, *Histoire naturelle de la santé . . . ,* 2nd ed., III, 174.

[18] F.-V. Raspail, *Manuel annuaire de la santé* (Paris, 1845), 1st ed., 56.

[19] F.-V. Raspail, *Cigarettes de camphre et camphatières hygiéniques* (Paris, 1839).

The subtitle of the pamphlet reads: "A remedy for many ailments that are slow to cure or even incurable and chronic; for the relief of complaints which do not call for the immediate presence of the doctor or no longer require it; for the soothing of pain in the doctor's absence." The text exhibited the mixture of medical, sanitary, and moral advice that was to characterize Raspail's writings. The more sanitation and hygiene could be encouraged, he believed, the less need there would be for medicine. Doctors would eventually become unnecessary. "Hygiene prevents medicine," read the oft-repeated epigraph on this first pamphlet.

Raspail's therapeutic armamentarium soon acquired a new weapon: sedative lotion. In one of his books he tells the story of its invention. In January 1840 he lived in a house whose plaster ceiling was cracked by water seeping from the tin roof. At night the temperature dropped rapidly. One night he caught cold and felt a violent headache. Camphorated alcohol compresses on the forehead merely aggravated the pain. He could neither read nor write, because the vision of his right eye was impaired. But it was imperative that he complete a toxicologic report for the trial of a Miss Boeglin of Colmar who was accused of having poisoned her father and mother. The trial on appeal was to be held very soon. What should he do? In a moment of calm he reasoned: if camphorated alcohol brings no relief, either the pain must be caused by congestion (in which case alcohol is injurious); or else the skull is preventing the remedy from reaching the source of the pain. "What if I used ammonia instead of alcohol as the vehicle for the camphor?" And why not add salt to help dissolve albumin in the blood? He compounded the mixture and later called it "sedative lotion," for as soon as he put some compresses on his forehead the pain subsided. He was able to write his report—and "Miss Boeglin was acquitted at Strasburg." [20]

Camphor had of course long been familiar to Europeans. It had been prized by the inhabitants of Southeast Asia, where the camphor tree grows wild, and its use had spread westward along with "arabic" numerals, the compass, paper, and gunpowder. "Alcanfor" reached Spain with the Arabs, and by the late Middle Ages it was sold all over Europe. Leopold Auenbrugger (1722–1809) recom-

[20] F.-V. Raspail, *Histoire naturelle de la santé* . . . , 1st ed., II, 577.

FORMULAS FOR RASPAIL'S MOST POPULAR REMEDIES

I. *Antiseptic and antiputrid medicines:*

a. camphorated alcohol	camphor	200	gr
	alcohol, 95 proof	1	liter
b. camphorated cream	camphor	30	gr
	pure wax	5	gr
	lard	100	gr
c. *"eau quadruple"*	zinc sulfate	4	gr
	kitchen salt	15	gr
	plant tar	0.5	gr
	aloe	50	gr
	water	1	liter
d. camphorated oil	camphor	30	gr
	olive oil	300	gr

II. *Febrifugal and sedative medicines:*

sedative lotion	ammonia	60	gr
	camphorated alcohol	10	gr
	ocean salt	30	gr
	water	1	liter

III. *Purgative and vermifuge medicines:*

a. purgative	aloe seeds
	castor oil
b. vermifuge	camphorated brandy
	asafetida
	male fern
	pomegranate root

IV. *Liqueur Raspail*

alcohol, 60 proof	1	liter
angelica root	15	gr
calamus	2	gr
myrrh	1	gr
cinnamon	0.25	gr
aloe	0.25	gr
clove	0.25	gr
vanilla	0.25	gr
nutmeg	0.25	gr
saffron	0.05	gr

Let stand in the sun for a few days. Filter. To each liter of the mixture add 800 gr sugar.

mended it as a specific for certain cases of insanity, pointing out that Albrecht von Haller (1708–1777) had also "found, employed, and praised" it.[21] In 1797 John Church, a young Philadephia physician, reviewed in his doctoral dissertation all the existing knowledge about the drug.[22] He had found that camphor was valued for its aromatic and sanitary properties and for its action as a stimulant, although, paradoxically, it also served as a sedative. The strong odor of camphor does not seem to have bothered Raspail's contemporaries: the Victorians were much more used to strong smells then we are and drugs did not then have to be odorless. In the early days of the Consulate a long memoir on camphor was read to the Paris Medical Society, and a comprehensive monograph appeared two years later.[23] Although not prominently featured in modern textbooks of pharmacy,[24] camphor is still used in modern medicine because of its antiseptic, anesthetic, stimulant, and somewhat sedative, properties. Indeed. L. J. Meduna (1896–1964), the discoverer of one kind of shock treatment for mental illness, at first used camphor in large doses to induce convulsive seizures in schizophrenic patients.[25]

In Paris, one hundred and thirty years ago, camphorated alcohol, camphor cigarettes, and the camphorated sedative lotion quickly formed a popular and inexpensive array of medicines. Raspail wrote:

[21] L. Auenbrugger, *Preliminary Experience with a Specific Remedy in a Specific Syndrome of Human Insanity* (Vienna, 1776), 4. The reference is to A. v. Haller, *Disputationes ad morborum historiam facientes* (Lausanne, 1957), I, 177.

[22] J. Church, *An Inaugural Dissertation on Camphor* (Philadelphia, 1797).

[23] S. Morelot, "Memoire historique et analytique sur le camphre," *Recueil périodique de la Société de médecine de Paris*, X (1801), 294–314. J.-P. Graffenhauer, *Traité sur le camphre considéré dans ses rapports avec l'histoire naturelle, la physique, la chimie, et la médecine* (Paris & Strasbourg, 1803).

[24] See, e.g., E. Kremers and G. Urdang, *History of Pharmacy* (Philadelphia, 1963, 3rd ed.).

[25] An excellent historical review of the clinical uses of camphor, with a copious bibliography, is to be found in J. Delaunay, *Contribution à l'étude du camphre depuis ses origines jusqu'à Raspail* (Paris, Faculty of Medicine Thesis, 1956). The author concludes: "Though he exaggerated its use, Raspail, this popularizer of genius, deserves credit for the important place which camphor and its derivatives successfully occupy in the modern therapeutic armamentarium" (p. 66). On the medical usefulness of camphor, see also: M. Gardel, *Camphre et sérum camphré* (Toulouse, Faculty of Medicine Thesis, 1913–1914). Among the works on camphor critical of Raspail, the best is: M. Foissac, *Du camphre* (Paris, Faculty of Medicine Thesis, 1866).

"Instances of success are so frequent that everyone today can cite more than one in the smallest village." [26] He recommended camphor against migraine, infections of the nose, eyes, and ears, toothache, cough, cold, asthma, grippe, whooping cough, incipient tuberculosis, heartburn, rheumatism, and skin diseases. He thus essentially advocated it as an anesthetic, as a mild antiseptic, and for its effectiveness in clearing the respiratory tract. He also recommended it for regular ingestion to insure general well-being. He himself "chewed it like bread." [27] This rather uncritical use may seem less astonishing if one remembers that many new drugs were then just only being isolated.[28] All his life Raspail was to remain faithful to camphor because he found it effective, cheap, and convenient—in fact, irreplaceable.

In the 1850s he devised the "Liqueur Raspail," an after-dinner drink somewhat resembling Benedictine [containing alcohol but no camphor!]. A poetic admirer once described it as a "dream from Ossian's paradise that found its way into Mahomet's heaven; the most subtle and exquisite gustatory perfume that I have ever known." [29]

For convalescents Raspail emphasized the need for fresh air, a nutritious diet, and salubrious living quarters. "Pure air is nourishment," he wrote, "for we assimilate its elements; it must be often renewed, for we constantly vitiate it by despoiling it to our advantage." [30] He advised that patients be fed appetizing food, liberally seasoned with onion, garlic, clove, cinnamon, or nutmeg. He was a stern critic of the prevalent reliance on fasting, leeches, and tightly closed windows.

His advocacy of "antisepsis" was meant particularly for surgeons.[31]

One cannot pay too much attention to cleanliness in an operation [he wrote]. Surgeons must above all be careful to wash their instruments

[26] F.-V. Raspail, *Histoire naturelle de la santé* . . . , 2nd ed., III, 392.

[27] *Ibid.*, 3rd ed., I, 214.

[28] Morphine was definitely characterized in 1817, strychnine in 1818, quinine in 1820, pure cocaine in 1860. See M. Bouvet, *Histoire de la pharmacie en France* . . . (Paris, 1937), 343–44; and E. Kremers and G. Urdang, *History of Pharmacy*, 319–20.

[29] T. Grimm, *Un grand méconnu: F.-V. Raspail* (Paris, 1910), 12.

[30] *Ibid.*, II, 435.

[31] Strictly speaking, as already pointed out, it is anachronistic to use the terms "antisepsis" and "asepsis" before Lister and Pasteur. See *supra*, p. 123, n. 32.

PARIS VOUS PARLE DE RASPAIL

A modern pamphlet advertising "Liqueur Raspail"
(Courtesy Moltzer & Co., Distillers of Liqueur Raspail, Arcueil, Seine)

before and after the operation with ammonia and rinse them afterwards
with alcohol. They will thus protect themselves from the majority of
the usual complications.[32]

After an operation he especially recommended repeated applications of camphorated alcohol around the wounds, and frequent
renewal of bandages saturated with camphorated salve.

Thanks to this simple medication, rigorously observed, I guarantee the
success of any surgical intervention: the patient will thus be protected
from the typhus which desolates our prisons and hospitals and from the
gangrene which all the antiphlogistic medication has never been able
to prevent but which, if my ideas are correct, it breeds and favors.[33]

[32] F.-V. Raspail, *Histoire naturelle de la santé* . . . , 2nd ed., III, 174.
[33] *Ibid.*, 1st ed., II, 506.

He argued, of course, from practical experience rather than experimental proof. Ammonia is simply a good cleansing agent, and alcohol will not kill all germs.

A distressing personal experience in 1841 helped shape Raspail's thought on surgical hygiene and post-operative care. His eldest son Benjamin developed a tumor on the knee at the age of eighteen. As it grew, Raspail became more and more alarmed. The leg finally had to be amputated at the knee. (It then weighed seventy pounds.) The sixteen-month illness, surgery, and convalescence all took place at home. Raspail was convinced that strict hygienic care with camphorated medicines had prevented sepsis, that a healthy diet had restored the patient, and that his own insistence on operating at the knee instead of the hip had saved his son's life.[34]

Given the large dose of pragmatic, sensible advice, and the emphasis on self-help, first-aid, sanitation, and hygiene in Raspail's writings, it is not surprising that they were eagerly read. The first edition of the *History of Health* sold out by 1845. Preparing a new edition, Raspail realized that his book was too voluminous and too expensive to reach the masses of poor people who needed his help the most. Therefore he wrote a *Health Annual,* which contained essentially the same information as the *History,* but abridged and simplified. It was of pocket-book format; prominence was given to detailed reports on Raspail's medical consultations, therapy, and cures. It sold for one-and-a-half francs.

The *Health Annual* met with instantaneous and unprecedented success. The business ledgers of the *Maison d'édition Raspail*[35] record the sale of 194,308 copies in the first five years, an average of more than 100 copies a day. Raspail and his two eldest sons acted as publishers. They drove hard bargains with the paper salesman, typesetter, printer, binder, and carefully planned their pub-

[34] *Ibid.,* II, 485–512.

[35] Founded in 1845, rue des Francs-Bourgeois St. Michel (later renamed rue Monsieur le Prince), with Benjamin and Camille as publishers, and with the help of initial capital from Raspail's old friend Nell de la Bréauté. (See G. Raspail, *La vie et l'oeuvre . . . ,* 113, and X. Raspail, *Raspail et Pasteur . . . ,* 164.) In 1859 the publishing house was transferred to 15, rue du Temple, next door to the newly founded Pharmacie complémentaire de la Méthode Raspail.

licity. The manual sold well from the start, to people as different as "a lady from Madrid" and "a peddler," but mainly to booksellers. One dealer alone, Dentu, sold 322 copies in the first six months. Gross receipts for the first eighteen months totaled 85,022 francs, more than half of which was profit. The Raspails became well-to-do almost overnight.[36] The *Annual* remained so successful that a new edition was issued almost every year. Raspail's most recent biographer asserts that "Even today [1948] the *Manuel-annuaire de la santé* has an assured and regular sale." [37]

The sales of the *Annual* were in fact boosted by Raspail's widely publicized prosecution for the illegal practice of medicine. At the trial he gave a glowing account of his training, competence, and solicitude. Even the district attorney, although prosecuting an illegal activity, was highly complimentary of Raspail's knowledge.[38] The scientist's friend Nell de la Bréauté, who lived near Dieppe, wrote on July 4, 1846: ". . . your defense has produced a miraculous effect, and has prodigiously enhanced your medical eminence in the people's eyes. Your *Manuel* will doubtless sell even better. People talk of nothing but your system. . . ." And again: ". . . the effect of this trial has been the opposite of what was expected . . . [Your opponents] have offered a platform to the most eloquent and superior man of our time, and thus rendered him a great service for which they deserve thanks." [39]

Even abroad the *Health Annual* was well received.[40] The Pref-

[36] The above facts result from the study of the Fonds Raspail at the Archives du Département de la Seine et de la Ville de Paris.

[37] G. Duveau, *Raspail*, 13.

[38] See *supra*, p. 136 and *infra*, pp. 195–97.

[39] Autogr. ms. letters, Fonds Raspail, Archives du Département de la Seine, LXXXV.

[40] Although research in New York, Washington, and Paris has not yielded a complete list of foreign translations, editions, and adaptations, the following will give some indication of the widespread and persistent demand for Raspail's book:

(a) H. Prater, M.D., Ph.D., *On the Injurious Effects of Mineral Poisons . . . Comprising an Epitome and Commentary on . . . the New System of Medicine of F.-V. Raspail: Every Man His Own Physician* (London, 1846); the copy of this book belonging to the National Medical Library in Washington includes the following manuscript epigraph by the author:

"We have heard of embalming after man's death,
When forever has left him the vital breath.
Thus the dead man is kept, no doubt, from decay,
And all sorts of vermin chased from him away;

ace to an English edition of 1853 urged the British to follow Raspail's therapy, citing his popularity in France:

M. Raspail's method of preserving health and curing disease has achieved a most unequivocal and truly legitimate success in France; . . . it has shaken and displaced . . . both the various systems of the old school of medicine, and the more recent importations, homeopathy and hydropathy. It is not too much to say that millions have derived solid and lasting benefit from M. Raspail's simple, plain, and lucid instructions in the difficult art of managing the health.[41]

Still more impressive—because it was written in a private letter to Raspail, with no idea of advertisement or gain in mind—is the following passage from a Catholic missionary in Nova Scotia:

Sir:

You may be surprised to receive a letter from a priest in North America. But this priest is a Frenchman. . . . When he left Paris for Nova

---

But here in this book of Raspail you will read,
That *during our life* of embalming we've need;
That insects assail us within and without;
That from these come all ills—both Fevers and Gout;
That *Camphor and Aloes*—these only can save us,
And keep that life sound which great Nature gave us.

.   .   .   .

We know some love smoking—smoke half the day;
To all our great smokers here then we say,
Adopt this new plan, smoke too all the night
Your camphor cigar, which ne'er wanteth a light!
Thus by you, *in your life,* no worms will be fed—
Quite enough to be eaten by them *when you're dead."*

(b) A. Fortier, *Annual Diary of Health,* or, *Family Physician and Druggist, containing the necessary Theoretical and Practical Manner of Preparing Medicines and Preserving or Curing Yourself of Disease, at Small Cost and with Promptitude, of all Curable Evils, and of Giving Relief to those who Labor under Chronic or Incurable Diseases* (New Orleans, 1846).

(c) Translations into German: (Leipzig, 1852, billed as *Dr. Raspail's neues Schutz- und Heilverfahren gegen die Cholera und die tausendfach erprobte, wahrhaft wundertätige Wirksamkeit desselben*); (also Bern, 1885).

(d) Translation into Swedish, 7th edition (Stockholm, 1886).

(e) Translations into Spanish: (Mexico City, 1850; Lima, 1856; Madrid, 1857, 1862, 1896; Barcelona, 1929).

(f) Translation into Portuguese (Lisbon, 1850).

[41] Raspail's *Médecine des familles* (Paris, 1843), rendered into English as *Domestic Medicine; or Plain Instructions in the Art of Preserving and Restoring Health by Simple and Efficient Means,* G. L. Strauss, Ph.D., ed. (London, 1853).

Scotia, he took with him one of your *Manuels de la santé* (1856) and this *Manuel* has become my traveling companion. I live in the midst of poor French Acadians, isolated on the Atlantic coast, far from the English towns, and without any doctor. . . .

This fact led me to study your *Manuel* so that I could learn to be helpful to my parishioners, owing to your good book. I have set up a pharmacy, I mix your drugs with the help of your formulas, and I distribute them. You will not be surprised to hear that your camphor cream and your sedative lotion work miracles. Everybody now owns them and praises them as the best remedies in the world. May you be blessed, Sir, for the relief which your book has brought. . . ." [42]

The use of the new method by a priest occurred no doubt less often than its propagation by ardent republicans who shared Raspail's political convictions. One of them—Sebastien Commissaire (1822–1900), a weaver from Lyons, and a deputy in 1848—gives a naïve, sincere, and explicit account of his medical and political adherence to Raspail that deserves to be quoted in full:

I want to say a few words about the reception accorded F.-V. Raspail's *Health Manual* in Lyons. Men of my age will recall that the population of Lyons went wild over the sanitary methods advocated by the illustrious chemist. In 1845, for a while, everyone except the doctors used the cigarette: men, women, children, young and old, rich and poor. On the streets, most men held a camphor cigarette between their lips, and ladies did not fear to be seen smoking one, while going for a walk.

The sale of cigarettes became very lucrative. Not only were they made out of quills, but of bone, ivory, or cocoanut—for all tastes and purses.

This enthusiasm lasted a few months; after that, only the serious followers of the method continued to use camphor cigarettes.

Raspail was an old republican. Everything that came from him was welcomed with warmth and enthusiasm by the republicans of Lyons. I became a convinced adept of the method. From that moment on, I spread double propaganda: for democracy and for the new method.

Young men seldom doubt their powers. Not content to treat my family, I even gave consultations to my neighbors. Soon my reputation spread, and I was called from quite far away to visit patients. My knowledge was being greatly exaggerated and I was turned into a doctor in spite of myself. The mass of workers was so ignorant in those days! and, as the proverb says, "In the land of the blind, the one-eyed hold the highest positions."

[42] Fonds Raspail, Archives de la Seine, LXXXVI.

My reputation was greatly enhanced by the fact that my consultations were free. I donated my time and my efforts. When I compounded sedative lotion or camphorated salve for the sick, I only charged them for the price of the ingredients I bought. My work was motivated by dedication alone. I hoped, by helping them, to convert them later to the republic.

During the month of November, 1845, I had the following adventure: a brother-in-law of Mademoiselle Jeanne developed an extremely violent case of cerebral fever. He had to be watched to prevent him from committing some mad action. A doctor was called, but, despite the strict observance of his advice, the patient grew worse. I was sent for and was informed of the sickness. I brought a liter of sedative lotion, a jar of camphorated salve, and I spent part of the night rubbing the patient and putting compresses on his neck and wrists. Gradually he quieted down and, between two and three o'clock in the morning, he fell asleep.

I sent the others to bed and I spent the rest of the night reading.

The patient awoke in the morning and spoke to me. The delirium had vanished and he was quite well.

The doctor arrived and smelled the odor of camphor and of ammonia. He grew angry.

"What is this? Who brought these drugs?"

"I did, Sir."

"Who told you to?"

"Raspail," said I, pointing to the *Health Manual.*

"You deserve to be prosecuted for the illegal practice of medicine."

"Prosecute him!," cried Jeanne's sister, "but my husband would be dead without him!"

The doctor quieted down and the patient got up the next day.

I must admit that the doctor's threat considerably chilled my enthusiasm. It had never occurred to me that I was committing a crime by curing patients free of charge. Subsequently, I was more careful. . . .[43]

Here was a man who had taken to heart Raspail's plea, published in his pamphlet on camphor cigarettes in 1839:

I ask those who have benefited from this method to propagate a useful and moral idea, instead of paying me a fee. They should not give alms, which is offensive. Rather, may they do a good deed before sundown, and thus relieve human suffering without wounding anyone's pride.[44]

[43] S. Commissaire, *Mémoires et souvenirs* (Paris, 1888), 2 vols., I, 128–30.
[44] F.-V. Raspail, *Cigarettes de camphre et camphatières hygiéniques . . . ,* 15–16.

Camphor soon reached a popularity that far exceeded Raspail's expectations.[45] A malevolent journal wrote in 1845: "The sales-girl, the glamour girl, the rabbit-fur salesman, the welfare-fund administrator all carry Raspail cigarettes in their mouths. You ask this herd of sheep why they 'smoke' them and they answer: 'I don't know, I just imitate others' " [46] Even among the educated the drug was widely used. In 1843 Sainte-Beuve recommended camphor cigarettes to his friend Juste Olivier, the Swiss historian and poet:

Camphor cigarettes can be very helpful in case of asthma if it is asthma of the lungs and not of the heart. In any case, camphor can do no harm. One inserts little pieces (not powder) inside a quill between two tampons of paper and one holds this quill in one's mouth by the narrow end. The paper tampons must not be too tight—tight enough to prevent the camphor from falling out but not so tight as to prevent the air from circulating. One must keep it in one's mouth a very long time, while talking and doing other things, without inhaling as if one were smoking; rather, one must keep breathing normally and not tire of the cigarette; well-being returns sometimes only after several days of use. (Consume as much as one cigarette per day.)[47]

Many years later Vincent Van Gogh also tried Raspail's cigarettes. A copy of the *Manuel-annuaire de la santé* appeared, decorated with onions, on a Still Life painted by Van Gogh around 1889. "[Raspail's] book," writes Carl Nordenfalk, "had not been placed [in the Still Life] merely as a coloristic note in the composi-

[45] In 1847 Raspail evidently found his *Annual* insufficient for frequent and informal communication with his growing flock of faithful followers. He therefore supplemented it with the monthly *Revue élémentaire de médecine et de pharmacie domestiques ainsi que des sciences accessoires et usuelles mises à la portée de tout le monde* (Paris, 1847–1849). Each issue contained most of the following: a "Clinic," a report on his most interesting cases; "Applied anatomy and physiology"; "New formulas and medicines," often mere restatements taken from the *Natural History of Health*; "Organic chemistry," and "Agriculture"—old favorites; "Morals and jurisprudence," inspired by his lawsuits; "Anecdotes"; and "Correspondence" with doctors all over France who used his methods.

[46] *Asmodée: Revue des journaux, ouvrages de médecine, chimie, pharmacie, et sciences accessoires,* Oct.–Dec. 1845, 77.

[47] *Revue Suisse,* May 21, 1843; reprinted in C.-A. Sainte-Beuve, *Chroniques parisiennes,* 48, n. See also "Raspail et Sainte-Beuve, *Aesculape,* Year 17, No. 11 (Nov. 1927), 284–87.

tion. It is a confession of the artist's faith in the possibility of mastering the destructive forces and fighting his way back to a normal existence." [48] Passionately concerned about his health, Van Gogh liked to increase his medical knowledge by talking with doctors. He seems to have derived considerable faith from Raspail's *Manuel*. Camphorated medicines helped him fight insomnia, and he recommended them to his brother Théo in a letter of January 1889.

Gustave Flaubert, ever on the lookout for human foibles, included Raspail's advocacy of camphor among the follies espoused by his heroes, Bouvard and Pécuchet, those two "shepherds tending their woolly flock of ideas." [49]

One day [Flaubert writes of one of these protagonists] he was accosted by a man who carried a sack on his back and offered him almanacs, sacred books, holy medals, and, lastly the *Manual of Health* by François Raspail. . . .

The clarity of the doctrine seduced . . . [Bouvard and Pécuchet]. All illnesses are caused by worms. They spoil the teeth, hollow out the lungs, expand the liver, wreck the intestine where they cause noises. The best means of getting rid of them is camphor. Bouvard and Pécuchet adopted it. They snuffed it, nibbled at it and distributed aloe pills. They even undertook to cure a hunchback. [50]

In *Madame Bovary* as well, "Raspail's medicines" appear among M. Homais' remedies. [51]

A pharmacy was soon needed where Raspail could send his patients with complete confidence. In 1839 he granted a pharmacist named Collas the exclusive right to manufacture and sell his camphorated salves, elixirs, powders, cigarettes, and snuffs. Collas also distributed a wooden doctor bag designed by Raspail. [52] In return Raspail was to receive medicines equal in value to Collas' profits for distribution among his patients. Collas netted about fifteen

[48] C. Nordenfalk, "Van Gogh and Literature," *Journal of the Warburg and Courtauld Institutes*, X (1947), 141.

[49] L. Trilling, *The Opposing Self* (New York, 1953), 185.

[50] G. Flaubert, *Bouvard et Pécuchet* (Paris, 1923), 84–85. In the newly discovered and published *Second volume de Bouvard et Pécuchet* (ed. Geneviève Bolléma, Paris, 1966) Raspail is quoted twice on p. 79 (*Histoire naturelle de la santé* . . . , 2nd ed. Introduction, p. LXII and LXIII, 98).

[51] G. Flaubert, *Madame Bovary* (Paris, 1957), 68.

[52] See illustration, p. 155.

hundred francs a year, enabling Raspail to give away a large quantity of drugs.[53] The association proved satisfactory, yet Raspail dissolved it after six years because "M. Collas, although wholly reliable in his dealings with my patients, both rich and poor, seemed to me to delay the propagation of the new method by his high prices." [54] Collas' successor Morel was to involve Raspail in a costly and damaging lawsuit. It seems probable that Raspail's record as a revolutionary in politics and a rebel in medicine prejudiced the case.

Morel was familiar with Raspail's personality, and he also knew the law. He had evidently decided to provoke his business partner into suing for dissolution, so as to gain control of a profitable enterprise. Raspail was unquestionably ill advised when, on November 8, 1845, he initiated legal pursuits against Morel who had been his pharmacist for only three months.[55]

It can hardly be a coincidence that the medical press began to print virulent attacks on Raspail at this very moment. Morel had many friends—and Raspail quite a few enemies. In December 1845 the scientific scandal sheet *Asmodée* suddenly branded Raspail as a "sad apostle of medical charlatanism" who "flaunts his publicity on markets and on public squares, at street corners, and in the newspapers." [56] The *Gazette médicale* wrote:

An ex-chemist, ex-naturalist, ex-author, ex-political writer who unfortunately lacks a medical degree has invented a system of medicine with camphor as its cornerstone. . . . His republican virtue . . . (which would subject medicine as well as politics to the spirit of '89) rebels against the suspicious authorities who restrict poor relief. We are afraid that the king's prosecutor will not take his reasons seriously.[57]

Raspail had by then been accused of practicing medicine illegally.

According to Raspail, the quarrel started when Morel would not let him or his sons enter the pharmacy, arguing that they were not licensed druggists. Raspail testified that Morel mixed impure salves

[53] F.-V. Raspail, *Nouvelle défense et nouvelle condamnation de F.-V. Raspail à 15,000 francs de dommages-intérêts* . . . (Paris, 1848), 7 and 41.

[54] F.-V. Raspail, *Histoire naturelle de la santé* . . . , 3rd ed., I, LXV.

[55] F.-V. Raspail, "Audiences préliminaires du 8 et 12 mai 1846, 7ème chambre (police correctionnelle)," *Procès et défense* . . . , 9.

[56] *Asmodée*, Oct.–Dec. 1845, 104.

[57] *Gazette médicale*, December 13, 1845.

and lotions, imitated Raspail's signature and paraph on his labels, and made his shop look like a stable.[58] The court ruled [59] that Morel had not in fact "failed to carry out his obligations," and that he should receive fifty thousand francs in damages. When Raspail appealed the verdict,[60] the judge found Morel's conduct objectionable, but thought it "could be explained by Raspail's hostile attitude." Damages were reduced to fifteen thousand francs, and Raspail was granted the dissolution of the partnership.[61]

[58] F.-V. Raspail, "Plainte portée par Raspail, père et fils, contre leur associé Morel, pharmacien, rue des Lombards, 14, et Choubard, leur commis dans la même officine, en escroquerie, abus de confiance, et contrefaçon de leur griffe," *Procès et défense* . . . , 9.

[59] Unluckily for Raspail the judge who presided at this trial had been the examining magistrate at the "Trial of the Fifteen" in 1832 when Raspail, then President of the *Société des amis du peuple,* had been condemned to fifteen months in jail and a fine of five hundred francs. See *infra,* pp. 170–72.

[60] See F.-V. Raspail, ed., *Résumé par ordre de dates des moyens présentés à la Cour le 1er et 8 décembre 1847 par F.-V. Raspail, appelant d'une sentence arbitrale qui le condamne à 50,000 francs de dommages-intérêts envers le Sieur Morel, pharmacien-droguiste, rue des Lombards, 14* (Paris, 1848).

[61] F.-V. Raspail, *Nouvelle défense* . . . , 21 and 44.

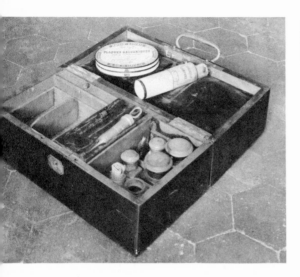

Raspail's doctor bag and labels currently used for Raspail medicines (Courtesy Musée de la Ville de Carpentras and Pharmacie Raspail, Paris)

The legality of Raspail's pharmaceutical activities demands careful study. The Law of April 1803 (21 Germinal, Year XI) clearly precluded his practice of pharmacy, since he had no training in this profession.[62] Of course he did not really claim to be licensed, and he distributed his medicines in association with qualified pharmacists (Collas, then Morel). This use of a figurehead, although not illegal, was condemned by doctors and pharmacists. An expert on French medical jurisprudence of the 1830s and 1840s denounced this subterfuge employed by druggists, herbalists, grocers, and doctors whom he stigmatized as "greedy, selfish men who want to get rich, who exploit the rights and degrees of others, and make use of their experience and social status. . . ."[63] It would be wrong to accuse Raspail of greed, but one can hardly blame the pharmaceutical profession for resenting the use of licensed figureheads by unlicensed practitioners, and the compounding of remedies—however

[62] See M. Bouvet, "Le régime de la loi de Germinal," in *Histoire de la pharmacie . . .* , and L. André-Pontier, *Histoire de la pharmacie* (Paris, 1900), 260–64.

[63] A. Trébuchet, *Jurisprudence de la médecine, de la chirurgie, et de la pharmacie en France* (Paris, 1834), 323.

effective—according to the formulas of a layman, however knowl-edgeable.[64]

From a legal point of view, were "Raspail medicines" market-able? The answer to this question depends upon whether they be-longed to the legal category of "secret remedies" and proprietary medicines. Doctors and lawyers had long protested vainly against these salves and potions which were for sale all over France. Ras-pail's medicines, in contrast with other proprietary drugs, had noth-ing secret about them. On the contrary, he sought publicity for his formulas so that doctors would become less and less necessary. From 1845 on he published the directions for compounding his remedies in his *Health Annual*.

The term "secret remedy" might have misled Raspail and his clientèle, but not after November 19, 1840, when the *Cour de cassation* redefined its legal meaning. Thereafter it was clear that Raspail's medicines belonged to a category that was defined and condemned as including "all pharmaceutical preparations not com-pounded in accordance with legally accepted and published for-mularies and pharmacopoeias; nor bought by the government and made public; nor mixed in each instance according to a prescription . . . from a doctor, . . . surgeon, or . . . health officer . . . ."[65]

But might they have been marketed as "inventions," protected by patents and trademarks? The question was being debated at the time, but there is no indication that Raspail was aware of this. A

[64] The protection of pharmacists against the incursions of unlicensed persons was one of the reasons for the founding, in 1824, of the Société de prévoyance des pharmaciens de Paris et du Département de la Seine. L. André-Pontier, *His-toire de la pharmacie*, 281.

[65] A. Trébuchet, "Des brevêts d'invention délivrés pour remèdes secrets," *An-nales d'hygiène publique et de médecine légale*, XXIX (1843), 209–10. Raspail himself finally acknowledged this legal classification. See F.-V. Raspail, *Revue complémentaire des sciences appliquées à la médecine et pharmacie, à l'agriculture, aux arts et à l'industrie*, III (1856), 37–40. That Raspail's medicines were ille-gal "secret remedies" after 1840 is confirmed, e.g., by the conviction of Brisset, a pharmacist, and Pradel, a pharmacy student, in 1856, for "selling secret reme-dies and for the illegal practice of medicine," because: "The medicines for which the chemist Raspail gives the formulas in his *Health Yearbook* have been pre-pared and sold by a great number of pharmacists since 1840. But these widely used preparations are not listed in the *Codex* and have just been included, by judgment of the tribunal . . . among the secret remedies." *Le Droit, Journal des tribunaux, de la jurisprudence, des débats judiciaires, et de la législation*. No. 151 (June 26, 1856), 637. See also H. Leclerc, *En marge du codex* (Paris, 1924).

committee of experts, reporting to the Minister of Public Works and Commerce, agreed that inventions were categorically different from remedies. The committee concluded that if the government patented medicinal remedies compounded by laymen, it would thereby sanction what the legal code condemned.[66]

Legislation concerning pharmaceutical products was indeed contradictory and confusing. A Parisian doctor complained:

The law is uncertain or misunderstood . . . [it contains] many contradictory provisions which further confuse matters. . . . [It happens that] the police prosecute an offense which the administrative authorities have abetted by selling a license for money.[67]

A lawyer concurred:

How can one proceed, seeing that the Decree of Prairial, Year XIII, departs from the Law of 21 Germinal, Year XI, which was invalidated by the Decree of August 18, 1810, which was itself modified by a third decree, of December 26, 1810; when one is forced to propose the annulment of this last decree since it precludes the execution of the Decree of August 18 but, seeing that the Council of State denied this annulment, all one can do is to let the Decree of August 18 fall into disuse. . . .[68]

At any rate, one of the government's objectives was achieved when Raspail lost his lawsuit against Morel and when he was condemned for the illegal practice of medicine. This frightened off some potential practitioners of his method and distributors of his medication. Witness, for example, this letter from a M. Sursol who asked

[66] See "Projet de lettre à M. le Ministre des Trauvaux Publics et du Commerce, touchant la concession de brevêts d'invention pour remèdes," par une commission composée de MM. Cornac, Gueneau de Mussy, Bouley, Lodibert, Adelon, *Annales d'hygiène publique et de médecine légale,* XIX (1838), 226–31.

[67] L. J. Delasiauve, *De l'organisation médicale en France sous le triple rapport de la pratique, des établissements de bienfaisance, et de l'enseignement* (Paris, 1843), 74–75.

[68] A. Trébuchet, *Jurisprudence de la médecine* . . . , 371–72. In the same book, this lawyer, asking for legal clarification and reform, demanded: "harsh and exemplary punishment against charlatans, i.e. against persons who practice medicine without a diploma or who sell secret remedies; against figureheads in pharmacy; against illegal and often shameful partnerships entered into by pharmacists. On all these points the law should be clear, positive, and harsh . . ." Preface, XIII–XIV.

a pharmacist friend whether he, as a grocer, could legally sell Raspail's products. The pharmacist,

. . . a man devoted to social ideas, told me that he himself often hesitated to advertise your specialties—not that he worries about being annoyed by the reactionary powers, he is used to that—but because he would turn the whole medical corporation against him. . . . He will consult the medical jury.
. . . We also have many doctors who do not disapprove of your method, but who lack the courage to practice it.[69]

For eleven years there was to be no special pharmacy that sold Raspail's drugs. But in 1858 Emile, his third son, opened the *Pharmacie complémentaire de la méthode Raspail*, 14, rue du Temple, and started a factory at Arcueil-Cachan, Seine, the next year. Emile was a chemical engineer, not a pharmacist, and therefore the legal battles continued. The correspondence between Paris and Boitsfort or Uccle, Belgium—where Raspail and Benjamin lived in political exile from 1853 until 1862—is filled with the details of litigation. In a letter to his brother Emile, for example, Camille commented in 1860:

With our name, we have to expect that all these old judges who have always been the bitter enemies of our dear father would only be too happy to ruin the sons. Maybe we'll get our revenge yet. . . . When one bears a political name, law becomes invalid, arbitrariness and vengeance take its place.[70]

But the family had learned from experience. Emile again used a figurehead pharmacist and, classifying some Raspail medicines as inventions, he obtained trademarks and patents to protect them (by a verdict of the Court of Appeals in 1863). On the other hand, by 1880 other Raspail products (notably camphorated alcohol, salve,

[69] Autogr. ms. letter from H. Sursol to Benjamin Raspail dated May 24, 1850. Fonds Raspail, Archives du Département de la Seine, LXXXV.

[70] Autogr. ms. letter dated Aug. 24, 1860, in the possession of M. Jacques Raspail. In 1869, the Paris Exposition of Fine Arts refused, for the third time, to hang two of Benjamin's paintings although they had been shown repeatedly in England, Holland, and Belgium. In a letter to the Superintendent of Fine Arts, Count de Nieuwerkerke, Benjamin protested: "Is it not clear that this exclusion is meant for the name I am proud to bear, rather than for my work?" "Lettre de Benjamin Raspail," *La révolution de 1848*, XXI–XXII (March 1924–Feb. 1926), 684–86.

and sedative lotion) were accepted into the French pharmaceutical *Codex*, which empowered all pharmacists to compound and sell them.

Emile's widow and sons continued the business after his death in 1887, but it was sold in 1904.[71] That same year a *Société anonyme des établissements Raspail* (owned by strangers) was incorporated in Paris. To this day it manufactures Raspail medicines and is connected with the Pharmacie Raspail, 20, rue Rambuteau, in Paris, which sells the now patented drugs, soaps, perfumes, toilet water, and toothpaste. The Liqueur Raspail is now distilled, sold, and widely exported by Moltzer & Co., Arcueil, Seine. Raspail himself was never associated with any of the commercial activity that blossomed from 1858 on, nor did he derive any pecuniary profit from it.[72]

While his medicines helped build his reputation, Raspail was personally offering medical advice to patients.

At first, I limited my services to my neighbors and the poorer people in my village. My dining room served as clinic when it rained too hard to let patients wait in the garden. All this was done without noise or publicity. My patients were not afraid of ruining their good name and treated me with the respect due to a friend.[73]

He was then living in the suburb of Montsouris. Fifteen years later, reminiscing about his medical beginnings, he wrote:

Patients thronged to my door and to my pharmacist; my marvelous cures kept adding to their number. Most internal illnesses, at the time, were caused by vermin which the current medical practices nourished with their diet, juleps, and syrups. My medication dispersed them as if by magic. In twenty-four hours patients were cured of a migraine, gastritis, or cough which the family doctor had carefully nurtured for years. How

[71] See Emile Raspail's will, made out in 1887, in the possession of M. Jacques Raspail.

[72] Raspail also invented many chemical manufacturing processes which might have brought him a considerable income, had he so desired. He did not try to patent his inventions but he often sued presumed imitators. For a list of these discoveries, see F. Raspail, *Biographie de F.-V. Raspail par son petit-fils, le Dr. François Raspail*, 15–17.

[73] F.-V. Raspail, *Manuel-annuaire de la santé* (1845), XIII.

easy it was to be a prophet! From everywhere patients came rushing to my hermitage at Montsouris.[74]

In 1845 Raspail transferred his office to the capital. He could not have been unaware of possible complications with the law, because he entered into association with a Dr. Pierre-Louis Cottereau (1800–1847), a licensed physician who was to sign all the prescriptions. In 1845 the two men opened a dispensary at 10, rue des Francs-Bourgeois, not far from the secluded Place des Vosges.

The first day that M. Cottereau and I opened our dispensary . . . [Raspail wrote in 1860], a crowd of people filled the rooms, the staircase and the courtyard and even spilled into the street. . . .

I treated the poor patients gratis; and often gave them medicines free. The rich went to M. Cottereau . . . he charged ten francs a visit.[75]

Raspail's clientèle was varied, although the majority were workers and their families, too poor to afford a doctor's fee and too proud or diffident to enter a hospital. In fact Raspail's popularity as a therapist affords the only logical explanation for the large political following he attracted in 1848 during the socialist phase of the Second Republic. He had by then refrained for twelve years from engaging in political activity. The membership of the radical "Club Raspail" and the 37,000 votes he polled as a candidate for the presidency, running against Louis Napoleon Bonaparte, must largely represent the thanks of devoted patients.

Artisans and bourgeois also called for his services. One can infer this from the great number of medical publications he sold from 1839 on: only literate customers would buy these. Reassured and guided by his writings, they eventually came to consult him in person. The well-to-do and even aristocrats came for help as well: Gabrielle Raspail mentions among her father-in-law's patients Prince Demidoff, the Duc de Fitz-James, the Marquise de Dampierre, the Comtesse de Pontavice, and the Princesse de Canino, widow of Lucien Bonaparte.[76]

[74] F.-V. Raspail, *Histoire naturelle de la santé* . . . (1860), LXIII.

[75] *Ibid.*, LXV and LXVI.

[76] G. Raspail, *La vie et l'oeuvre* . . . , 3. See also an affectionate letter from the Princesse de Canino to Raspail, probably written in the mid-1840s. Autogr. ms. letter No. 69, Fonds Berner, Bibliothèque de La Chaux-de-Fonds, Switzerland.

Typical of many notes from friends, acquaintances, or admirers, who recommended patients to Raspail's attention, was the following note of June 1, 1847, from Etienne Cabet, the Utopian experimenter: "Cabet sends fraternal greetings to Raspail and begs his kind attention for good father Loiset who would like to consult him about his wife's health." [77] Another appeal came on behalf of Gustave Flaubert's sister, who lay dying of puerperal fever in Rouen. Maxime du Camp reports the incident: "Caroline was dying and [Raspail] alone might save her. I couldn't believe my eyes: Raspail in the house of Flaubert's father, in the very temple of scientific medicine—that was like putting the devil in a holy water font." Yet Du Camp was asked to fetch Raspail. Finally, at night, he found Raspail's house at Montrouge. No one answered, and he had to climb over the wall. At last there was a light and a voice. "My hat in one hand, my letter of introduction in the other, I flew up the three stairs and was welcomed by a gun which Raspail aimed at my chest shouting: 'Stop there!' I couldn't help laughing and I said: 'Read first, then you can shoot later.'" They left for Rouen on the first train; but Caroline was beyond help. As usual Raspail refused all proffered remuneration—3,000 francs this time.[78] But he did stay for dinner.[79]

Raspail showed sympathy for each patient—an attitude in contrast to the growing fashion of focusing on interesting medical cases. Many persons came to him for reassurance, for his special brand of medical advice mixed with supportive therapy and with admonitions about sanitary practices and hygienic precautions. His published case histories reveal this humanitarian approach. They sound as spontaneous as a spoken consultation. His solicitude also renders plausible the high percentage of improvements and cures he obtained with camphorated medicines. His success far exceeds the

[77] Dossier Raspail, No. 1684, Archives nationales.

[78] M. Du Camp, "Souvenirs littéraires," Pt. V in *Revue des Deux Mondes*, XLVII (Oct. 1, 1881), 485–86. Raspail evidently moved from Montsouris to Montrouge sometime in the late 1840s.

[79] The incident was discussed at one of the famous literary "Magny dinner parties," on January 31, 1863, when Ste.-Beuve compared Raspail's fear of persecution to that of Rousseau and commented that the scientist "had paid Flaubert's father the greatest possible compliment by dining at his house without fear of poisoning." E. and J. Goncourt, *Journal*, VI (Monaco, 1956), 22.

known therapeutic qualities of camphor, and must be due in part to the psychological impact of his kindly interest.

The urge that Raspail felt to help his fellowmen had first driven him to abandon pure scholarship for the practice of medicine. But the demand for his services soon made him feel harassed, and in his eagerness to help he made a compromise with thoroughness. In 1847, for example, he informed his patients[80] that he would from then on reserve Tuesday afternoons for the owners of the *Natural History of Health.*

Provided you know how to read . . . [he admonished his patients], you would be guilty toward a host of others if you asked me for five extra minutes. For, with five minutes per person, I need nine hours to see one hundred-and-eight patients; and there are days when I have one hundred-and-fifty to two hundred to see. You can understand that, in order to be just toward all, sooner or later I would have to be still more laconic and, in most cases, I would have to be content, after having diagnosed the sickness, to indicate the page of the treatment in the book.[81]

Eventually he was driven to plead with his patients to consult his books only and refrain altogether from visiting him. "I urge patients," he wrote, "first to apply the methods of the *Manual* . . . ; the chances are that, in most cases, especially in the early stages of a sickness, they will not need my help. The aim of all my efforts is to teach everyone to do without me. . . ."[82] His method implied a high regard for the average person's intelligence and a low opinion of physicians. Himself a man of the people, he shared the popular distrust of doctors. He conveyed the conviction that the healing art was an easy discipline, obtainable for little money, and accessible to common sense. The democrat in him was gradually defeating the doctor.

The careful scientist of the 1820s thus emerged ten years later as a medical sectarian. Historically, Raspail indeed belongs to a generation of medical "system-makers." A monistic pathology and monistic treatment were typical of doctors such as John Brown

---

[80] By printing in his *Revue élémentaire de médecine* a notice to this effect and also posting it at his dispensary.

[81] F.-V. Raspail, *Revue élémentaire de médecine* . . . , I (1847–1849), 274.

[82] *Ibid.*

(1735–1788) in England or Benjamin Rush (1745–1813) in the United States. Only, by the time Raspail reached maturity as a medical thinker, the day of systems was past. Observation, statistical analysis, and experimentation were by then widely recognized as the only avenues along which medicine could make progress. It is curious to find that in his work as a chemical microscopist Raspail had carefully followed modern scientific methods, whereas a decade later as a physician he acted with impulsive zeal, leaving no time for criticism or self-doubt.

Popular attitudes of the day may help to explain Raspail's actions. Since medicine still seemed unreliable in the early nineteenth century, patients sought refuge in cults and faiths. Raspail's age produced the followers of Gall and Spurzheim's phrenology, of Sylvester Graham's health cult, of Vincenz Priessnitz' water cures, and of Samuel Hahnemann's homeopathy. Popular confidence in Raspail, partly induced by his political leadership, may have helped cast him in the role of a medical cultist. This would not be an exceptional development, since the intellectual style of an era often influences medical and scientific practices and even research. Individuals often adapt themselves to the image which their followers have created. Raspail's sense of mission, his scorn for contemporary medicine, and the characteristic traits of his therapy suited the part of the medical cultist to perfection. He was in many ways typical of the charismatic medical practitioner in an age of Utopian Socialism when medical science was as yet unable to cope with many diseases.[83]

[83] George Rosen, in his highly interesting review of Gumpert's *Hahnemann: The Adventurous Career of a Medical Rebel* (New York, 1945), draws the portrait of the "typical" leader of a medical "cult." The description is a good likeness of Raspail. See *Bulletin of the History of Medicine*, XVIII (November 1945), 461–62.

*On n'améliore pas en bouleversant, mais
en modifiant, et les modifications sont
lentes et successives.*

F.-V. Raspail

VII

ARSENIC AND CIVIL RIGHTS

THROUGHOUT HIS LIFE RASPAIL BATTLED against the law. There is an engaging nobility in his fight, for one hundred and thirty years ago the law in France was unjust. The poor were not protected equally with the rich; republicans could not exercise the civil liberties that the constitution promised.

All over Europe, Utopians, socialists, republicans, and philanthropic reformers were attacking the status quo in order to help the common man. Raspail joined in this attack whenever he could. Any effort to promote civil rights received his immediate, enthusiastic support. He was a born fighter who gained special satisfaction from assailing entrenched authority. He would give of his time, money, oratory, organizational talent, and he would risk his safety and his life, all with a spontaneity born of passion.

In the realm of politics, Raspail's efforts were circumscribed by the degree of freedom that various governments in power during Raspail's long life afforded French citizens. Under the Restoration, republican political activities had to be confined to illegal secret societies, such as the carbonari, which Raspail joined soon after they were introduced into France. Civil liberties were reaffirmed in 1830 under the July Monarchy, but were then gradually withdrawn during the following five years. As long as there was an opportunity to agitate, every minute of Raspail's time, and all his energies and thoughts were engaged in the fight for civil and political equality.

In Raspail's mind this fight for freedom was by no means confined to politics: chemistry, pharmacy, and medicine were also involved. If he would liberate science from political control, then he must face the dilemma of the modern scientist. He must take sides in the political struggles that affected the interests of his profession, regardless of the consequences for his work. Can one man serve both masters: be a dispassionate investigator in his laboratory, coldly analytic and factual in scientific writing, and be at the same time the passionate advocate of a cause in the courtroom, on the political rostrum, or in a pamphlet or newspaper?

The famous examples that come to mind would seem to indicate that political passion and scientific objectivity can be combined by exceptional persons—but that society will exact its price by imposing either suffering or compliance. Galileo, who taught Copernican astronomy despite his awareness of the Vatican's censure, ended his life as a martyred prisoner; Rudolf Virchow fought on the barricades regardless of professional consequences, but eventually watched the defeat of liberalism in Germany; Robert Oppenheimer risked his career and endured official ostracism. Raspail went further: he sought out the opposition as soon and as often as he could.

Raspail's efforts on behalf of social justice in chemistry, pharmacy, and medicine involved him in controversy with the most powerful man in French medical politics. He first encountered this dangerous opponent in 1823 in the role of expert chemist for the prosecution, when Raspail, as expert for the defense, attempted to save a man from being convicted of arsenic poisoning. Three more trials for murder by arsenic followed, culminating in the world famous Affaire Lafarge. In each case Raspail was pitted against this most eminent of French forensic medical men, the former professor of legal medicine and toxicology at the Faculty of Medicine in Paris and soon to be its dean: Mathieu-Joseph-Bonaventura Orfila (1787–1853). Their dramatic duel lasted twenty-five years; Raspail was to acquit himself brilliantly against formidable odds. In the end Orfila, exasperated by the popularity of Raspail's medical system, had him indicted in 1846 for the illegal practice of medicine.

Orfila personified all the traits that Raspail hated most: he was arrogant, conceited, and ruthless. And he was supremely successful. More than that he represented the Establishment: he was Catholic, monarchist, in favor at court, anti-republican, opposed to reform. In his beliefs and opinions, Orfila was the antithesis of Raspail. But they were equally proud and obstinate. It seems as if Raspail instinctively chose an opponent so powerful as to render his own civil rights efforts all the more noble, if somewhat desperate.

The tribulations of Raspail between 1830 and 1836 serve as an illustration of Louis Philippe's dealings with republican leaders, and with the clubs and newspapers of the democratic opposition. After failing to win Raspail's adherence, the government proceeded to subject him, in the course of five years, to a total of twenty-seven months in prison and eight hundred francs of fines, not counting the much heavier financial penalties imposed on his newspaper, the *Reformer*, which died of exhausted funds and the forced absence of its editor.

Among those who shared Raspail's political convictions, dismay and distrust of the government displaced initial enthusiasm soon after July 1830. Louis Philippe, by promising a strict adherence to the Charter of 1814 (flouted by his predecessor) granted his republican opponents the right to meet, criticize the régime in word and print, and pursue their social and political aims peacefully. The privilege of trial by jury was restored in October 1830. Of 520 indictments during the first four years of the July Monarchy, only 188 resulted in fines and imprisonment.[1] But soon it became evident that in order to fulfill the promises of the Charter, the July Monarchy would have to liberalize the Napoleonic Code. As it turned out, the government did little to relieve the pressure of censorship,

[1] J. Isaac, and Ch.-H. Pouthas, *Révolution, empire, première moitié du 19ème siècle* (Paris, 1929), 526.

and did not in any way relax restrictions on the right of assembly. Finally, in the summer of 1835, an attempt on the king's life provided the excuse of the abolition of those very freedoms that Louis Philippe had solemnly sworn to uphold in order to reach the throne.

Prosecution and, at times, persecution, was the logical penalty for Raspail's course of action. It started in 1830, when news of revolution first reached him. He was jubilant, and rushed into the street to fight. Like many another liberal, he firmly hoped for the establishment of a republic in which all citizens would obtain the basic freedoms. When he helped storm the barracks of the rue de Babylone, a shot touched his forehead. The wound was not serious, but it did earn him the July Cross, the only decoration he ever accepted from King Louis Philippe.

Soon after the fighting, he wrote this letter to the Provisional Government:

August 1, 1830.

Gentlemen:

Coming home to my garret, I put down my musket for a moment and, seeing my two children, I feel impelled to write in order to ask for work. I address this request to my country, for which I have suffered for fifteen years . . . I am asking for instruments and quiet, in order to serve [science] with still greater success. . . .

Raspail, National Guard,
chief editor of the *Annales
des sciences d'observation*.[2]

The royal government was at first favorably inclined and attempted to make a friend of Raspail. On March 13, 1831, he was awarded the Legion of Honor.[3] He refused it, however, writing to the Minister of the Interior that acceptance would betray his comrades who had died on the barricades. He signed the letter "Raspail, plain citizen."[4] He was then offered the post of Curator-General of the *Muséum*, an offer that was withdrawn when he announced his

---

[2] Fonds Raspail, Archives du Département de la Seine, XXXV.
[3] See *Le Moniteur universel*, March 19, 1831.
[4] "Raspail, homme du peuple," J. Saint-Martin, *F.-V. Raspail*, 29.

Bronze medallion by David d'Angers, 1835 (Courtesy Musée Carnavalet, Paris) Photo Bulloz

intention completely to reorganize its collections.[5] Eugène de Mirecourt tells the story:

Louis Phillippe, so eager to corrupt, tried to win this dangerous antagonist. He ordered a review of National Guard artillery, expressly to try and seduce Raspail who belonged to this unit.

His Citizen-Majesty reviewed the ranks, stopped in front of our hero and spoke a few kind words. The gunner choked, not knowing what to say.

But the next day, when a government messenger stopped at his home with the offer of a position at the Botanical Garden, Raspail got even and said:

"Tell your master that I shall accept nothing from those who stole our republic!"

[5] X. Raspail, "Notice," *Catalogue de livres anciens ayant fait partie de la bibliothèque de F.-V. Raspail,* XIV–XV.

That was frank, but hardly tactful.[6]

The king persisted [7] and sent the young ladies Montalivet to deliver a set of costly baby clothes to Raspail's home when his third child, Emile, was born. The incorruptible republican haughtily rejected the gift.[8]

Now the government lost patience. A letter Raspail published in *La Tribune* on February 18, 1831, on the subject of the uprising at Saint-Germain l'Auxerrois,[9] caused his first indictment. "Look at the National Guard [he had written], its members are so convinced of the reactionary tendencies of the government that the most enlightened among them, so far the well-intentioned dupes of the golden mean, have blushed, these past few days, whenever they donned their uniforms. . . ." [10] Raspail seemed to welcome his prosecution under the press laws. "I shall enter the arena [cried this romantic], to win my spurs and begin to fight the king's justice." [11] On May 10, 1831, he arrived in court, dressed in his National Guard uniform and wearing the July Cross. The jury found him guilty; he was sentenced to three months in prison and a fine of three hundred francs. Owing to a strange and admirable gentlemen's agreement, he was allowed to finish teaching a course on organic chemistry, and was not jailed until July 9.[12] On that day he began an acquaintanceship with French prisons that was to become intimate and extensive.

Released after this first term, he found life busier than ever, for

---

[6] E. de Mirecourt, *Raspail*, 41–42.

[7] Casimir Périer (1777–1832) who began his stern ministry on the day when the Legion of Honor was offered to Raspail, exclaimed: "He must accept or else rot in a dungeon!" F.-V. Raspail, *Réforme pénitentiaire: Lettres sur les prisons de Paris* (Paris, 1839), I, 165.

[8] X. Raspail, *Procès de l'almanach Raspail* . . . , 120–21.

[9] A commemorative service for the Duc de Berry (whose assassination in 1820 had endangered the Bourbon succession) was held in this church. This act of legitimist devotion at a time of economic depression and hardship so infuriated the crowds that they invaded the church and destroyed the sacristy and the adjoining episcopal residence. The mob was belatedly dispersed by the National Guard, and it is to this action of the government that Raspail took exception.

[10] Cited in J. Saint-Martin, *Raspail*, 28. See also F.-V. Raspail, *Réforme pénitentiaire* . . . , I, 277.

[11] *Ibid.*, I, 217.

[12] He explained that this convenient arrangement applied to terms of less than four months. *Ibid.*, II, 338–39.

he was elected president of the "Friends of the People," the most active democratic society of the early 1830s.

> . . . my life is a constant whirl [he wrote]; . . . I walk across Paris six times a day; meetings are scheduled at all hours . . . every night there is a gathering, an earnest discussion which affects the heart and excites the mind; at midnight there are still people waiting at my door; at five o'clock in the morning I am awakened, I talk while dressing, in order to leave in time.[13]

Under his leadership, the Friends of the People founded adult education classes in Paris: in grammar, writing, arithmetic, history, hygiene, and sanitation. He encouraged nursery schools and the "adoption" by each educated member of five or six families—in order to raise their living standards and moral values.[14]

The Society was under constant police surveillance.[15] "This mixture of philanthropy and politics," comments Georges Weill, "might rapidly win over the mass of Parisian workers to the republican party. The Society became all the more dangerous for the government because it would not engage in conspiracy." [16] By the end of 1831 Raspail found himself implicated in the "Trial of the Fifteen," which brought him to national notice. The Society was about four hundred strong in Paris by this time.[17] It was now charged with breaking the law on assembly and with advocating the violent overthrow of the government. In speeches for the defense, on January 10, 11, and 12, 1832, Raspail took full advantage

---

[13] *Ibid.*, II, 316–18.

[14] *Ibid.*, 326–37, *passim*.

[15] A pamphlet entitled "To the People, from the Society of the People's Friends" was denounced as seditious on July 5, 1831, by the "Library Bureau" of the Ministry of the Interior. The district attorney had the printer fined. (Archives nationales, Series BB[18], 1197, dossier 5662.) Again in 1832 pamphlets distributed by the Society were seized from soldiers stationed in Strasbourg. The district attorney at Colmar was informed that "The aim of such a publication is obvious: it is to provoke disobedience of the law . . . prosecution of the authors is indicated, provided one can hope that it be crowned with success." Archives nationales, Series BB[18], 1205, dossier 7104.

[16] G. Weill, *Histoire du parti républicain en France, 1814–1870*, 68.

[17] F.-V. Raspail, *Défense et allocution du citoyen Raspail, président de la Société des amis du peuple, aux assises des 10, 11, 12 janvier 1832* (Paris 1832), 1.

of the publicity which trial by jury affords. Regardless of censorship, court proceedings could then be reprinted gratis and circulate freely. The republicans were to make plentiful use of this inexpensive propaganda. Indeed, the speeches and the behavior of the defendants in the early 1830s show that they were conscious of addressing a wider audience than the court. Raspail wrote:

. . . before my trial [of 1831], no newspaper, however fearless, would have dared print one single line of my principles of political morality; now I have won the privilege of expressing my thoughts in all Parisian and provincial newspapers. . . . So many privileges, in so little time and for so little money, upon my word, that's not expensive! [18]

At the trial in January 1832, Raspail explained his club's goals to the jury: the Friends of the People were striving for an elected executive with a short term in office; a constitution that would guarantee decentralization; salaries for deputies; universal military service without replacement; juries chosen by lot from among all citizens; freedom of the press, assembly, and worship; the right to work;[19] and the abolition of the death penalty.[20] He argued quietly, with logic and conviction, revealing himself a leader of impressive courage, equally committed to popular rights and civil peace. "We seek to enlighten the masses; we deposit our demands at the feet of the sovereign people." [21] But in the heat of argument he was sometimes carried away. He spoke fiery, frightening words. Tchernoff rightly insists that this aggressiveness was generated by the milieu, and was not inherent in Raspail's calmly reasoned thought:

. . . under violent words he hides moderate ideas. The scientist thinks, and calmly discusses the articles of his program. The man feels the effervescence of the surrounding milieu. Extremely sensitive, constantly in touch with the crowd, struck by the sight of misery which he seeks out and observes daily, he is sometimes overcome by the revolutionary

[18] F.-V. Raspail, *Réforme pénitentiaire* . . . , I, 297.

[19] How far he was ready to go in demanding this right is not quite clear. He said: "No one should ask for work in vain; the state protects the unemployed, whatever their profession." F.-V. Raspail, *Défense et allocution* . . . , 11–12.

[20] These goals represent a mixture of traditional republican demands with new, socialist aims, such as the guarantee of the right to work which Louis Blanc was to emphasize a few years later in his *Organization of Work*.

[21] F.-V. Raspail, *Défense et allocution* . . . , 7.

ardor of the extremists. But, being a rational person, he rejects the mirage of 1793: his ideal is the republic, not the Convention.[22]

Yet the court would not see things this way. Raspail's egalitarianism was evident: "Taxing necessities is theft," he argued, "taxing luxuries, restitution." [23] His speeches attacked Louis Philippe for his failure to set up a republic and denounced the king's victory celebrations as a waste of the people's money. "Perish the traitor," he cried, "especially if he bears the title of king! . . . One should bury alive, under the ruins of the Tuileries, a citizen who demands from our poor France fourteen million francs to live on." [24] When the judge attempted to impose silence, Raspail exclaimed, "You are presiding over the funeral of our freedom . . . respect our words!" [25]

Given the violence of these utterances, it is remarkable that the jury acquitted all defendants. The judges, however, decided that certain rousing statements in Raspail's defense speech rendered him guilty of attempted subversion and outrage against the magistracy. They sentenced him to fifteen months in prison and to a fine of five hundred francs.

Sainte-Pélagie, in Paris, was his first place of confinement, and later, after five days in the antiquated, filthy jail of La Force,[26] the prison at Versailles. Near it his wife, with their nine- and five-year-old sons and a baby, rented a two-room apartment. Madame Raspail brought all his meals and was allowed to spend evenings with him.[27] Thus life in jail was made bearable, and Raspail, a

[22] I. Tchernoff, *Le parti républicain sous la monarchie de juillet. Formation et évolution de la doctrine républicaine* (Paris, 1901), 250–1.

[23] F.-V. Raspail, *Défense et allocution* . . . , 12.

[24] *Ibid.*

[25] *Ibid.*, 2. It was at this same trial that Godefroy Cavaignac, another defendant and the son of the popular revolutionary hero, proudly declared: "My father was one of those who, in the midst of the National Convention, proclaimed the republic . . . and defended it in war. . . . Today, when I have at last the opportunity of pronouncing a word proscribed by so many, I declare without affectation or fear: in my heart and my convictions, I am a republican." Quoted in G. Weill, *Histoire du parti républicain* . . . , 72.

[26] F.-V. Raspail, *Discours . . . dans l'assemblée générale de l'Association républicaine pour la liberté de la presse et reproduit pour sa défense devant la cour d'assises qui l'a acquitté* (Paris, 1834), 14.

[27] He was also permitted to have other visitors; see, e.g., this note from Alexandre Dumas dated October 21, 1831: "My dear Raspail, I am going to the police

philosopher at heart, settled down to work. Perhaps he would never have written his books on agriculture, chemistry, and botany but for the leisure of prison life.

Soon after his release, in April 1833, Raspail rejoined the republican agitators, whose organizations had in the meantime undergone important changes. The clubs of the early 1830s had succumbed to the harassment of the police. Henri Gisquet (1792–1866), the Police Prefect of Paris, wrote in his *Memoirs:* "The government and the conspirators were engaged in a relentless daily struggle. . . . I ordered the local branches [of clubs] dispersed as soon as they were founded, I had their papers confiscated, their members arrested." [28] When Raspail returned to the scene, three new associations had been formed: the Society for Popular Education, the Free Press Club,[29] and the Society for the Rights of Man and the Citizen.[30] From 1833 to 1835, they channeled and led the republican agitation—much to the government's concern.

today for a permit to visit you. I shall bring what you asked for." Archives nationales, Dossier Raspail, No. 1684.

Or, see the childhood reminiscences of Georges Daremberg, the son of Charles Daremberg, the famous medical historian: "On Sundays, we used to go to Versailles to visit our fellow-scientist Raspail, the distinguished micrographer who was imprisoned—although under lenient conditions—for political crimes against the government of Louis Philippe." G. Daremberg, *Les grands médecins du 19ème siècle* (Paris, 1907), 4.

[28] Quoted in G. Perreux, *La propagande républicaine au début de la monarchie de juillet* (Paris, 1930), 307.

[29] This society worked through six committees which inquired into police raids and arrests, furnished legal help to defendants and unbiased information to jurors, offered assistance to prisoners, their families, and businesses, and labored to obtain fair legislation on press matters. (Lafayette was a member of this last committee.)

[30] "This society," commented Louis Blanc—[as translated by a contemporary Englishman]—"from a poor beginning, had taken a quick and strong hold on the country. In 1833, its power at Paris rested upon the ardor of upwards of 3,000 *sectionnaires* . . . it acted upon the provinces by numerous societies which had been formed on the same model. . . . Its object was to keep up the movement made by the people in 1830. . . . It left no means unemployed, but brought into play subscriptions on behalf of political sufferers, or of convicted journals, popular lectures, traveling orators, and active correspondence: so that, in the very midst of the state, revolt had its government, its administration, its geographical divisions, and its army." L. Blanc, *History of Ten Years, 1830–1840* (London, 1844), II, 180.

Raspail has been accused of constant and excessive worry about police spies and stool pigeons. True enough, he was always on the lookout for such traitors, and was wont to blame the police for any minor losses or adverse occurrences that happened to him. He was extremely suspicious, and changed his domicile frequently. The sympathetic critic Eugène Spuller wrote:

Among the republicans of this era, François-Vincent Raspail was most inclined, owing to the incidents of a hard life and to his temperament, to be tortured by fear of the police. This fear became a monomania: he never lost it, not even during the last years of his long existence.[31]

This "monomania" should be reconsidered in the light of documents such as the following letter:

Departmental Police   Melun, July 12, 1834
1st Legion

To the Minister of the Interior

Sir:

I have just learned that Raspail . . . has come to Lagny to visit M. Auguste Petit, known for his extremist opinions, and has participated in an anti-governmental dinner party.

Raspail's apparent purpose is to learn about cereals and agriculture from peasants, farmers, and millers. The information seems necessary for the book he is writing; but since the trip might conceal a political purpose, I thought it my duty to keep you informed.

Raspail will be discreetly watched during his stay. . . .[32]

During the summer of 1833, Louis Philippe decided to build fortifications around the capital. At a military review by the king on July 28, the third anniversary of the "Three Glorious Days" of 1830, anti-militaristic and anti-government shouts were heard. Even the National Guard joined in the cry: "Down with the bastilles!" Over two hundred citizens were thrown into jail, and a lawsuit was started against the Society for the Rights of Man which had,

[31] E. Spuller, *Histoire parlementaire de la seconde république* (Paris, 1891), 84.
[32] Archives nationales, Series F⁷, 6784, dossier 2. This series contains many documents which prove that the slightest movements of suspect individuals were reported to the Minister of the Interior by the departmental police [gendarmerie]; e.g., Series F⁷, 6783.

so the government charged, instigated this outburst to subvert the army and overthrow the régime. It was no coincidence that on August 23, 1833, as he was leaving a meeting of the Free Press Club (over which he had presided because the Marquis de La-fayette failed to appear) Raspail was arrested.[33] He was held in custody for three months, only to be acquitted by a jury to whom he explained his social and economic philosophy in a remarkable speech—a summary, he said, of his words to the Free Press Club.

. . . I profess . . . the following doctrine: that the land belongs to the state which promises to exploit it in the interest of all.

Far from me the thought of establishing thereby this distributive fan-tasy commonly called land law [*loi agraire*], an absurd idea. . . .

Far from me also the thought of demanding now, or even in the near future, the realization of our theory. This idea can only be fruitful after having been ripened by a thorough discussion of its implementation. To establish it after a sudden upheaval or a revolt would be to strangle it at birth and make it the scourge of mankind.

One does not improve by overthrowing but by modifying, and change is slow and cumulative. . . .

Then he appealed to the rich and explained his own role: "Oh rich men . . . instead of cursing and jailing the writers who warn you of the storm, add your efforts to theirs . . . and conjure the lightning which is about to strike! Oh, why can I not act as media-tor in this ancient quarrel?" [34] Not only did he reject class war, but he also called for friendship between peoples. "He is the first," comments Georges Weill, ". . . among French republicans, to re-pudiate war-mongering and foreign conquests, the first who under-stood that war has no place in a democracy." [35]

Although Raspail was acquitted in November 1833, he was not released. Rather, the government chose to include him in the "Trial of the Twenty-Seven"—all members of the Society for the Rights of Man—which opened on December 11, 1833. Besides its alleged connection with that year's July demonstrations, the Society was accused of defiance toward a government injunction of April 10 which had ordered it to disband. Its very existence was therefore

[33] F.-V. Raspail, *Histoire naturelle de la santé.* . . , 3rd ed., III, 453.
[34] F.-V. Raspail, *Discours . . . dans l'assemblée générale.* . . , 6 and 10.
[35] G. Weill, *Histoire du parti republicain.* . . , 113.

illegal. At the eleven-day trial, Raspail and three lawyers outlined
the peaceful objectives of the Society and the advantages of a free
press, denying any revolutionary intentions. After that, the twenty-
seven defendants refused to answer any questions. The jury voted
"innocent." Raspail was finally set free two days before Christmas.[36]

But the respite was brief. Four months later, Lyons, Paris, and
several other cities were shaken by serious workers' revolts. The
government decided to wipe out republican and socialist clubs and
newspapers in one monster trial before the Chamber of Peers
which judged attempts at subversion. Of 2,000 persons arrested,
164 were kept in jail. (Raspail was not among them.) The Parisian prisoners, held at Sainte-Pélagie, had over a year to map their
strategy. They drew up a list of defenders, and Raspail's inclusion
in this list accounts for his initial presence in court. But soon he
had a better reason to be there. The *Réformateur*, Raspail's own
newspaper, published an article entitled "The Legislative Butch-
ers"[37] for which the editor, M. R. Louis Jaffrenou, was indicted.

The defense presented by M. Raspail [wrote Louis Blanc, in the quaint
words of his contemporary translator], did not overpass, in the slightest
degree, the bounds of calm and becoming discussion, philosophical and
dignified. But all the powers of the day seemed carried away by some
resistless frenzy. M. Jaffrenou, acting editor of the *Réformateur*, was
sentenced to one month's imprisonment and to pay a fine of ten thousand francs.[38]

These penalties were subsequently doubled in retribution for an
"Open Letter to the Accused."[39]

The English writer Frances Trollope (1780–1863), who attended
the trial in the Chamber of Peers, gave this account in her book
Paris and the Parisians in 1835:

Never did effrontery go farther than in some of the defenses which
have been set up for the accused *gérants* of the journals in question.

---

[36] See *Procès des vingt-sept ou de la Société des droits de l'homme et des
élèves de l'Ecole polytechnique* (Paris, 1834).

[37] On May 23, 1835; see Archives nationales, Series C 764, dossier 7. On the
Réformateur, see infra, p. 179–80.

[38] L. Blanc, *History of Ten Years. . . ,* II, 343.

[39] *Procès des accusés d'avril devant la cour des pairs* (Paris, 1834–1835), 2
vols., I, 140–59.

For instance M. Raspail expresses a very grave astonishment that the Chamber of Peers, instead of objecting to the liberties which have been taken with them, do not rather return thanks for the useful lesson they have received.

He states too, in the same defense, as he is pleased to call it, that the conductors of the *Réformateur* have adopted a resolution to publish without restriction or alteration every article addressed to them by the accused parties or their defenders. This resolution, then, is to be pleaded as an excuse for whatever their columns may contain! The concluding argument of this defense is put in the form of a declaration, purporting that whoever dooms a fellow-creature to the horrors of imprisonment ought to undergo the same punishment for the term of twenty years as an expiation of the crime. This is logical.

There is a tone of vulgar, insolent defiance in all that is recorded of the manner and language adopted by the partisans of these Lyons prisoners, which gives what must, I think, be considered as very satisfactory proof that the party is not one to be greatly feared.[40]

Contrary to Frances Trollope's judgment, E. D. Pasquier, the President of the Tribunal, was impressed with Raspail's defense of civil rights: "In the Chamber of Peers I heard but two truly eloquent speeches," he told his friend Sainte-Beuve, "that of Montalembert and that of Raspail." [41] Louis Blanc commented that Raspail, "a gentleman of high intellectual distinctions, celebrated more especially in the annals of science, excited the astonishment of the court by the picturesque force of his language and by the facility he displayed in passing from considerations of the most elevated kind to the most familiar reflections." [42] And Lamennais, the great Catholic socialist, wrote: "It will be hard to forget Raspail's beautiful and calm defense. These words of a gentleman, elevated, penetrating, full of idealistic argument, obtained a prison sentence of only one month for the editor of the *Réformateur,* but could not prevent the maximum fine for the paper." [43]

On July 28, 1835, four weeks after this trial, Giuseppe Fieschi killed eighteen persons in an attempt to assassinate King Louis

[40] F. Trollope, *Paris and the Parisians in 1835* (New York, 1836), 366–67.

[41] Quoted in R. Blanchard, "Notices biographiques: François-Vincent Raspail," *Archives de parasitologie,* VIII, 31.

[42] L. Blanc, *History of Ten Years. . . ,* II, 348.

[43] Quoted in G. Raspail, *La vie et l'oeuvre. . . ,* 52. [Sought unsuccessfully in Lamennais' published work.]

Philippe. The king and his sons escaped unharmed. The next day, Raspail was arrested at three o'clock in the morning, eight miles outside Nantes where he had been invited to preside at a democratic banquet.[44] Adolphe Thiers, the Minister of the Interior, had personally ordered his arrest by a telegraphed message.[45] Raspail was then brought to Paris in a police wagon,[46] and interrogated on August 13 by a magistrate named Zangiacomi. Zangiacomi then dictated to a clerk his version of the interview—according to the astonishing practice then current. The conversation was, at first, polite, ranging from science to politics. But then Raspail, indignant at his arrest and encouraged by the noncommittal attitude of the jurist, felt "prompted by his respect for individual liberty to remind the magistrate of his legal duties." [47] Zangiacomi seems to have made a practice of goading and trapping republicans.

He was notorious [writes the *Encyclopédie Larousse*], for the passionate zeal with which he persecuted the republicans. . . . He would transform a cross examination into a formal accusation. He would finish a sentence begun by the suspect, . . . induce him to incriminate himself and others . . . ; any means seemed fair to him against the accused. He intimidated witnesses, blamed one of them for having a deported brother, and forbade the use of the term "citizen" in court. . . . In his presence, the lawyers had a virtually impossible task.[48]

Zangiacomi evidently set a trap for Raspail when he asked:

If you were in my position and if you republicans won out, what would you do to me? "Strange question," Raspail replied. "I do not think that I shall see my hopes realized in my lifetime. . . . But if I should hold you in my power under similar circumstances I should, instead of torturing a sick man, be content to send you for a day or two to Charenton [the insane asylum], where you would be given a few showers; the next day I would have the pleasure of shaking hands with

[44] Letter of July 31, 1835, from the district attorney at Rennes to the Minister of Justice. Archives nationales, Series BB[18], 1359, dossier 2379.

[45] F.-V. Raspail, *Procès perdu, gageure gagnée, ou Mon dernier procès* (Paris, 1857), 61.

[46] F.-V. Raspail, *Mémoire à consulter. Pourvoi en cassation. . .* , 6–7.

[47] F.-V. Raspail, *Mémoire présenté à la section criminelle de la cour de cassation* (Paris, 1835), 5.

[48] Article "Zangiacomi," in *Encyclopédie Larousse*.

you, a converted enemy, since you would then shout louder than I: Long live the Republic! [49]

As a result of this lesson, Raspail was pronounced "guilty of insulting M. Zangiacomi" and was condemned to two years in jail and five years under police surveillance. The verdict was appealed before the courts of Paris and then Rouen and was twice reduced: to two years' confinement, then to six months.[50] At last, Raspail was set free on January 15, 1836, his spirit unbroken, his republican convictions unshaken. But the government had succeeded in wrecking his newspaper, his chief tool for political opposition.

Raspail had founded the *Reformer* in the fall of 1834, giving it a quietly didactic tone. The masthead carried the subtitle: "A daily paper dedicated to the new interests: material and moral, industrial and political, literary and scientific." Raspail had secured the required deposit of 100,000 francs from the family of his friend de Kersausie (who was then in jail)[51] and sent a prospectus to all members of the defunct Society of the Friends of the People.

In the *Reformer*, "one of the most influential republican newspapers," [52] Raspail had the opportunity to reiterate and expand his ideas regarding the renovation France must undergo if the bulk of her people were to lead happy lives. Reforms were urgent, but revolutionary violence would only mean a general setback. Agreements must be reached among all social classes. Education must be lay; worship strictly private. Decentralization of power was essential; local collaboration could be constructive and fruitful. Just as in his medical writings he put the burden of progress on the indi-

---

[49] F.-V. Raspail, *Procès perdu. . .* , 64.

[50] *Ibid.*, 67–68.

[51] René-Théophile Guillard de Kersausie (1798–1868), a Breton nobleman, was a lifelong friend and comrade-in-arms of Raspail. He was a nephew of Théophile de la Tour d'Auvergne, the aristocratic soldier who fought with the rank and file in the American and French revolutionary wars and earned the title of "First grenadier of France." De Kersausie left the army in 1830 because yet another monarchy had emerged from the Revolution; he was implicated in the Trial of the Twenty-Seven and in that of the April Defendants of 1834. He left France in 1837, returned in 1848, only to be exiled in 1849. The amnesty of 1859 brought him back to Paris where he died. "Kersausie," commented Eugène de Mirecourt, "is a blameless republican, loyal, chauvinistic, and ignorant." *Raspail*, 31, n.

[52] E. Hatin, *Bibliographie historique et critique de la presse périodique française* (Paris, 1866), 392.

vidual citizen, so in his political thought he expected democracy to be the collective achievement of free men.

The *Reformer* [writes Weill], was, after the *Globe* of the Saint-Simonians, the first daily to be motivated by ideas of large-scale social reform. It hoped to educate its readers and neglected minor news and daily politics. Most of its readers were poor people. . . . Raspail did not idolize Paris; rather, he addressed the provinces which he believed more serious and calm, and able to think for themselves.[53]

As soon as the police heard about the *Reformer*, Raspail became the target of denunciations, searches, lawsuits, and fines. He felt himself surrounded by police spies: "Among the newspaper personnel, I had at the most two friends on whom I could count: I distrusted everyone else." [54] The *Reformer* lasted from October 8, 1834, to October 27, 1835,[55] during which time it underwent close to twenty trials and provoked 115,000 francs worth of fines (of which it paid 100,000).[56] Its editor, M. Jaffrenou, served almost twelve months of jail sentences.[57] On October 29, 1834, Raspail even fought a duel with M. Cauchois-Lemaire, the editor of the periodical *Bon-Sens*. Raspail had challenged his opponent for calling *Bons-Sens* a democratic newspaper, although it had not taken a strong stand against the government.[58]

By the end of 1835, the battle for civil rights was lost. The press had "undergone 1,173 lawsuits, paid fines amounting to 7,110,005 francs, seen fifty-seven newspapers killed, and its writers jailed for 3,141 years.[59] And Louis Philippe continued to restrict voting priv-

[53] G. Weill, *Histoire du parti républicain.* . . , 114–15.

[54] F.-V. Raspail, *Réformes sociales* (Paris, 1872) I, 19.

[55] After Raspail's imprisonment at the end of July, 1835, his colleagues Louis Blanc and Armand Marrast served as editors. E. Hatin, *Bibliographie historique* . . . , 392.

[56] F.-V. Raspail, *Procès perdu.* . . , 66.

[57] J. Saint Martin, *Raspail,* 55 ff.

[58] The duel took place on October 29, 1834, in the Bois de Vincennes. Cauchois-Lemaire fired first and missed. Raspail shot his adversary through collar, tie, and shirt, without hurting him. *Ibid.,* 53–5.

[59] A. Saint-Ferréol, *Les proscrits français en Belgique ou la Belgique contemporaine vue à travers l'exil* (Brussels, 1870–1871), 2 vols., I, 34. Now and then, a merchant would be fined or jailed for selling pamphlets, posters, scarves or handkerchiefs imprinted with a picture of Raspail, whose face and name were now familiar to all Frenchmen. See Archives nationales, Ministry of Justice, Division of Criminal Affairs and Pardons. Series BB[21], 411, dossier S 9-7483, June 8, 1837.

Raspail at the *Reformer* office (Painting by Latil, 1835)

ileges to a small, wealthy electorate. Their economic outlook was his own: all were afraid of socialism. Urbanization, and the numbers and class consciousness of the workers were now growing fast enough to frighten the middle classes. The workers' demands must be resisted, or else the newly acquired wealth would have to be shared. Politics and economics thus conspired to encourage the ruling classes to monopolize the power they had but recently wrested from the Bourbon kings.

Seeing that legal avenues for political protest were closed after 1835, one imagines that Raspail welcomed with alacrity the opportunity of a murder trial that would afford him a confrontation with his enemy of long standing: M.-J-B. Orfila. By 1839, Orfila, Dean of the Paris Medical Faculty, was the expert on whom the government often relied when toxicological knowledge was needed in lawsuits to which the state was a party.

Born into a humble family at Mahon, Minorca, in 1787, Orfila had studied medicine at Valencia, Barcelona, and Madrid. Dissatisfied with the mediocre instruction prevalent in his country, he went to Paris in 1807, obtained a medical degree in 1811, and began teaching chemistry. Three years later he wrote to his father:

I have met in Paris men of the highest distinction: counts, dukes, marquesses, and other eminent individuals. The persons I see most often are the Princess de Vaudémont and the Prince de Talleyrand. . . . Nature has endowed me with a superb voice. I have made such progress that there is perhaps no one in Paris at this moment who sings as well as I do. . . .[60]

In 1818, one of his many friends informed Orfila that the professorship of legal medicine at the Paris Faculty might soon become vacant and that he might be chosen, provided he acquire the French nationality. Turned Frenchman, Orfila was indeed appointed professor of legal medicine in 1819. Four years later he yielded his chair to Royer-Collard and became professor of medical chemistry. Both medical and legal chemistry grew considerably in his lifetime, owing in part to great advances in the study of poisons.[61] Orfila himself contributed to this progress. In fact his main works, *A Treatise on Poisons* (1813), *Elements of Medical Chemistry* (1817), and *A Treatise on Legal Medicine* (1847), helped establish his specialty as a recognized academic subject. From 1831 to 1848 he served as Dean of the Medical Faculty of the University of Paris. The supreme power he wielded in French academic medicine under the July Monarchy was equalled only by his belief in himself.

Endowed with the most promising gifts [writes the *Encyclopédie Larousse*], with an attractive, graceful, and seductive physique and a ravishing voice, Orfila was received everywhere with alacrity. He knew how to combine his love of society and its pleasures with an extraordinary facility for work. Surrounded by eager friends anxious to promote him, he joined to this powerful element of success an ever unruffled confidence in himself which sometimes helped to hide his incompetence. . . . After becoming Dean of the Faculty he considered himself the

[60] A. Fayol, *La vie et l'oeuvre d'Orfila* (Paris, 1930), 132.
[61] See G. Bass, *Die Gerichtsmedizin als Spezialfach in Paris von 1800 bis 1850* (Zürich, 1964).

representative of the government rather than the leader of the medical profession. He was too quick to consider men who did not share his political opinions or who fought his scientific doctrines as his personal enemies. He was drugged by the incense offered by a circle of intimates, an élite for whose advantage the rest of the medical corps was practically sacrificed. For a while no doctor was nominated, promoted, decorated or rewarded without his intervention or consent.[62]

Orfila and Raspail had first come face to face in the Boursier case of 1823 before the Court of Appeals in Paris.[63] Five years later they engaged in rival tests and arguments on blood stains—Raspail reading his reports to the Philomatic Society, and Orfila presenting his papers before the Academy of Medicine. The five papers that this dispute occasioned [64] reveal how much Orfila and Raspail disliked each other. Orfila tried to brand Raspail as a careless scientist, while Raspail denounced Orfila as an unscrupulous climber. The papers also show that Raspail was as eager to prove an impecunious defendant innocent as Orfila was bent on obtaining convictions.

In 1836, after the great struggle for civil rights was lost, Raspail's duel with Orfila moved onto the national and even the international stage because arsenic, long favored by murderers, became detectable thanks to the Marsh test.[65] The medical, biochemical,

[62] Article "Orfila," in *Encyclopédie Larousse*.

[63] Raspail refers to this encounter. Corroborative evidence is lacking.

[64] J.-M.-B. Orfila, "Recherches sur différents points de médecine légale: caractères distinctifs des taches de sang, de rouille et de jus de citron sur des instruments," *Journal général de médecine, de chirurgie, et de pharmacie*, C (1827), 226–29.

F.-V. Raspail, "Sur les moyens, soit chimiques, soit microscopiques, qu'on a tout récemment proposés pour reconnaître les taches de sang en médecine légale," *Ibid.*, CII (1828), 335–50.

J.-M.-B. Orfila, "Nouveau mémoire sur le sang considéré sous le rapport médico-légal," *Ibid.*, CII (1828), 350–62.

F.-V. Raspail, "Réponse de M. Raspail à la lettre que M. Orfila écrivit le 19 janvier à la Société philomathique," *Ibid.*, CII (1828), 362–72.

F.-V. Raspail, "Réponse à quelques faits qui se trouvent dans le Mémoire que M. Orfila a lu, le 29 janvier 1828, à l'Académie royale de médecine," *Ibid.*, CII (1828), 373–84.

[65] In 1836 James Marsh (1789–1846), an English doctor and chemist, developed a chemical test which permitted the identification of minimal quantities of arsenic. The following year the Marsh test became widely known in France, and from then on all judicial inquiries into sudden deaths, where murder by arsenic was suspected, centered on the testimony of expert chemists.

pharmaceutical, and legal ramifications of arsenic poisoning then became so involved and far-reaching that the Academy of Medicine and the medical press dealt with the subject throughout the 1840s.

Immediately after the Marsh test became known, Orfila began intensive research on arsenic. Between January and September 1839, he read to the Paris Academy of Medicine five long papers on the poison.[66] In one of these he asserted that "there normally exists in the human body a small quantity of an arsenical compound, probably calcium arseniate" but that the arsenic taken by mouth can be recognized by its place in the body.[67] This possibility of locating ingested poison was a fruitful theory for the coroner to pursue. Only Orfila, in his passionate wish to find arsenic and obtain convictions, confused matters hopelessly during murder trials: he devised a method of stewing the corpse (a *"pot-au-feu"*) and then filtering and distilling the resulting liquid. No jury could tell the origin of the arsenic he would triumphantly produce—nor did the chemists for the defense have any raw material left on which to conduct their own tests. In August 1839, Orfila discussed before the Academy of Medicine the presence of arsenic in the soil of cemeteries. He had obtained arsenical stains in experiments with cemetery earth and thought it conceivable that minute quantities of

---

The quantities of arsenic involved in the tests made at these trials were tiny. Expert testimony was complicated by the fact that a small quantity of arsenic is found in man's bones. Some thought that this "natural" arsenic could be differentiated from the drug administered by a killer. Others focused on the location of arsenic in the corpse, arguing that its presence in the stomach, intestine, liver, or spleen indicated murder. In any case, careful study and research were needed before chemists and physicians could testify to murder in a court of law with any assurance.

[66] J.-M.-B. Orfila, "Mémoire sur l'empoisonnement par l'acide arsénieux," *Bulletin de l'académie de médecine*, III (1838–39), 426–64 and 676–84; "Mémoire sur les moyens de s'assurer que l'arsenic, obtenu des organes où il a été porté par absorption, ne provient pas des réactifs, ni des vases employés à la recherche médico-légale de ce poison," *Ibid.*, 1049–73; "Mémoire sur un nouveau procédé pour constater facilement dans nos organes la présence d'une préparation arsénicale qui aurait été absorbée," *Ibid.*, 1106–20; "Quatrième mémoire sur les terrains des cimetières, sur l'arsenic qu'ils peuvent fournir et sur les conséquences médico-légales que l'on doit tirer de l'existence possible d'un composé arsénical dans ces terrains," *Ibid.*, IV, 40–56; "De l'arsenic naturellement contenu dans le corps de l'homme," *Ibid.*, 178–203.

[67] J.-M.-B. Orfila, "De l'empoisonnement par l'acide arsénieux," *Ibid.*, III, 680.

arsenic might be absorbed, on rainy days, by corpses buried without a coffin. That September he confidently summed up his findings: "In a medico-legal inquest in cases of arsenic poisoning one can always ascertain with accuracy whether the arsenic obtained from the blood or the organs of the corpse is natural arsenic and whether it derives from an arsenical compound ingested or externally applied." [68]

Orfila's assertions were hotly contested by a distinguished Italian ophthalmologist from Naples, Francesco Rognetta (1800–1857), renowned for introducing eye surgery into France, and at the time of the debate professor of surgery at the Ecole Pratique de Médecine in Paris. Rognetta communicated his findings to the Academy of Medicine, where a subcommittee was formed to study his experiments. The results were submitted to the academicians for the grand debate on arsenic the summer of 1840.

This was not the only annoying challenge to his omniscience that Orfila was to experience. The Academy of Sciences, thinking no doubt that arsenic belonged to *its* domain, appointed its own committee. E. P. Danger (1802–1855) and C. F. Flandin (1803–1891), both chemists specializing in toxicology, presented their own papers to the Academy of Sciences between December 1840 and February 1841. They found no "natural" arsenic in the human body and none in the earth of cemeteries, and they urged that the Marsh test be performed with great skill and caution—since insufficiently carbonized animal matter might produce stains with both the appearance and the physical characteristics of arsenic.[69]

In order to end the dispute between the partisans of Rognetta's "Italian School," Orfila's supporters, and those of Danger and Flandin, the Academy of Sciences appointed yet another committee, and thought it politic to invite the Dean of the Medical Faculty to the debate. He came to supervise in person the sixteen experiments designed to substantiate his own theories, and the thirty-three more, devised by other scientists. The struggle came to a climax in the battle royal held at the Academy of Medicine,

[68] J.-M.-B. Orfila, *Ibid.*, IV (1839–40), 190.
[69] E. P. Danger and C. F. Flandin, "Recherches médico-légales sur l'arsenic," *Académie des sciences, Comptes-rendus hebdomadaires des séances,* XI (July–Dec. 1840), 1038–40, and XII (Jan.–June 1841), 118–19 and 335–36.

where the clauses of the final report were voted on point by point, often paragraph by paragraph. It would seem that personality clashes provided the real substance of the debate, since by the summer of 1840 all scientific points had been conceded: there *was* some arsenic in human bones; the soil of cemeteries rarely contained arsenic and was unlikely to contaminate a buried corpse; and the Marsh test was excellent. It would reveal the presence of even two millionths of a gram of arsenic in a liquid. Why, then, a debate that took up almost seven meetings of the Academy in July and August 1840, and discussions which generated "so much confusion that the president adjourned the meeting?" [70]

One reason was that Orfila had numerous enemies among academicians, as indeed among doctors[71] and the enlightened public. They would be happy if he were proven wrong. The Academy of Sciences seemed to have taken on the study of arsenic (and given so much attention to Danger and Flandin) partly because of the self-assurance with which the Dean was holding forth on the poison at the Academy of Medicine. Letters addressed to Raspail at the time of the three murder trials in which he challenged Orfila clearly indicate that numerous physicians, pharmacists, lawyers, and a large section of the public, admired him for the painstaking way he questioned Orfila's chemical analyses and for his courage

---

[70] *Ibid.*, 946.

[71] Another professional publication where Orfila took violent issue with a colleague who dared disagree with him was the *Annales d'hygiène publique et de médecine légale*. See A. Devergie, "Mémoire sur l'empoisonnement par l'arsenic: nouveau procédé pour retrouver l'arsenic absorbé," *Ibid.*, XXIV (1840), 136–80; and Orfila's rebuttal: "Empoisonnement par l'arsenic: observations sur le dernier mémoire de M. A. Devergie," *Ibid.*, 298–313.

And two years later: A. Devergie, "Note communiquée aux membres de la commission de l'Institut, chargés d'apprécier les nouveaux travaux sur l'arsenic," *Ibid.*, XXVII (1842), 186–97; and Orfila's reply: "Lettre à M. le rédacteur des *Annales d'hygiène publique et de médecine légale* sur le meilleur moyen à employer pour la recherche de l'arsenic, dans les cas d'empoisonnement," *Ibid.*, 447–53.

Or, again: J.-M.-B. Orfila, "Mémoire sur quelques moyens proposés dans ces derniers temps pour découvrir l'arsenic dans les organes où il a été porté par la voie de l'absorption," *Ibid.*, XXVIII (1842), 73–96, where Orfila attacked the results obtained by Fordos and Gelis in France, Pettenkoffer in Munich, and Gianelli in Florence.

in opposing this powerful antagonist.[72] Raspail thereby may well have gained readers for his books and newspapers, customers for his camphorated medicines, and votes for his legislative and presidential candidacies in 1848, 1869, and 1874.

The murder trials of Louis Mercier and of Antoine Rigal in 1839 again brought Raspail and Orfila together in court.[73] Each was eager to humiliate and defeat his antagonist. Mercier and his wife were charged with the murder of their son by arsenic. Louis Mercier had brought several children into his second marriage, among them Nicholas, who was mentally defective. The young wife found this boy's uncleanliness so repugnant that she threatened to leave Mercier. When Nicholas died soon thereafter, the neighbors grew suspicious.[74] Legal proceedings were initiated, and the court of Dijon was to try the case. The prosecution chose Orfila as chemical expert. The lawyer for the defense first approached Dr. Francesco Rognetta, but then refrained from inviting him to

[72] See, e.g., Ms. No. 2388: Letters from Arrault, pharmacist; Gendrin, physician. Fonds Raspail, Muséum.

Dr. A.-F.-H. Fabre (1797–1853) satirized Orfila and praised his opponents in *Némésis médicale illustrée* (Paris, 1840) 102–3:

"De notre Faculté le doyen autocrate

. . . . .

Signale chaque erreur comme une découverte,
Et fait du corps humain une cornue inerte;
Et puis, sans se douter qu'en un sol sablonneux
L'arsenic délayé filtre et pénètre mieux,
Prononce, dût-il faire une double victime,
Qu'un cadavre enfoui l'a reçu par un crime;
Orfila le savant fait du doute un devoir,
L'ignorance toujours a foi dans son savoir;
Mais elle trouve aussi de vigoureux athlètes,
Toujours prêts à sonner ses honteuses défaites,
Et qui lui font rêver comme un épouvantail
Couërbe ou Rognetta, la *Lancette* ou Raspail."

[73] The indictment of Antoine Rigal of Albi, in May 1840, for the murder by arsenic of his wife Thérèse brought an almost exact repetition of Raspail's role in the Mercier case and is therefore not discussed here in detail. See F.-V. Raspail, *Procès et défense* . . . (Paris, 1846), 57.

[74] F. Rognetta, *Procès de Dijon. Consultation médico-légale sur un cas de mort attribué à l'empoisonnement par l'arsenic* (Paris, 1839), 6.

Dijon for fear that Orfila would attempt to have the Italian expelled from France.[75] Rognetta suggested Raspail, who accepted only after pointing out that his politics might be detrimental to his client's case.[76] Orfila, one gathers, had the reputation of fighting on grounds far removed from his scientific competence.

Several local expert chemists had performed the Marsh test on the remains of Nicholas Mercier and had found no arsenic. Orfila came, and by reducing the body to a "stew," extracted from it two grains of the poison. He then produced "large and beautiful arsenic stains," commenting that evidently the provincial experts "had not used the new methods which alone can destroy the organic matter" and reveal the arsenic.[77] A disagreement on methodology turned into a power struggle where the Dean of the Medical Faculty lost no occasion to underline his own superiority.

In his defense of Mercier, Raspail explored at great length the possibility that the microscopic quantity of arsenic, sufficient to kill Mercier, might have been introduced accidentally into the corpse while it was buried, or during its transportation to the laboratory— especially since the remains had been handled with great negligence. A heated verbal fight between Raspail and Orfila ensued— but to no avail. The jury found young Mercier's father guilty of murder, although it exonerated the young wife. Maître Monget, the lawyer for the defense, wrote to Rognetta:

The accused was killed by moral proofs; chemistry is not responsible for the verdict. M. Orfila was beaten by M. Raspail; Orfila was very weak, from the point of view of science, when confronted by that formidable athlete.[78]

Rognetta replied to Monget:

On perusing M. Orfila's report, I was struck by the incredible audacity with which this chemist asserted the existence of a crime when, from

[75] After the trial Orfila endeavored to do this. "Evidently M. Orfila imagined," Rognetta commented, "that his power with the Police Prefect could change the properties of arsenic and transform his toxicological heresies into the truth." Rognetta, *Ibid.*, 99.

[76] *Ibid.*, 44.

[77] J.-M.-B. Orfila, "Mémoire sur plusieures affaires d'empoisonnement par l'arsenic récemment jugées par les cours d'assises du royaume," *Mémoires de l'académie de médecine*, IX (1841), 9.

[78] F. Rognetta, *Procès de Dijon. Consultation médico-legale*, 5.

the toxicological point of view, everyone was in doubt as to the details of the incriminating facts. . . .

My work received the approval and support of a scientist whose authority has great weight, M. Raspail, and it served as the basis of the speech for the defense. I am happy that a man of such great merit agrees with my judgment of M. Orfila's procedures. I have been fighting him for a year, in the interest of science and of society.[79]

Soon after Louis Mercier was sentenced and his wife acquitted, arsenic poisoning became the subject of national public curiosity, owing to the "Affaire Lafarge."

At a world-famous trial, Madame Lafarge, née Marie Cappelle, stood accused of having poisoned her husband with arsenic.

I am innocent [she wrote to Raspail], and very unhappy; I suffer and appeal to your science and to your heart. Many people, whose adverse judgment was a torture for me, were convinced in my favor by some chemical experiments. Then M. Orfila arrived and I was hurled back into the abyss. You are my only hope; give this slandered victim the help of your wisdom; come and save me when all else fails! [80]

Whoever inspired this letter knew Raspail. The scientist left for Tulle by the first available coach—which broke a wheel and reached its destination eight hours after the verdict was rendered.

Raspail came too late to win Madame Lafarge's acquittal, but he did think the verdict might be appealed. After paying the convicted murderess a visit that moved him deeply, he scrutinized the trial records, particularly the chemical experts' report.[81] The scientific aspect of the "affaire," Raspail found, was treated with incredible negligence. The body had been exhumed eight months after death, and no record was available of either the exhumation or autopsy.[82] The viscera needed for chemical examination had

[79] *Ibid.*, 2.

[80] F.-V. Raspail, "Lettre à M. le Dr. Favre," *Gazette des hôpitaux*, II, 2nd series, No. 114 (Sept. 26, 1840), 453.

[81] F.-V. Raspail, *Mémoire à consulter à l'appui du pourvoi en cassation de Dame Marie Cappelle, Veuve Lafarge, sur les moyens de nullité que présente l'expertise chimique* (Paris, 1840).

[82] Although no record of the autopsy could be found in Tulle, Raspail later did obtain it in Paris, from the lawyer for the prosecution, Maître Paillet. F.-V. Raspail, "Réfutation de la réponse de M. Orfila aux écrits de M. Raspail sur l'affaire de Tulle," *La Lancette française: Gazette des hôpitaux. . .* , III, 2nd series, No. 1 (Jan. 2, 1841), 1.

been fetched on horseback, without due precautions, from Le Glandier, the hamlet where Lafarge was buried. Local specialists had then conducted three sets of inconclusive chemical analyses. But the prosecutor would not be denied. Here was a woman already convicted of theft, and who was known to have loathed the man who married her under false pretenses and brought her to a forsaken smithy in Corrèze. Would she have hesitated to kill? The government must obtain a conviction. In these straits the prosecution called an expert endowed with a gift for oratory who would crush these provincials under the might of his phrases. Orfila did not disappoint them. He began his presumed chemical report with the words: "Lafarge died of poison: I shall prove it." [83] After twenty-four hours he was on his way home, having found what he called "an imponderable quantity of arsenic" [84] and having seen Madame Lafarge sentenced to hard labor for life. The Court of Appeals sustained the verdict.[85]

Raspail was indignant at Orfila's arrogance, and was skeptical, as always, of his chemistry.[86] In his "Lettre à M. le Docteur Favre," published two weeks after the trial in the *Gazette des hôpitaux*, Raspail argued that out of Orfila's three analyses, the only conclusive one was made with Orfila's own potassium nitrate. Raspail also underlined the strange fact that Orfila presented to M. Bories, a local pharmacist, the whole box of reagents he had brought from Paris *with the exception* of the potassium, zinc, and potassium nitrate, portions of which Orfila used in his experiments and the

[83] F.-V. Raspail, "Réfutation de la réponse de M. Orfila aux écrits de M. Raspail sur l'affaire de Tulle," *La Lancette française: Gazette des hôpitaux. . .* , II, 2nd series, No. 148 (Dec. 19, 1840), 593.

[84] F.-V. Raspail, *Accusation d'empoisonnement. . .* , 33.

[85] In the early days of the Second Republic, Raspail hoped for a review of the case. But the revolutionary government was wholly occupied with weightier matters. Madame Lafarge was finally pardoned by Louis Napoleon Bonaparte, after twelve years in prison. She died soon after her release. She left some remarkable *Memoirs*. (*Mémoires de Marie Cappelle* [Brussels, 1841–1843], 4 vols.)

[86] One could find a very small quantity of arsenic anywhere, Raspail exclaimed in a passionate outburst, even in the chair of the presiding judge! This quip seems to have been made at a banquet given in honor of Raspail at Dijon. (See J. Wogue, *Raspail*, 56). Wogue also mentions a song composed for the occasion, ending with the refrain: "Et quand Raspail arriva,/ Orfila fila fila."

remainder of which he took back to Paris. The reader was left to draw his own conclusions.[87]

Madame Lafarge herself believed in Raspail's argument. As late as March 4, 1848, she wrote to Armand Barbès, asking for his intervention to free her:

Surely you know and love Raspail. . . . He will tell you that there never was any poison involved. He saw the results of M. Orfila's tests; he questioned the other experts. . . . He was convinced of the extreme bad faith brought to this case. . . . M. Orfila did not permit his potassium to be tested; more than that, he took it back to Paris with him, knowing that M. Raspail was on his way to Tulle. . . .[88]

The Affaire Lafarge aroused compassionate interest all over Europe; in the era of Romanticism this was not surprising. Heinrich Heine, for example, at the time a newspaper correspondent in Paris for the *Augsburger Allgemeine Zeitung,* reported that:

Since her condemnation, Madame Lafarge is being discussed even more passionately than before. Public opinion is entirely in her favor since M. Raspail, the most upright man in France, has thrown the weight of his opinion into the balance. One has to consider, first, that here a strict republican takes a stand against the interests of his own party since his assertions directly challenge the jury, one of the most popular institutions of the new France. Secondly one has to remember that the man on whose judgment the jury based the condemnation is a notorious schemer and charlatan, a burr on the mantle of the great, a thorn in the flesh of the oppressed, one who flatters the mighty, despises the weak, deceives as a speaker, and sings off key. By heaven! if one remembers these things one can no longer doubt that Marie Cappelle is innocent and that not she should be pilloried on the Tulle market place but the famous toxicologist and Dean of the Faculty of Medicine in Paris, namely M. Orfila! Those who know the dealings of this vain egotist, even slightly, from closer observation are convinced in their innermost beings that he will shun no opportunity to show off his scientific specialty or to further the lustre of his fame! . . . The consensus of public

[87] In a fairly objective review of Orfila's part in this battle between chemists, Julien Raspail, a physician, also concluded that the amazingly large quantity of arsenic in Orfila's third analysis must have come from the Dean's own reagents. (J. Raspail, "L'Affaire Lafarge," *La Revue,* CIV (Sept. 15 and Oct. 1, 1913), 179–95 and 377–95; 384.)

[88] P. Muller, "Madame Lafarge sous la 2nde république," *La révolution de 1848,* IX (1912–1913), 450.

opinion is that there was no poison in the body of Lafarge but all the more in the heart of M. Orfila. Those who agree with the judgment of the Tulle jury form a very small minority and have lost their former assurance. Among them are persons who do believe in the poisoning but consider this crime as a form of self-defense and in many ways justifiable.[89]

In France the Affaire Lafarge has remained one of those famous lawsuits which have never been settled satisfactorily. The beauty of the victim, the horror of imagining her trapped by a repulsive blacksmith, her appealing *Memoirs,* all helped keep Madame Lafarge's image alive.[90] She has even been the subject of a film in which Raspail appears as the valorous knight vainly attempting to rescue a wronged lady.[91]

In the eight years between the conviction of Madame Lafarge and the outbreak of the Revolution of 1848, Orfila relentlessly pursued Raspail in the medical press and in the courts. The all-powerful Dean might have been content with his victories over Raspail, since the jury had voted for the prosecution in all four murder trials. But Orfila was irked by Raspail's growing popularity. The *Natural History of Health* (1843), the *Health Annual* (1845), and his camphorated medicines were gaining for their

[89] H. Heine, *Französische Zustände: Lutezia* (vol. 9 of *Sämmtliche Werke,* Hamburg, 1884, 12 vols.), 224–25.

[90] In a volume written for the collection "Great Forgotten Lawsuits," for example, the author wrote: "Orfila isolated no more than an atom of poison—so minute an atom [*sic*] that, as he himself said, 'it would have been difficult to weigh,' and which, according to the defense, 'was hardly enough to kill a fly.'" L. André, *Madame Lafarge, voleuse de diamants* (Paris, 1914), 153.

See also: Balthazard, *Orfila et l'Affaire Lafarge* (Paris, 1920). J. Beaudéant and A. Pasturel, *Affaire Lafarge: Une réhabilitation qui s'impose. Etude juridique et psychologique d'une cause criminelle célèbre* (Paris, 1913). G. de Chapel d'Espinassoux, *Conflit d'Orfila et de Raspail* (Montpellier, 1926). "Madame Lafarge," *Figaro,* in feuilleton, Feb. 28 to May 1, 1864. E. Gril, *Madame Lafarge devant ses juges* (Paris, 1958), with an impressive bibliography. T. Manceau, *Quelques vérités nouvelles sur le procès Lafarge* (Toulouse, 1847). H. Ramet, *La madone de l'arsenic* . . . (Paris, 1936). E. Saunders, *The Mystery of Madame Lafarge* (London, 1951). J. Shearing, *The Lady and the Arsenic* . . . (London, 1937). NB also *Correspondance de Marie Cappelle* (Paris, 1913), 2 vols.

[91] R. Coulom, *L'Affaire Lafarge: une histoire vraie* (Paris, 1938).

author national fame and a lucrative income. In at least one case Raspail's detailed critique of Orfila's chemistry saved a man's life.[92] Lawyers, doctors, and journalists, such as Dr. A.-F.-H. Fabre, editor of the *Gazette des hôpitaux*,[93] supported Raspail largely because they hated Orfila. In 1843 the Dean withdrew from his position as expert in court for reasons that sound unconvincing.[94] At this very time Raspail was being attacked in *Asmodée*[95] and *Esculape*[96] and was being prosecuted by his ex-pharmacist Morel [97] and the mutual aid society of Parisian doctors.[98]

[92] On May 20, 1842, Marcel Barthe, a lawyer from Pau, wrote Raspail an urgent letter asking for advice with regard to experiments which local chemists had performed, with the help of the Marsh test, on a corpse suspected dead of arsenic poisoning. Raspail's immediate reply, and his writings in the *Gazette des hôpitaux*, evidently helped the lawyer convince the jury of the accused murderer's innocence.

"Your letter helped me save a man's life. . . . Your writings, your letter, and the report of the Academy of Sciences occasioned by your learned critique of M. Orfila's experiments, gave me the means of defeating the accusation. The moral proofs were also favorable to the defense.

"I know no greater satisfaction than to wrest a poor innocent man from the hands of justice. Much of this joy should be yours." Archives nationales, Dossier Raspail, No. 1684.

[93] As early as 1836, Fabre had attacked the Dean in a satirical poem "L'Or-filaïde ou Le siège de l'Ecole de médecine" (in *Némesis médicale*, Paris, 1836). See also *supra*, p. 187, n. 72.

[94] In the Preface to his *Traité de médecine légale* (Paris, 1848, 3 vols.), Or-fila complained about the low calibre of medical experts in the courts: "These improvised half scientists aim only at publicity and at being counted among the experts. Their temerity has lately become so outrageous that con-scientious men have stopped assisting the tribunals rather than tolerating col-laborators or antagonists whose revolting ignorance and unbridled charlatanism make lying a game."

He concluded with an unmistakable reference to Raspail: "I had to offer these explanations in order to justify the decision I took in 1843 to refuse the numerous requests of the courts. My refusal was not motivated by fear of new battles—as has been spitefully insinuated—since my efforts have *always* been successful. Rather, my refusal was caused by the overweening distaste I have felt, all my life, for debate with men whose ineptitude equals their bad faith."

Raspail wrote in 1848, that after the Affaire Lafarge the Academy of Medi-cine had requested from the Ministry of Justice that Orfila be no longer used as toxicological expert. "From that time on the 'Prince of science' no longer appeared in poison trials." F.-V. Raspail, *Nouvelle défense* . . . , 12 n.

[95] See *supra*, pp. 151, n. 46 and 153, n. 56.

[96] See *infra*, pp. 194–95.

[97] See *supra*, pp. 153–54.

[98] See *infra*, pp. 195–96.

Orfila, doubtless the power behind these efforts, considered Raspail a medical charlatan and political subversive whereas he thought of himself as the guardian of French medicine and law. He had no appreciation for the solace Raspail brought to the suffering poor, and saw only the would-be physician whose activities must cease. Viewed in historical perspective, the quarrel between Orfila and Raspail is as old as medicine. Like any other organized profession, physicians wish to regulate and control the practice of their specialty. They want to exclude, and wish the law to prosecute, anyone who is not trained and who does not practice their art according to their rules. Doctors on the whole tend to be conservative, not only in their social outlook but in their professional views as well.

Human needs, misery, and ailments, on the other hand, have often responded to treatment other than the strictly medical. The healer, apothecary, midwife, barber-surgeon, monk, confessor, and priest have, through the ages, dealt with a large share of human pain, and have relieved it to the best of their sometimes considerable ability. But the medical profession frowns on them all, as soon as they transgress the limits of their competence.

The anti-Raspail campaign in the medical journal *Esculape* is typical of the manner in which Orfila and his supporters tried to harass Raspail. This "nasty little journal, printed and distributed at Orfila's expense," [99] lasted only from 1839 to 1841. These were of course the years of the Mercier, Rigal, and Lafarge murder trials and of Raspail's first pamphlet on camphor cigarettes. In the winter of 1839–1840, *Esculape* launched into a lengthy discussion of pharmacists who gave medical consultations. The undesirable type of pharmacist was described in these words—(the clock mentioned was Raspail's own):

You enter a pharmacy divided into two compartments: on one side the luxurious, visible part with its display of drugs; on the other, a mysterious cabinet hidden from the passer-by: very full green curtains cover the window entirely and shield all secrets from outsiders. If curiosity, or a less futile purpose, entices you to enter this private office, you find it furnished in a soberly luxurious manner: books, a bronze clock whose face is encircled by the mantle of Time, a beautifully wrought desk,

[99] Rognetta to Raspail, Ms. letter of October 14, 1839, Fonds Raspail, *Muséum.*

paper weights with heads of Hippocrates, and, finally, the god of this little temple, majestically seated in a big chair with sculptured arm rests, awaiting the moment to render his oracles. You are in the office usually directed by the head of the establishment himself or by a student who dropped out of school: this is an excellent way to make money, since the free consultation is handsomely paid for at the cash register in the store. But the question of probity? . . . .[100]

In a similar vein a French physician wrote in 1843:

In defiance of the law, which demands that medicines be sold only on a doctor's written prescription, all pharmacists stock a variety of more or less potent mixtures such as creams, unguents, syrups, pills, chocolates, elixirs. They sell them as openly as a grocer peddles his sugar and soap. And on the pretext of unimportant or innocuous ailments, they even venture to offer remedies, advice, and care to people who are confident of the pharmacist's knowledge, convinced of the benign nature of their own afflictions, and eager to economise on a doctor's visit. One could also point to numerous greedy pharmacists who use this popular habit for shameful speculation and who gain a hold over patients in order to substitute multiple, unknown, complex, and lucrative drugs for the simple and adequate medication a doctor would have prescribed.[101]

Raspail thus found himself indicted for the illegal practice of medicine at a time when physicians and pharmacists were already aroused by the many unlicensed incursions into their practices and were eager to defend their prerogatives. He was accused by the *Association de prévoyance des médecins de Paris,*[102] whose president was P. E. Fouquier, King Louis Philippe's physician, and whose

[100] *Esculape, Journal des spécialités médico-chirurgicales* (Paris, 1839–1841), 3 vols. in 1, Oct. 7, 1839.

[101] L. J. Delasiauve, *De l'organisation médicale en France sous le triple rapport de la pratique, des établissements de bienfaisance et de l'enseignement,* 73.

[102] F.-V. Raspail, *Procès et défense de F.-V. Raspail poursuivi le 19 mai 1846 en exercice illégal de la médecine devant la 8ème chambre (police correctionnelle) à la requête du ministère public, et sur la dénonciation formelle des sieurs Fouquier, médecin du roi, et Orfila, doyen de la Faculté de médecine de Paris, agissant comme vice-président et président d'une association anonyme de médecins.*

This society had been founded in 1833 by Orfila, and was one of numerous similar ones throughout France, designed for mutual help among its members and for the detection and prosecution of any medical activities or medicinal preparations offered by unauthorized persons.

vice-president was none other than Dean Orfila. The prosecution was helped in preparing its case for the trial on May 19, 1846—so Raspail believed—by Morel, who had planted informers among Raspail's dispensary patients. These persons now appeared in court as witnesses. In order to establish that Raspail had actually been practicing medicine, they testified that although Dr. Cottereau had always *signed* all prescriptions, Raspail had *dictated* them. They also testified that Raspail had charged high fees, whereas he had always proclaimed that he treated the needy free of charge.

The district attorney was astonishingly complimentary, however.

M. Raspail is known to all as a practitioner who offers his ministrations to everyone, whose publicity is widespread, whose dispensary welcomes all ailments, who competes with doctors certified and authorized by the law. His activities are so obvious, so well known, that many believe them to be legal, and would be greatly astonished to learn that M. Raspail is not a doctor.[103]

Raspail sparred with some witnesses, including Dean Orfila, and then spoke in his own defense. He was not a doctor, but a chemist, he said: "Chemistry is a science, whereas medicine is a trade." [104] He despised the medical degree: "Only men without a degree are compelled to study constantly, whereas the diploma suffices to confer innate knowledge and to act as a substitute for ignorance." [105] Not only had he given free consultations for eight years, but also free lectures at the Faculty of Medicine in 1828, 1830, and 1836, where doctors vied with students to learn from him.[106] "For eight years I have been consulted by doctors about my prescriptions and asked to instruct them in the use of my method." [107] Carried away by emotion, Raspail then revealed that no diploma or degree had ever seemed to him worth acquiring since he had won the highest distinction imaginable as a very young man: a word of praise from Napoleon.

. . . The eyes of the eagle that soared above France and above the

[103] F.-V. Raspail, *Procès et défense* . . . , 22.
[104] *Ibid.*, 27.
[105] *Ibid.*, 14.
[106] *Ibid.*, 32. This is an exaggerated account of his lectures on the microscopic method. See *supra*, p. 126.
[107] *Ibid.*, 33.

world, whose fascinating glance gave birth to giants, those eyes lowered themselves on me, in the recesses of my province. What I then felt, no! gentlemen, you will never imagine it . . . during my solitary life this memory has preserved all its initial freshness. . . . I concealed this distinction in my innermost self, as one would hide an eagle in one's arms. . . . This title, however modest, seemed so great to me, that it has left no room for any others; not even the greatest could, in my eyes, displace it. I have sworn but one allegiance because I have never found anything as great to love as the one who then seemed to us the genius of France, the armed precursor of world civilization. Can you, today, offer me anything as magical? [108]

He summed up his defense with this challenge:

Go ahead, gentlemen, and use the remnants of your power against a man who has refused to be your teacher and whom you now denounce: four years from now, there will be no more doctors like you, there will only be magistrates charged with caring for the public health; and humanity will have taken another step toward progress.[109]

He was then convicted and condemned to pay the maximum fine, fifteen francs. He left the courtroom saying: "Yes, I have done something illegal, but eminently moral; here are my fifteen francs, the maximum penalty, and I bid you good day." [110]

Despite his condemnation Raspail opened a new dispensary, rue Culture Sainte Catherine (now 5, rue de Sévigné), and practiced medicine there alone.[111] Dr. Cottereau had died, and Raspail knew that the maximum penalty he would incur was trifling. In February 1848, a new revolution would again make him exchange the role of doctor, pharmacist, and man of science for that of the militant republican.

[108] *Ibid.*, 36.   [109] *Ibid.*, 50–1.   [110] *Ibid.*, 75.
[111] A marble plaque commemorates the fact. See *supra*, p. 135.

VIII

REVOLUTION

AGAIN

THE FIRST SIX MONTHS of 1848 were fateful for France. Rarely was the overthrow of the government welcomed by so many Frenchmen of varied political opinions and of different social stations as was the demise of Louis Philippe's monarchy. Hopes were high for a better future, and opportunities for leaders were plentiful.

The establishment of a republic in 1848 appeared to many liberals as a foregone conclusion, owing to the lack of an acceptable alternative and to the patriotic and reverent memories that the First Republic inspired. The degree of political equality that such a régime should bring also seemed to present no major problem. Universal suffrage, although feared by some, was decreed without difficulty.

What really divided Frenchmen were the social and economic issues: the late 1840s were a time of economic crisis for all of Europe. Prices were high and tempers short. Industrialization had progressed far enough in France to swell the labor force and to render its problems a matter of serious national concern. A feeling of solidarity was beginning to pervade the working class.

Republican convictions among the workers were usually coupled with socialist aspirations. Every variety of socialism had its spokesman: the disciples of C. H. de Saint-Simon (1760–1825) aimed at awakening the social conscience of industrialists, while the spiritual sons of F.-C.-M. Fourier (1772–1837) worked for the establishment of utopian communities; Louis Napoleon Bonaparte (1808–1873) predicted the "extinction of pauperism"; H. F. R. de Lamennais (1782–1854) expressed the views of socialist Catholics; and Louis Blanc (1811–1882) dealt with the "organization of work." Karl Marx (1818–1883), familiar with conditions in France since his visit in the midforties, predicted the ruin of the bourgeoisie. J.-P. Proudhon (1809–1865), the staunch idealist, preached anarchy and the abolition of private property, while Auguste Blanqui (1805–1881), who spent thirty-six years in French jails, advocated a violent social revolution to clear the way for a better world.

These numerous exponents of socialism and republicanism were unprepared to wield political power. The censorship laws of 1835 had effectively deprived potential leaders of any experience in the practical business of politics. Instead of political pamphlets they had written many of those ponderous tomes that censorship permitted. Never had they addressed a large political meeting—only a few fellow members in a secret society. Each leader was eager to attract adherents, but was slow to join with others of similar convictions. The result was that the many leftist groups never merged into one strong party. Louis Philippe, through his repressive legislation, had effectively prepared the speedy failure of the republicans and socialists who overthrew him.

The people of Paris played a major part in the short-lived republican experiment of 1848. As has happened so often before and since, the inhabitants of the capital assumed that they could shape events for all of France, and that the country would follow them. On February 24, the fate of the regency was being decided at the Palais Bourbon, after King Louis Philippe had abdicated in favor of his ten-year-old grandson. The people of Paris simply ignored the Chamber of Deputies, and the crowds, by-passing the Palais Bourbon, made for the City Hall as soon as they learned that the

monarchy was tottering. The first concern of the republican leaders
was to draw up lists: at the Chamber of Deputies, at the two leading opposition newspapers (the *National* and the *Réforme*), and
at the City Hall, lists of candidates for a provisional government
were being composed, amended, and read to "the people" for their
approval. Popularity was a powerful factor in the Paris of February
1848.

Raspail was out of touch with politics when the February Revolution occurred. But he was in personal contact with many thousands of Frenchmen, owing to his medical work and especially the
Manuel-annuaire de la santé. The role of popular leader in the
revolution was for him the natural outgrowth of his past as republican club president and journalist and of his ten years as medical
adviser to the people.

His immediate goal was to see a republic established. He envisaged this régime as a welfare state and confidently expected an
equitable solution of all major problems owing to the judicious
exercise of universal suffrage. According to Raspail, the political
principles he had set down in the *Réformateur* in 1835 still applied:
the election of the head of state for a short term by all male citizens
of voting age; decentralization of power; regional association between the various economic classes and productive groups; cooperation and mutual constructive assistance. He drew no clear line
between the political and the social purposes of a government. Like
many socialists he was eager to see the administration busy itself
with relieving the plight of the poor. He was suspicious and fear-
ful lest the people be cheated out of the fruits of their successful
revolt—as had happened in July 1830.

The acknowledged fact of Raspail's personal popularity in Paris[1]
roused hopes among republicans that he could be their leader. A
clearly formulated and practicable program, and a limited list of
specific, realistic, political and economic demands, might have
earned Raspail's inclusion in the Provisional Government formed
on February 25, or at least his election to the National Constituent
Assembly in April. But Raspail had not prepared any detailed, con-

[1] As one significant indication of Raspail's popularity, Georges Duveau cites
the fact that many pipe bowls were carved in his likeness in the spring of 1848.
G. Duveau, *Raspail*, 6.

crete proposals; he was not eager for legislative or executive power. He wished to stay in the streets during the revolutionary disturbances, and to be with the crowds, close to "the people." Once the republic was established, he envisaged his role as that of a teacher and trusted counselor of the masses. He hoped to restrain them from destruction and bloodshed, and he was ready, if need be, to act as their spokesman toward government and society.

Among the moderates and conservatives, Raspail's popularity with the crowds raised apprehensions that a clearly formulated platform might have allayed. His words justified doubts about his commitment to legality. Was he a revolutionary like Auguste Blanqui? How far would his socialism go? Was he a communist like Etienne Cabet?

During the evening hours of February 24, Paris was filled with rumors. In the suburb of Montrouge, where Raspail then lived, it was widely believed that an Orléanist regency had been established. A group of workingmen came to consult Raspail, and in the early hours of the 25th, he led them to the City Hall, which was surrounded and filled by the victorious but worried insurgents. He managed to enter the building, while his men disarmed the guards,[2] then elbowed his way to the council chamber where the self-styled Provisional Government was deliberating.[3] He was granted a short interview, first with a general—he thought it was either d'Hautpoul or Lamoricière—and then with André Marie, a member of the government. "The people," declared Raspail, ". . . for I have 20,000 men behind me, demand . . . the republic!" He was politely assured that all would be well and returned to calm his followers. Mounting a table, he shouted: "In the name of the French people, I proclaim the republic, one and indivisible!"; and then: "And death before a firing squad to anyone who even mentions a regency!" Asked why he did not desire a place in the

[2] In Léonard Gallois' version, this episode reads: " 'The people is at home here!' cried the democratic leader; he mounted the stairs, followed by the crowd which shouted: 'Long live the republic! Long live Raspail!' But, on his urging, his formidable escort stopped to wait on the stairs. *Histoire de la révolution de 1848* (Paris, 1849), 5 vols., I, 127. See the bas-relief on Raspail's statute, *supra*, p. 128.

[3] The story goes that Louis Blanc, seeing Raspail arrive, exclaimed: "Tiens, voilà Monsieur Raspail! Qu'en ferons-nous? [Camphrons-nous]," E. de Mirecourt, *Raspail*, 88.

government, he replied: "Because, my good men, I shall hold office only if I am chosen by universal suffrage. . . . I shall watch the work of the republic, but I shall not try to profit from it." [4] He implied that he could easily have become a member of the executive. The following year, at his trial for attempted subversion, he was quite explicit: "It was entirely up to me, on February 24, to be a member of the Provisional Government. On that day I held the Hôtel de Ville in my power." [5] Although his self-centered view of history made for an exaggerated account of the part he played in the February Revolution, it is true that his popularity was a potent factor and that he exerted his considerable influence for civil peace.

The voluminous literature about the first six months of 1848 shows that this peace was even then being undermined by a widening social and economic rift. A divergence of fundamental interests soon split apart the various political groups that had cooperated in the overthrow of the July Monarchy. Moderate republicans were content with the new order, and had no wish to tamper with the social fabric. But radical republicans were dismayed by the delegates chosen in the April elections: most of the deputies were wealthy enough to have qualified for the Chamber under Louis Philippe, and three-fifths of them were between forty and fifty years old. No leader of the Parisian clubs, no candidate of the Luxembourg Commission, and none of the well-known socialists had been chosen. The moderates had won a solid majority. "The democratic and social republic was defeated." [6] The Left felt betrayed.

The modern historian can date the defeat of socialist hopes from the elections of April 23 and 24, eight weeks after the February Revolution. An optimistic contemporary like Raspail would not give up so easily. He had, since February 25, been a

---

[4] This whole episode is reported by Raspail a quarter of a century later in "Ma proclamation de la république le 24 février 1848," *Réformes sociales*, 88–95.

[5] *Procès des accusés du 15 mai devant la Haute Cour de Bourges* (Paris, 1849), 17. (Henceforward referred to as *Procés . . . du 15 mai*.)

[6] Ch. Seignobos, *La révolution de 1848—Le second empire*, vol. 6 of *Histoire de France contemporaine, depuis la révolution jusqu'à la paix de 1919* (Paris, 1921), 83–84, *passim*.

leading spokesman for the workers of Paris. He was giving voice to their hopes as well as their fears through his newspaper, the *Ami du peuple,* his club, and his leadership in the demonstration of May 15.

The *Ami du peuple en 1848* and the "Club des amis du peuple" enabled the erstwhile scientist and doctor to pursue his main purpose after the February Revolution: to teach republicanism. His habit of writing regularly for an unseen but responsive public was well established after five years of composing the *History of Health and Sickness* (1843), the *Health Annual* (from 1845 on), and the *Revue élémentaire de médecine et pharmacie domestiques* (1847–1849). The public he addressed after February 1848 was largely the same as before. Only the emphasis in his writing and teaching changed from public health to the public weal. In his mind there was a close logical link between the two pursuits. The ethical basis of his medical teaching subserved his political aims: individual self-respect would strengthen a man's desire to pursue the political freedoms of assembly, speech, and religion as much as it would bolster his resolve to follow a regimen of hygiene and physical moderation; responsible community relations were as essential for labor peace, and the active participation of all in political life as for preventive medicine.

In naming his newspaper *Ami du peuple,* Raspail implied a somewhat misleading identification with Jean-Paul Marat. But the masthead of the paper carried a much more conciliatory message than the name of Marat would indicate. It read: "God and country. Complete freedom of thought. Unlimited religious toleration. Universal suffrage." At first Raspail was jubilant:

Progress has settled on the barricades . . . it advances with giant steps and covers great distances on the wings of electricity. The telegraph turns to the left to tell us that freedom has arrived at Brussels; it turns to the right and we learn that liberty has reached London and Berlin. . . . Long live the European republic! . . . In a year, long live the universal republic! [7]

But he must also have made offensive remarks, for an unbiased source reports that:

[7] F.-V. Raspail, *L'ami du peuple en 1848, an premier de la république reconquise,* No. I, 1.

When the *Ami du peuple* was published, frightening rumors spread, and the students made an auto-da-fé of the second issue, on the Place Saint-Michel. This execution was perhaps touched off by a sentence in the first number which read: "Neuilly, that boudoir of decrepit royalty, has gone up in flames; thus the people have purified the hearth of governmental corruption." [8]

Student rioting seems to have made little lasting difference to Raspail. From March 12 on, the *Ami du peuple* was reissued, a biweekly, one-man analysis and commentary on the news. A critical attitude toward the government set the tone of the newspaper. Legislation, whether adopted or merely proposed, was usually judged insufficient. When the death penalty was abolished, for example, Raspail approved, but he immediately demanded complete political amnesty as well.[9] He also discussed the merits of candidates and incumbents. Citizen Lamartine, for example, was for him a source of "sentimental and poetic utterances—entirely bereft of political ideas or concrete plans. . . ." [10] Louis Napoleon Bonaparte's political ambitions seemed to Raspail a "foolish illusion." [11]

Although critical of the government, the *Ami du peuple* did not adopt a revolutionary tone and, on the whole, deserves inclusion in Seignobos' edifying description of the press in the spring of 1848 as "full of doctrinal pieces and professions of faith, appeals, wishes, protestations, usually couched in noble and sentimental phrases; familiarity was unfashionable. . . . The polemics about the suffering poor were passionate, bitter, indignant, but never rude or insolent." [12] It is fair to asume that the objectives and the tone that Raspail imparted to his newspaper he also carried to the rue Montesquieu on Saturday nights, when he addressed the "Club des amis du peuple," familiarly known as the Club Raspail.

Political clubs were as necessary to the republicans of 1848 as they had been to their elders in 1789. Fifty years of silence had

[8] E. Hatin, *Bibliographie historique et critique de la presse périodique française,* 439.

[9] F.-V. Raspail, *L'Ami du peuple* . . . , I, 1. For Respail's lifelong advocacy of total amnesty, see *infra,* pp. 286–88.

[10] *Ibid.*

[11] *Ibid.,* X, 1.

[12] Ch. Seignobos, *La révolution de 1848* . . . , 39.

strengthened rather than strangled the desire for political debate. Newspapers could raise issues and express opinions, but nothing could take the place of personal contact with candidates and leaders. Clubs were already numerous in Paris when Raspail decided to open his own on March 25, one week after the successful popular demonstration of March 17 and one month before the first elections by universal suffrage held by the Provisional Government.

The best known left-wing popular societies already in existence were Armand Barbès' *Club de la révolution*,[13] Louis-Auguste Blanqui's federated *Société républicaine centrale*, and Etienne Cabet's federated *Société fraternelle centrale*.[14] Each club had an acknowledged leader, and its membership figures give an indication of the leader's popularity. Blanqui's club had about 1,000 members, Barbès and Cabet could claim between 3,000 and 5,000, whereas the *Club Raspail* boasted close to 6,000 members, including 1,000 women, which was then quite unusual.[15]

Raspail's club met to hear and choose candidates for political office, to discuss national legislation, and to consider joining street demonstrations in Paris. But it met mainly to listen to its president. The club had neither regular officers nor committees and hardly ever an agenda.[16] An admission fee of ten centimes was used to defray the rent and help some of Raspail's indigent patients.[17]

Mine was a conference rather than a club [Raspail later explained]; I acted as professor, and every Saturday I would lecture on politics to a large audience. It was not a club, for there were no officers. I was alone, and was not affiliated with any other group. I presented my ideas candidly to my numerous friends. Instead of teaching at the Medical

[13] Armand Barbès (1810–1870) was one of the most active and dedicated republican revolutionaries during the first half of the nineteenth century. A deputy in the Constituent Assembly of 1848, a leader of the May 15 demonstration, he became Raspail's companion in Vincennes prison, before the High Court at Bourges, and in the fortress of Doullens. Barbès' life sentence was commuted in 1854; he died in exile at The Hague.

[14] The federations resulted from an amalgamation of several Parisian clubs.

[15] The only scholarly, thorough discussion of Raspail's club, from the Marxist point of view, is Suzanne Wassermann, "Le club de Raspail en 1848," *La révolution de 1848*, V (1908–1909), 589–605; 655–74; 748–62.

[16] *Ibid.*, 596.

[17] *Procès . . . du 15 mai*, 69 and 115.

School, I was teaching at the Salle Montesquieu which is more centrally located and within easier reach for the five thousand workers, tradesmen, and other citizens who made up my regular, orderly audience.[18]

Daniel Stern, in her *History of the Revolution of 1848,* analyzed Raspail's political philosophy and described the nature of his teaching:

M. Raspail had a good mind for politics, and understood better than anyone else the need to accustom the bourgeoisie to a republic slowly, without violence. . . . Although his doctrines, based on a pantheist philosophy, tended to radical communism . . . he protested consistently against any immediate or violent change. . . .

Those who dreamt of social reform through a sudden upheaval of property, he said, would be more than guilty; they would be out of their minds; they would be wild men spitefully destroying their enemies' harvests and crowning their stupid vengeance with their own deaths. *Equality of rights is an immutable law; equality of property would not last two hours.*

The categorical phrasing of even his wisest ideas, his touchiness, his austerity isolated Raspail from parties and factions. He wielded a very great personal influence among the people of the faubourgs. His medical knowledge enabled him to relieve sickness and suffering which the talkers in the clubs were content to describe, and which ambitious men knew how to exploit. But his was an isolated, moral influence, secretly envied and counteracted by the party leaders. Raspail never held the initiative in the revolutionary movement.[19]

The candidates for political office who were asked to present their views at Raspail's club in 1848 ranged from socialists like Cabet, Esquiros,[20] and Agricol Perdiguier,[21] to noblemen such as

[18] *Ibid.,* 17. A modern historian confirms Raspail's description: "At the *Club Raspail* and at the *Société fraternelle centrale,* presided over by Cabet, up to 5,000 men, women, and children gathered at night to hear the leader of their sect, their master, preach to them." Ch. Seignobos, *La révolution de 1848* . . . , 41.

[19] D. Stern, *Histoire de la révolution de 1848,* III, 132–33.

[20] Henri Esquiros (1814–1876) was a popular author of extremist republican convictions, best known for his *Evangile du peuple* (1840), *Histoire des montagnards* (1847), and *La vie future au point de vue socialiste* (1857).

[21] Agricol Perdiguier, nicknamed "Avignonnais-la-Vertu" (1805–1875), was a popular figure among Parisian workers and politicians of the Left, as well

his friend Guillard de Kersausie,[22] and even the Prince de la Moskowa[23] and the Marquis de la Rochejaquelein,[24] whose recent conversion to republicanism Raspail found convincing. They were all endorsed, although the Club did not propose an official list of candidates at election time. Raspail wished to limit his activities to educating all the voters he could reach,[25] and training them in the responsible use of their new right.

Raspail alone, among French leaders, seems to have realized that the most favorable course for republicans to pursue would have been to hold national elections immediately after the February Revolution—before the defeated government forces had time to recover.[26]

The elections could easily have been held within ten days [he wrote

---

as among Romanticist writers, such as Eugène Sue and George Sand. Born, like Raspail, in Vaucluse, and a carpenter by trade, Perdiguier had perfected his professional know-how during a traditional "tour de France." He believed in reviving and extending the medieval corporations and was thus, in a way, a forerunner of syndicalism. After the revolution of 1830, he settled in Paris. His best-known book was *Le livre du compagnonnage* (1840).

[22] See *supra*, p. 179, n. 51.

[23] Napoléon-Joseph, Prince de la Moskowa (1803–1857), was the oldest son of Marshal Ney. An Orléanist under Louis Philippe, he turned republican in 1848, and into an ardent supporter of Louis Napoleon Bonaparte shortly thereafter. He married a daughter of the wealthy banker Laffitte in 1828, and married his only daughter to Persigny, Louis Napoleon's alter ego, in 1852. He was a long-time president of the Jockey Club in Paris, best known for living in ruinous luxury.

[24] Henri-Auguste Georges du Vergier, Marquis de La Rochejaquelein (1805–1867), a soldier by profession, served in the House of Peers during the Restoration and as a deputy of the extreme Right under Louis Philippe. In 1848 he proclaimed himself rallied to the republic. In a famous speech to Raspail's club he declared, on April 1, 1848: "Monarchy is really and truly dead, citizens. The role of the pretenders is over, and if one of them dared attack the republic, I would be his most determined enemy." Having been elected to the Constituent and to the Legislative Assemblies, he turned into an ardent supporter of Louis Napoleon Bonaparte and became a senator in 1852.

[25] The extent of Raspail's influence in the provinces is not easy to document. It certainly reached into Lyons and Marseilles, both cities which later sent him to the legislature as their deputy. F. Dutacq reports that, when the Lyons Democratic Society decided to correspond with Parisian clubs in the spring of 1848, Raspail "the aged tribune," was chosen as the man to contact. A regular correspondence ensued. See F. Dutacq, *Histoire politique de Lyon pendant la révolution de 1848 (15 février–15 juillet)*. (Paris, 1910), 294.

[26] F.-V. Raspail, *Ami du peuple* . . . , February 28.

on March 30], they would have been, like universal suffrage, the result of general enthusiasm. . . . Why did you delay the elections? . . . The lists weren't ready, you say? . . . Could they not, with a little good will, have been drawn up in three or four days? No, . . . you mistrusted the mass of our citizens. . . .[27]

His voice went unheard, both by the moderate republicans who wanted elections soon (but only after voting procedures could be properly organized), and by the socialist republicans who pressed for a long delay so that the country could be educated to its new rights and privileges.

That Raspail exerted his considerable influence in favor of moderation and legality is even more strikingly shown by his refusal to participate in the street demonstrations of March 17 and April 16, which were launched in the hope of intimidating the Provisional Government. Raspail's absence from these disturbances needs to be pointed out, since many historians have simply assumed that he helped organize and lead them.[28] Given this moderation on two occasions, it is surprising to find Raspail at the head of a popular insurrection on May 15. A logical explanation of his apparently contradictory attitudes is afforded by an analysis of these three popular demonstrations. The first two marches were aimed at the Provisional Government in the Hôtel de Ville. The immediate issues were the date of the elections, the democratization of the National Guard, and the removal of troops from the Paris region.[29] The first demonstration earned some success, the second only the growing bitterness

---

[27] *Ibid.*, March 30.

[28] See e.g., J. Vidalenc, *Louis Blanc* (Paris: Collection du centenaire de la révolution de 1848), 49; and A. R. Calman, *Ledru-Rollin and the Second French Republic* (New York, 1922), 126. In Duveau's *Raspail* this important point is left vague; but Suzanne Wassermann, who analyzed the *Ami du peuple* with care, makes it quite clear that Raspail disapproved of these manifestations and stayed away.

[29] On March 17, 150,000 men marched on the Hôtel de Ville. An executive committee of thirty members carried the petition. The clubs headed the marchers, the workers followed, each trade carrying its banner. The thirty leaders met and talked with the government. A delay of two weeks for the elections to both the National Guard and the National Assembly eventually resulted. The "people" had gained a small victory.

On April 16, the mood of the crowd was tense. They wished again to delay

of the workers and the increased resentment and fear of moderates and conservatives.[30]

On May 15, on the other hand, the demonstrators had an altruistic motive, although they were also impelled by resentment against the National Constituent Assembly. The purpose was the popular demand that France send soldiers to the rescue of Poland. Tsar Nicholas I had just crushed a Polish revolt, one of the many uprisings sparked by the overthrow of Louis Philippe. Friendly feelings for faraway Poland had been fashionable among Frenchmen for a least a century—dating back to the days when Louis XV was given a Polish bride and France espoused the cause of her father, Stanislas Leczinski. This sympathy toward Poland, prevalent among the workers of Paris in the mid-1840s, had no rational basis; it was motivated by enthusiasm for Poland's national aspirations toward which France had shown the way in 1789, and to which Napoleon I had given concrete form by creating the Grand Duchy of Warsaw. Raspail concurred in this sympathy. He even wrote a pamphlet[31] to publicize his support for the faraway, presumably liberty-loving country. French ardor was also fostered and fanned by citizens of Polish extraction, some of whom were deputies under the Second Republic. In their fervor the workers were blind to the fact that French military help for Polish nationalists was quite impracticable. But Poland's cause furnished an effective theme for a republican and socialist workers' demonstration on May 15, 1848.

The Constituent Assembly, convening at the Palais Bourbon, distrusted and feared the crowd. On May 12, a decree had been passed

---

the elections and, it was rumored, "change the composition of the government." When the demonstrators arrived at two o'clock from the Champ de Mars, they found the Hôtel de Ville surrounded by so many members of the National Guard that they had to advance two by two, between rows of guardsmen who shouted "Down with the communists!" No more concessions were made. The moderates had gained the upper hand.

[30] On April 17 Raspail resigned from the National Guard. The document announcing this decision gives no reasons. See *Lettre Affiche aux Braves Gardes Nationaux de la Commune de Gentilly*. Fonds Raspail, Archives du Département de la Seine, XXXV. He had held the rank of commander of this batallion.

[31] F.-V. Raspail, *De la Pologne sur les bords de la Vistule et dans l'émigration* (Paris, 1839), tr. into Polish (Poitiers, 1840).

forbidding petitioners personal access to the assembly hall.[32] Insurgents who presented their demand for help to Poland at the rostrum were thus breaking the law. Raspail, together with Sobrier,[33] Albert,[34] Blanqui, and Barbès, headed the two hundred thousand marchers. He had written the petition, he read it to the Assembly, and his name was to figure on several lists of potential members for a provisional government.[35] He was also seen near the Hôtel de Ville that evening. He was deeply implicated and was arrested that night.

The demonstration had in fact gone much further than Raspail had intended. The mob got completely out of hand. Once the Assembly hall had been invaded ". . . there was an abominable confusion of speeches, cheers, and shouting. The President was summoned to surrender his bell; he refused. Several men rushed up to him. The excitment was at a pitch. A crime, a revolution seemed imminent." [36] Thus reported the *Moniteur*. Alexis de Tocqueville, a member of the Assembly, was more annoyed than frightened by the mob.

Some of the intruders [he wrote], were openly armed, others showed glimpses of concealed weapons, but none seemed to entertain a fixed intention of striking us. Their expression was one of astonishment and ill will rather than enmity; with many of them a sort of vulgar curiosity in course of gratifying itself seemed to dominate every other sentiment. . . . They dripped with sweat, although the nature and condition of their clothing was not calculated to make the heat very uncomfortable for them, for several were quite bare breasted. There rose from this multitude a confused noise from the midst of which one

[32] For a highly interesting analysis of the temper of the crowd in Paris during the week-end of May 13–15, see L. Lévy-Schneider, "Les préliminaires du 15 mai 1848," *La révolution de 1848*, VII (1910–1911), 219–32.

[33] Marie-Joseph Sobrier (? –1854), was an enthusiastic republican who spent a part of his fortune helping political prisoners under the July Monarchy. In 1848 he published *La Commune de Paris* which advocated the most far-reaching reforms in favor of the working class. After the 15th of May he was imprisoned with Raspail at Vincennes, tried at Bourges, and condemned to seven years' detention. Pardoned in 1852, he died two years later, a very ill man and partly insane.

[34] Albert, whose real name was Alexandre Martin (1815–1895), had been the only working class member of the Provisional Government of February 1848.

[35] *Procès* . . . *du 15 mai*, 2.

[36] *Le Moniteur universel*, No. 138 (May 17, 1848), 1061, col. 1.

sometimes heard very threatening observations. I caught sight of men who shook their fists at us and called us their agents. This expression was often repeated; for several days the ultrademocratic newspapers had done nothing but call the representatives the agents of the people, and these blackguards had taken kindly to the idea.[37]

At the height of the excitement, one of the mob, Huber,[38] mounted the tribune of the Chamber and shouted: "In the name of the French people, deceived by its representatives, I declare the National Assembly dissolved!" And to the President of the Assembly: "You are no longer needed here. Go away!" Then, turning toward the insurgents, Huber yelled: "And now, let's all go

[37] A. de Tocqueville, *Recollections,* J. P. Mayer, ed. (New York, 1949), 128–29.

[38] Aloysius Huber (1815–1865), by profession a tanner, was by avocation a revolutionist. A member of many secret societies in the 1830s, he was imprisoned several times. In 1848 he refused to join the government, preferring to agitate. He was one of the main organizers of the May 15 demonstration. It is not impossible that he acted as a police agent who incited the republicans and socialists to violent and subversive acts so that they could be jailed by the government.

Raspail was convinced of Huber's sinister role. The ascertainable facts derive mainly from the testimony, before the High Court at Bourges, of M. Monnier, General Secretary to the Police Prefect, Caussidière. Monnier read documents from Huber's file in the police archives. They included letters handwritten by Huber, proving that he was in the government's pay in 1838 already, that he had amassed evidence in prison and in London, in order to denounce political prisoners and help foil a plot against King Louis Philippe. In early May 1848 he was awarded the governorship of Raincy castle, a sinecure.

On May 15 it was Huber who pleaded with Raspail to lead the demonstration, and to read his own petition for Poland. It was Huber who, at the Palais Bourbon, proclaimed the Assembly dissolved. Although jailed in 1848 and condemned to deportation in 1849, he was pardoned on February 10, 1852 by Louis Napoleon, at a moment when most other republicans and revolutionaries were being exiled or deported. (See Archives nationales, Series BB[21], 549, dossier S3322.) He ended his days in considerable luxury, financed from mysterious sources. He died suddenly in 1865.

Concerning his role on May 15, Huber himself protested violently against the allegations of Monnier, Raspail, and Blanqui. He returned to France of his own free will in 1848 (but after the Bourges trial) in order to "defend his honor." He tried in vain to have Raspail and Blanqui brought to Versailles from Doullens, nor was he ever cleared of the suspicion that he had been a secret agent of Louis Philippe. See *Procès du citoyen Huber devant la Haute Cour de Versailles* (Paris, 1849).

For an interesting sidelight on this complicated story, see J. Bossu, "Il y eut en 1848 Hubert et Huber," Chronique et Bibliographie, *La révolution de 1848,* XXXVI (1939), 77–78.

to the Hôtel de Ville!" [39] Although some of the leaders actually made their way across the Seine to the City Hall—the traditional seat of insurrectionary Parisian governments—there was such a lack of coordination and planning that the demonstration simply petered out. Two hundred and eighty persons were arrested, and the leaders were sent to the prison of Vincennes. Meanwhile, at the Palais Bourbon, the National Assembly, "still very incomplete, resumed its sitting; it was six o'clock." [40]

In the eyes of the Constituent, and subsequently the Legislative Assembly, the wild demonstration of May 15 was not an effort to win help for Poland but an attempt to overthrow the moderate republican government and set up a socialist one. Its leaders must therefore be brought to justice. A decision as to the legal procedures applicable to the suspects in the prison of Vincennes was deferred until after the adoption of the new constitution. The debates in the National Assembly on January 20 and 22, 1849, ended with a vote of 466 to 288 for the course of action proposed by the government, which was to try the prisoners before a special High Court. This court would not meet until March 7, 1849, so that Raspail and his companions were held in "protective custody" for ten months. The defendants would eventually be summoned before five judges chosen from the Courts of Appeal and thirty-six jurors taken from among members of the departmental General Councils.[41] The conservative sympathies of such a court were a foregone conclusion. In addition the tribunal would sit in the small provincial town of Bourges where popular demonstrations in favor of the prisoners were much less likely than in Paris and could, in any event, be more easily controlled.[42]

The competence of this court was challenged by the accused and by their supporters.[43] Raspail and his fellow prisoner Quentin[44]

[39] *Procès . . . du 15 mai*, 2.

[40] A. de Tocqueville, *Recollections*, 138.

[41] *Le Moniteur universel*, No. 25 (January 25, 1849), 241.

[42] P. de La Gorce, *Histoire de la seconde république française* (Paris, 1911), II, 124–25.

[43] F.-V. Raspail, *Départ des prisonniers de Vincennes, leurs adieux au peuple; les dernières paroles des citoyens Barbès, Raspail, Blanqui, et Huber, adressées au Président de la république, Louis Napoléon* (Paris, 1849).

[44] Auguste-François Quentin. Very little is known about him, except that he was born in 1800 at Angers.

even took legal action to have the government decree annulled. But to no avail.[45] One of the deputies who opposed the creation of a special tribunal, a liberal and the author of an excellent *History of the Constituent Assembly*, gives this illuminating analysis of the debate:

It was useless to tell [the deputies] that they were violating the eternal principles of morality and justice which demand that the accused be punished only according to laws which exist when the crime is committed; it was vain to retell the unhappy history of special tribunals; it was pointless to pile up the opinions of jurists, legislative texts, cornerstones of jurisprudence. After two days of solemn debate, the Assembly decided that a High Court of Justice would meet at Bourges, to judge the authors and accomplices of the 15th of May.

When the Assembly was invaded, the Constitution had not been voted, the institution of a High Court of Justice did not exist, common law alone was valid. The defendants should have been handed over to a jury. However great their crime, they had the right to expect that no special law, voted after the event, would affect them, that no court other than a jury would punish them. Morality and justice demanded this.

Nevertheless they were put in an exceptional position. Instead of being mere defendants before an ordinary court, they were offered the special opportunity of posing as political victims.

The principles at stake were argued with wonderfully forceful logic and at times with great eloquence by Ledru-Rollin, Crémieux, Dupont de Bussac, and Jules Favre. . . . It was no use. Eloquence, common sense, and truth were foiled by political passion, stoked with skill, and the Assembly committed the injustice of deviating from the magnificent course it had followed on May 15, which would have meant to regard the defendants with pity and to abandon them to ordinary justice.[46]

The workers of Paris did not share the Assembly's feelings. Grateful for Raspail's advocacy of their demands on May 15, they nominated him for a seat in the National Constituent Assembly in

[45] *Le Moniteur universel*, No. 49 (February 18, 1849), 540–41.

[46] L. Babaud-Laribière, *Histoire de l'assemblée nationale constituante* (Paris, 1850), 2 vols., II 19–21. In the Constituent Assembly of 1848 Léonide Babaud-Laribière (1819–1873) voted consistently with the Left. In June 1870 he was elected Grand Master of Freemasonry in France. Under the Third Republic he served as Prefect of Charente, and of Pyrénées Orientales.

June and again in September 1848. Defeated on June 4 and 5 (although he had 72,000 votes), he was elected with but 67,000 votes on September 22.[47] One of his supporters wrote him an Open Letter which reads in part:

Yes, we nominated you, and this causes us joy and pride.

We nominated you because you want the democratic and social republic . . . because your soul is strong and your heart warm for truth; because you have loved the proletarians since your birth; . . . because you are a wise and honest citizen; . . . because you are unhappy and unjustly pursued . . . because, ever since the morrow of the February Revolution, instead of seizing sinecures like so many others, you courageously took the pen which the people restored to you . . . , because your whole life has been a long apostolate. . . .[48]

His popularity had also reached the provinces. In Lyons he was well known because his defense of the "April prisoners" in 1834 was widely remembered.[49] Lyons chose him as a candidate in the September elections as well. He did not win, but he earned the satisfaction of receiving 34,185 votes.[50] Perhaps the most dramatic gesture of his supporters was to propose his name for the presidency of the Second Republic.[51]

The reasons for choosing a political prisoner as presidential candidate were complex. Actually, political radicals had long agreed on Ledru-Rollin, but the socialists did not like him. In the end the socialists decided to vote for Raspail, partly to honor him, and partly—since he had no conceivable chance of success—to protest against the institution of the presidency.[52] Although the dimensions

[47] See *Procès-verbal de recensement général, Elections partielles, Seine, 17 septembre 1848,* Archives nationales, Series C, 1328, No. 180.

[48] Ch. Marchal, *Lettre à F.-V. Raspail, représentant du peuple* (Paris, 1848).

[49] See *supra,* pp. 176–77.

[50] See F. Dutacq, "L'élection d'un représentant du Rhône à l'Assemblée nationale au mois de septembre 1848," *Revue d'histoire de Lyon,* VII (1908), 443–69.

[51] Raspail's friends in Lyons published a proclamation which reads in part: ". . . We want Raspail for president . . . because his fifty years of blameless life are the best guarantee of support for the two great principles of morality and the family." (Quoted in G. Raspail, *La vie et l'oeuvre* . . . , 92.)

[52] See Anon., *La présidence entre Ledru-Rollin et Raspail: Appel aux sentiments de l'unité démocratique et sociale* (Paris: Dépôt central chez Chapuy, n.d. [1848]). This pamphlet favors Raspail and warns: "Ledru-Rollin is no dem-

of the Napoleonic victory in the presidential election came as a shock to many, the defeat of F.-V. Raspail by Louis Napoleon Bonaparte was hardly surprising.[53] Unsuccessful in 1848, the prisoner's supporters in Paris and Lyons triumphed twenty years later under the Liberal Empire when they elected him a deputy from the Rhône Department.

How actively the imprisoned Raspail was able to participate in these exciting and ultimately rewarding events we can only surmise. Some election posters which have survived carry his picture; others feature open letters to the voters, appealing for their support, explaining his platform, and expressing his thanks for their continued devotion.[54] One of these, addressed to the "Citizen-electors of the Seine" by the "old martyr of your holy cause" whom they had just chosen as their deputy, has the ring of Raspail's prose and bears the stamp of his convictions. Dated "From the dungeon of Vincennes, on September 22, 1848," it reads in part:

ocratic socialist; Raspail has always been one"; or again: "Revolutionary electors, you must vote on grounds of principle, justice, and true politics, for Raspail the man of truth, the stalwart socialist, the true Friend of the People!"

For a lucid account of the changing waves of opinion among newspapers, clubs, and factions in the fall of 1848, see A. R. Calman, *Ledru-Rollin . . .* , ch. XVII, "A Presidential Candidate."

[53] It is amusing to note that Raspail received twice as many votes as the poet Lamartine. The official results of the elections were as follows:

Louis Napoleon Bonaparte	5,434,226
General Cavaignac	1,448,107
Ledru-Rollin	370,119
Raspail	36,900
Lamartine	17,910
General Changarnier	4,790

See J. M. Thompson, *Louis Napoleon and the Second Empire* (New York, 1955), 96.

[54] F.-V. Raspail, *Propagande électorale: prêtres et socialistes* (Paris, n.d.) purports to be a conversation between a peasant, a schoolmaster, and a priest. The priest defines socialists and communists as "persons who take away your land"; to the schoolmaster they are "men who share their possessions with you." The peasant is convinced by the teacher's arguments and decides to vote for Raspail.

F.-V. Raspail, *Aux citoyens-électeurs des 4 et 5 juin* (Paris, 1848). In this poster, Raspail thanks the voters, calls for civil peace, and reaffirms his belief in universal suffrage.

F.-V. Raspail, *Aux citoyens-électeurs du Rhône* (Paris, 1848), relates to his unsuccessful candidacy in Lyons which he calls "An honor for you! A consolation for me!"

Political campaign por-
traits of 1848, 1869, and
1876 (Courtesy Ar-
chives du Département de
la Seine)

I bless your victory which has allowed me to measure your power . . .
in the electoral field.

Citizens, my brothers, you must never again agree to fight on any
but legal grounds.

Be conscious of your own strength: you are nine against one; why
should you need to fight, as long as you advance together?

Take your opponents by the hand and let them join your ranks;
forget the past and live for the achievements of the future.

In addition to this stress on legality, he also made a renewed appeal
for regional collaboration. Despite bitter personal hardship, his tone
was still that of teacher and guide.[55]

With membership in the National Constituent Assembly,
Raspail expected to obtain parliamentary immunity and to be
released from the Vincennes prison at once.[56] "I am ready to leave,"

[55] F.-V. Raspail, *Aux citoyens-électeurs de la Seine, Merci!* (Paris, 1848).
[56] An anonymous admirer published a *Biographie de François-Vincent Raspail,*

he wrote to his constituents, "and waiting for the door of my cell to open, so as to take the place you have assigned to me." [57] The decision to free him was up to the Assembly. Its agenda on September 26, 1848, included the admission of its newly elected members, among them Louis Napoleon Bonaparte and François-Vincent

---

Représentant du peuple (Paris, 1848), essentially a plea that the government judge and free Raspail speedily, so that he might occupy his seat in the National Assembly. Another friend and admirer wrote: ". . . your nomination is a good omen for the maintenance of the republic. . . . Where are you now, doubtless at home, for universal suffrage must have broken your chains and your next letter will be postmarked Montsouris. . . ." Autogr. ms. letter from Josué Hofer of Mulhouse, 25 September, 1848, in the possession of M. Jacques Raspail. And one Gustave Leroy composed a song called *Raspail, représentant du peuple* (n.p. [Paris], n.d. [Fall 1848]).

[57] F.-V. Raspail, *Discours de M. Ledru-Rollin, prononcé au banquet du Châtelet le 22 septembre 1848 suivi des remerciements de F.-V. Raspail* (Paris, 1849), 18.

Raspail.[58] As is well known, the prince's credentials were challenged unsuccessfully, and his humble, patriotic speech, haltingly delivered with a heavy German accent, convinced all present that they had nothing to fear from the awkward, ungainly nephew. The case of the political prisoner came next. A report from the credentials committee was immediately followed by a letter from the attorney general which the assembly's president, Armand Marrast, read to his colleagues. The letter was enlarged upon by the attorney general himself, present because he was also a deputy. Raspail, it was argued, must first be tried for his participation in the May 15 demonstration, and then, if declared innocent, he could take his place in the Assembly. Parliamentary immunity could not be retroactive and cover a "crime" committed before the immunity was valid.[59] "A citizen charged with a crime, caught in the act, must be tried according to the laws of the land. . . . The rights of justice precede the rights of politics in this case, and are therefore preeminent." [60] This highly debatable argument, the crux of the matter, was attacked by several speakers. The point under discussion had great significance: How to determine the legal rights of a deputy when France had no constitution that spelled out such rights? In this fluid situation power and law rested with the majority of the Assembly itself. The law courts had only the Codes to guide them, and they were silent on matters such as parliamentary immunity.[61]

[58] Strange as it may seem, many workers evidently supported both of these candidates. When Gustave Lefrançais expressed his surprise he was told: "In voting for Bonaparte, we shouted 'Down with the butcher of June!'; in supporting Raspail, 'Long live socialism!' " *Souvenirs d'un révolutionnaire* (Paris, 1886), 68–69.

[59] This was an entirely new problem for which no precedent existed in France.

[60] *Le Moniteur universel*, No. 271 (September 27, 1848), 2608, columns 2–3, *passim*.

[61] The abstract legal problem focuses on this technicality: whose prisoner was Raspail from May 15, 1848 to March 7, 1849 [when the Bourges trial opened] —the prisoner of the executive or of the judicial branch of the government? He had been arrested, on May 15, by the National Guard (the 8th company of the 2nd battalion of the 11th legion); thus he was the prisoner of the executive branch; had he been handed over—technically speaking—to the law?

Raspail himself seemed to think so, since on October 21, 1848, he attempted to obtain, from the local law court, a decision which would permit him to attend Assembly sessions, to which he was willing to be taken from prison, and from which he would return to Vincennes. The judge refused to comply, "given

"Why could not Raspail be freed temporarily?" it was asked. He could be counted on to appear whenever the lengthy preparations for the trial were terminated. In the heat of debate, Eugène Raspail,[62] a nephew and a deputy from Vaucluse, made the mistake of diverting the argument from the matter of principle at stake which had impressed the listeners. He pleaded that Raspail be released *so that* he could argue his case before the assembly. This conjured up May 15. Shouts of "But we've seen and heard him already!" ended the discussion and lost the case. The Constituent Assembly, although it validated Raspail's credentials, voted that

---

the present situation." General Cavaignac, Head of the Executive Branch, was informed of Raspail's wishes, but ignored them. (See Letter to the Minister of Justice, Oct. 25, 1848 and other documents in Archives nationales, Series BB[30], dossier 1.)

The author wishes to thank M. Pierre Laroque, President of the Section for Social Affairs, Council of State, for his enlightening discussion of this legal point.

[62] Eugène Raspail (1812–1888) served as deputy from Vaucluce in the Constituent Assembly where he voted consistently with the extreme Left. He figures in four episodes recorded in the *Moniteur*: he was arrested on May 15, 1848—but soon released for lack of evidence (*Le Moniteur*, No. 138 [May 17, 1848], 1062, col. 1); in September he defended Raspail's right to be seated in the Assembly (see above); in January, 1849, he spoke against transferring the trial of the May 15 prisoners to Bourges (see *supra*, p. 212); and in April, 1849, he slapped a deputy who had just testified at Bourges, giving new evidence that was damaging for Raspail. The astonishing fact about this evidence was that M. Point volunteered it ten months after the event *because* he had heard some deputies say that Raspail's guilt was doubtful. "Ah," Raspail thereupon exclaimed, "so I was innocent, and I would still be innocent without you, Monsieur!" (*Procès des accusés du 15 mai* . . . , 70.) Eugène had slapped M. Point at the door of the National Assembly. Therefore the deputies voted to suspend his immunity so that criminal proceedings could be initiated. The eventual outcome was a condemnation to two years in prison and a thousand francs fine. (See "Demande en autorisation de poursuites contre le sieur Raspail (Eugène) à raison de voies de fait commises contre son collègue, le citoyen Point, représentant du peuple; Rapport du commissaire spécial de police de l'assemblée, séance du 11 avril 1849," Archives nationales, Series C, 908, No. 22; and "Dépêche du ministre de la justice relative au jugement correctionnel rendu, par défaut, contre le citoyen Eugène Raspail pour outrage et voies de fait envers son collègue le citoyen Point; Expédition du jugement," Archives nationales, Series C, 908, No. 27 and BB[30], 363, dossier 3.) Eugène escaped imprisonment by fleeing to London. Whether he ever paid the fine is not known. See also, L. Blanc, A. Blanqui, F.-V. Raspail, et al., *Almanach républicain démocratique pour 1850* (Paris, n.d.), 138. He returned to France sometime after the amnesty of 1859 and ended his days peacefully as director of the gas-light company of Avignon.

he must await trial first.[63] From a legal point of view, it would seem that Raspail was being wronged, and that temporary freedom, at least, was owed him.[64] But he was now best known to the deputies as a hothead who had infringed upon the inviolability of a republican assembly; they would rather stretch legality to keep him in jail than tempt fate by setting him free.

In the ten months elapsed between the "crime" of May 15 and the trial of its perpetrators, the republican and socialist cause lost the sympathies and support of the middle class. The rift between this class and the workers widened into a chasm, owing to the fiasco of the National Workshops, the fighting between government troops and the workers in June, and the strangling of the opposition by an increasingly conservative government. Could Raspail and his comrades expect a dispassionate attitude from the special court that was to judge them? Louis Blanc doubted this when he wrote from London on April 7, 1849: "The crime judged at Bourges has a well-known name: it is called *socialism*." [65] And Blanqui told his judges: "You are a dangerous expedient set up by politicians eager for vengeance." [66]

And yet the trial (which lasted from March 7 to April 2, 1849) was on the whole conducted in an atmosphere of fairness and calm. This was due not only to the presiding judge, Bérenger de la Drôme, but also to Raspail, the senior socialist defendant. Apart from a few outbursts of anger provoked by injurious remarks from witnesses, Raspail was consistently respectful of judge and jury. In several instances he acted as spokesman for his colleagues,

---

[63] When the trial at Bourges was in progress, the Assembly voted that any deputy condemned to "grievous or degrading punishment" [*"peines afflictives ou infamantes"*] would forfeit his deputy's mandate. With his condemnation on April 2, 1849, Raspail would thus lose his seat in the Assembly.

[64] This was also the opinion of many citizens, one of whom wrote to General Cavaignac on June 21, 1848: "Why don't you set Raspail free and make him render medical services . . . and you will have to feed one prisoner less. . . . This idea may still reach you in time, just as it occurred to me when I saw camphor cigarettes in the mouths of all the workers among whom I am ending my long life." P. Sirodon to General Cavaignac, Archives nationales, Series BB[30], 333, dossier L.

[65] L. Blanc, *Pages d'histoire de la révolution de février 1848* (Paris, 1850), 4.

[66] *Procès . . . du 15 mai*, 14.

which was helpful to all concerned, since Barbès and Albert refused, as a matter of principle, to defend themselves, Blanqui lost
his temper too easily, and men such as Flotte,[67] Quentin, or
Borme[68] were unused to public speaking. Raspail, being something of an expert on the Napoleonic Codes and on the rights of
political prisoners, argued effectively, in lawyers' language.

The public was greatly astonished to learn [commented Léonard Gallois]
that this great citizen was as good a lawyer as any law professor. To
struggle in this manner with the attorney general and his assistants
seemed to be mere play for the chemist Raspail who reminded his
antagonists more than once of the provisions and texts of our codes of
instruction and procedure. Raspail defended himself with vigorous
arguments . . . and his condemnation seemed impossible.[69]

All participants, to be sure, were aware of the wide press coverage
of this trial. They addressed the entire French reading public as
well as the court. But Raspail and his colleagues mainly fought
hard to regain their freedom. The presiding judge never curtailed
their right to speak nor to challenge any of the two hundred and
forty-six witnesses.[70]

Of the twenty defendants, eight had fled.[71] Most important
among those present were Raspail, Blanqui, Barbès, Albert, and
General Courtais, the commander of the National Guard in Paris
in 1848,[72] who had neglected his duty of protecting the Assembly
from the mob on the fateful day. The minutes give the following
description of Raspail:

Age fifty-four, chemist, writer, representative of the people in the
National Assembly. Born at Carpentras, Vaucluse; address: 55, rue de
la Tombe-Issoire, Montrouge, near Paris; height: 1 m 76; hair and

[67] Benjamin Flotte (1815– ?) was a cook by profession. He emigrated to
New Orleans and grew rich, but antagonized the slave owners because he be-
friended the negroes. He died poor.

[68] Daniel Borme (1822– ?) was a chemist.

[69] L. Gallois, *Histoire de la révolution de 1848*, IV, 415.

[70] The prosecution called on 168 witnesses, the defense produced 78 more.

[71] But one of these, Léopold Villain, came to Bourges of his own free will
when the trial opened.

[72] A. G. H. Courtais (1790–1877) served under Napoleon I; in 1842 he was
elected to the Chamber of Deputies where he voted with the liberal opposition.
After the events of May 15 he was imprisoned at Vincennes, tried at Bourges,
and acquitted. He returned to private life and died in obscurity.

eyebrows: light blond; forehead: high; eyes: blue-grey and protuberant; nose: regular; mouth: large; chin: round; face: oval; coloring:
high.[73]

The defendants were dressed "simply but not without elegance," [74]
and Raspail usually came into court with "voluminous files under
his arm." [75] The prisoners were formally charged with having attempted to alter or destroy the government and with fomenting
civil war.

Raspail, as was his wont, spoke in his own defense, although
two lawyers had been assigned to him. In his first major speech
he challenged the competence of the court. He maintained that
the defendants should be tried in Paris by a regular jury. He also
took issue with the nature of the accusation, arguing that his own
behavior on May 15 should be considered a misdemeanor, not a
crime against the state. He complained of having been held in
protective custody for the unnecessarily long period of ten months.[76]
The court considered his objections, but denied their validity.[77]

In his second speech Raspail turned to the major points raised to
prove his guilt. In every instance he clashed with Maître Baroche,[78]

[73] *Procès . . . du 15 mai*, 7.

[74] *Ibid.*, 8.

[75] *Ibid.*, 16.

[76] The prosecutor explained that of the 280 persons who had at first been
arrested, only 20 were now accused; 800 witnesses had been heard; 3,000 documents now constituted the files.

[77] *Procès . . . du 15 mai*, 12–13. Always sensitive to suffering, Raspail
seized the opportunity to protest against the inhumane treatment of political
prisoners. The "ambulatory prison cells" in which the defendants had been
transported to Bourges must have been built by "an ignoramus unfamiliar with
the theory of breathing: it is impossible that a man should not repeatedly faint,
in the course of a four-hour trip." (*Ibid.*, 13.)
A few days later Raspail informed the court that the prisoners were unable
to sleep at night because the guards came to check on their presence every
fifteen minutes and made a great deal of noise. This protest created enough
public interest for the President to summon the Director of Prisons. The man
sent word that he was indisposed, and the underling who represented him
denied everything. The court was satisfied. (*Ibid.*, 79–80.)

[78] Pierre-Jules Baroche (1802–1870), a lawyer, had begun his political career
as an anti-Orléanist liberal and served as representative in the Constituent Assembly. But popular agitation frightened him and he turned into one of Napoleon III's most consistent and most rewarded supporters. He resigned as Vice
President of the Council of State in 1863 and, on September 4, 1870, fled to
the island of Jersey where he died.

the prosecutor, and neither side gave an inch. The Club Raspail was denounced as a haven for revolutionary oratory; the prosecution was not in the mood to make distinctions between fervent republicanism and subversion. Raspail's intention to follow instead of lead the 200,000 demonstrators on May 15, was discussed. As the defendant explained: the original petition that was to have been presented to the Assembly had got lost, and some of the leaders prevailed upon Raspail to read his own version. This was an odd turn of events, but one which gained general credence.[79] Crucial to Raspail's defense were the next two points: he maintained throughout that General Courtais had *admitted* him into the Palais Bourbon,[80] and that the Assembly President, P. J. B. Buchez, had *invited* him to read his petition[81] for armed intervention in Poland.[82] Buchez, called to Bourges as a witness, remained as weak and vague in his testimony as, according to all sources, he had been on May 15. He said, for example:

I could not have given Raspail permission to speak since the Assembly, in its decree of May 12, had forbidden that petitions be brought before it by outsiders. . . .

[79] Significantly, the correspondent of a provincial newspaper had described the May 15 manifestation as "calm, peaceful, numerous, strong, imposing. . . . I was told that citizen Raspail would certainly head the demonstration and thus I felt reassured; for I have always considered Raspail as a superior and very wise man." Quoted in L. Gallois, *Histoire de la révolution de 1848*, II, 114.

[80] The verbatim report reads: "A juror: 'Does the defendant Raspail declare that General Courtais invited him to enter the Assembly building?'—*Raspail*: 'Yes, Sir.'" *Procès . . . du 15 mai*, 18.

In a recent monograph on the National Guard, Louis Girard writes: "This [revolutionary] 'day' came as a complete surprise to units that were just getting settled. . . . The Third Legion had stationed 150 men inside the Palais [Bourbon] but only thirty were left: the rest had gone to lunch." L. Girard, *La garde nationale* (Paris, 1964), 307.

[81] There is no need to doubt Raspail's veracity when he stated during the trial: "We debated at first whether the petition should be read or only deposited; we decided it should be read and we wanted Louis Blanc to read it because he was a deputy. But there were shouts: 'No, it must be read by a citizen who is not a deputy.' I thought then that this might be a means of quieting the excitement and I read the petition." *Ibid.*, 29.

[82] On the subject of Poland, Raspail waxed emotional: ". . . yes, Poland has my deep sympathies. . . . In 1838, I published a manifesto called *Poland on the Vistula* . . . , which proves that I had toward the Poles written commitments, commitments of the heart." *Ibid.*, 17.

. . . I might have said to some persons around me: "I hope that after Raspail has read his petition, they'll all quiet down." [83]

Turning to Raspail, his erstwhile companion in carbonaro conspiracy, Buchez added, somewhat sententiously: "If you want my opinion, I have only one explanation for your behavior, considering that you are a mature and reasonable man: it is that you were being led and pushed further than you intended to go." [84] Alexis de Tocqueville, an eyewitness, thought Buchez' behavior in the Assembly far from heroic:

Buchez, the President, whom some would make out to be a rascal and others a saint, but who undoubtedly, on that day, was merely a blockhead, rang his bell with all his might to obtain silence, as though the silence of that multitude was not, under the present circumstances, more to be dreaded than its cries.[85]

Whether or not Raspail had Buchez' permission to read the petition will never be known. The court, at any rate, did not believe so.

Three further points were discussed in the effort to establish Raspail's guilt: the tone of his utterances to the insurgents after he finished reading the petition; his inclusion in lists of prospective leaders of a revolutionary government; and his true destination during circuitous carriage rides after he left the Palais Bourbon. On the first point, even the official Act of Accusation was clear: "Raspail insisted that the crowd evacuate the hall to permit the Assembly freedom of discussion." [86] Ledru-Rollin testified in Raspail's favor on this point. Many witnesses agreed.[87] That his name appeared on lists of men who would head a putative revolutionary government, with Raspail possibly the minister of education, he did not deny; but he disclaimed any responsibility for such a choice and any intention of accepting the honor.[88]

[83] *Ibid.*, 108.
[84] *Ibid.*
[85] A. de Tocqueville, *Recollections*, 130.
[86] *Procès . . . du 15 mai*, 2.
[87] *Ibid.*, 97.
[88] See also Raspail's account of this day twenty-six years later before the *Cour d'assises de la Seine*. X. Raspail, *Procès de l'almanach Raspail . . .* , 126–28.

Maître Baroche, the prosecutor: "Did M. Raspail not know that his name figured on the lists of the provisional government?"

Raspail: "I knew it, but I said: No, I decline, because anything I accept must be legal; I would never have wanted to be part of a government chosen by thirty men. . . ." [89]

After leaving the Palais Bourbon, did Raspail attempt to reach the Hôtel de Ville? The Act of Accusation noted ominously: ". . . witnesses . . . have testified to . . . Raspail's presence" near the Town Hall.[90] Had he asked to be taken there, or was he being driven, against his will, somehow a prisoner of the crowd that surrounded his carriage shouting "Vive Raspail"? Four cabdrivers and several eyewitnesses testified. The route Raspail had followed was established beyond doubt. A carriage had taken him and two other men from the Palais Bourbon along the quais to the Ile de la Cité where he got off at the Pont d'Arcole, across the bridge from the City Hall. Someone talked with him there. He then walked away, never crossing the bridge to the right bank of the Seine. He reached the Place Maubert in the company of a Dr. Veyne, and hired another carriage which, after many detours, took him to the Latin Quarter, rue des Francs-Bourgeois-Saint-Michel, his son's home. There he was arrested.

To judge from the verdict, the jury concluded that Raspail's destination was indeed the City Hall and that his intention was to participate in the choice of an insurrectionary provisional government. Raspail denied this with vehemence.[91] But the jury must have been equally convinced that he tried to calm the crowds, as much as he was able, and that it was against his nature to foment civil war. The witnesses and Raspail agreed that he was exceedingly tired on the evening of May 15. A fainting spell had over-

[89] *Ibid.,* 70–71.
[90] *Ibid.,* 2.
[91] A touching incident took place at this point during the debate. When the prosecutor stated that Raspail's intention to reach the Hôtel de Ville was self-evident, a young man in the audience shouted: "That's not true!" The judge had him seized and would have dealt harshly with his lack of respect to the court, had not Raspail identified him as a twenty-year-old friend of his son's, and, with tears in his eyes, pleaded that the young man's loyalty not be severely punished. Everyone was moved, and the young man got off with twenty-four hours in jail. *Ibid.,* 109.

taken him at the Palais Bourbon. By late afternoon he was so exhausted from the excitement, the noise, the heat, the crowds, and the effort furnished on a day that had begun with a walk from the Place de la Bastille across most of Paris that he had no other wish than to go home.

Given the political circumstances surrounding this case, the verdict pronounced by the court on April 2 comes as no surprise. Barbès and Albert were sentenced to deportation; Blanqui to ten years in prison, Sobrier to seven, Raspail six, Flotte and Quentin five. Six of the lesser defendants were acquitted, as was General Courtais. Only Barbès, Albert, and Blanqui were found guilty of the second count: fomenting civil war.[92] Within the range of guilt assessed by the jury, Raspail's share seems to have been judged fairly. But the punishments meted out by the judges were quite harsh.[93] Raspail never admitted that on May 15 he had violated the law.

[92] Extenuating circumstances were found valid in the cases of Sobrier, Raspail, Flotte, and Quentin. The six defendants who were absent were condemned to deportation. Huber was reported to have returned to France and to be in jail.

[93] The guilty defendants also had to bear the cost of the trial. Raspail's family, some years later, had to pay a bill for 12,000 francs. F.-V. Raspail, *Procès perdu* . . . , 26 n.

*Owe nothing to favors; join no cliques;
expect everything from your work, your
reputation as your daily bread; do good
without hope of remuneration; serve
your country despite its recalcitrance; be
indulgent without being duped—this
is the line for a Raspail to follow.**

IX

THE REBEL AS
PATRIARCH

MAY 15, 1848, MARKED THE END of an epoch in Raspail's life for
more than political reasons. The last thirty years of his existence
were to be filled with prison, exile, tragedy. Madame Raspail's
death in 1853 was to be an ever-present sorrow. When his prison
sentence was commuted and he was banished, he dejectedly left his
beloved country and, for nine years, he lived in a small town near
Brussels. Belgian law prevented the practice of his medical skills,
but it did allow the publication of his journals. He produced no
more original research, although science was always on his mind.
His writings became increasingly philosophical and encyclopedic,
concerned with the past and the future, denying the present. He
lived in a private world, as the elderly will, with the ideals of his
youth, the memory of his political leadership, his work, his children,
and grandchildren. The extraordinary fact about this white-haired

* Raspail's inscription on his son Xavier's copy of the *Histoire naturelle de
la santé.*

227

old man is that during his fourteen years' absence he became a
living legend and thus a force in the political life of France. He
was to make his presence felt under the Liberal Empire and the
Third Republic.

For the five years following May 15, 1848, Raspail lived in
prisons—at Vincennes until the Bourges trial and thereafter in
the fortress of Doullens in Artois. When he was led off to serve his
jail term, incurred mainly for rashness and lack of judgment, Raspail was already an experienced prisoner whose habits in confinement were well established. His chief concern was to maintain
communication with the outside: political, medical, and familial.
This link with political followers had become vital after his election to the National Constituent Assembly on September 22,
1848. At Vincennes, as a suspect before the trial, he was allowed
pen and paper, but his writings were censored and his visitors
supervised. He probably participated in the composition of his own
campaign literature in June and September, 1848,[1] but his newspaper, the *Ami du peuple,* ceased publication with his arrest on
May 15, and his club, like all other republican and socialist clubs,
was closed. A review in which he had interspersed medicine and
pharmacy with politics[2] also ceased publication in 1849 when,
writing from the "Vincennes dungeon," he told his readers: ". . .
now that I am again in jail, you may be sure that knaves are gaining control of the body politic. . . ."[3]

He had to abandon his patients, which worried him most of all.
The dispensary of the rue de Sévigné had to be closed, for Dr.
Cottereau, his associate, had died in February 1847. True, Raspail continued to publish his *Health Annual,*[4] but this seemed
a pittance to a man who knew the extent of the people's medical
needs. An anguished *Appeal to Humanity*[5] was wrung from him
when he learned of the June massacres in 1848. He pleaded with

[1] See *supra,* pp. 215–16.
[2] F.-V. Raspail, *Revue élémentaire de médecine et de pharmacie domestiques
ainsi que des sciences accessoires et usuelles mises à la portée de tout le monde*
(Paris, 1847–1849), 2 vols.
[3] *Ibid.,* II, 387.
[4] Only in 1848 and 1853 was the *Annual* not published, for reasons which
Raspail's biography fully explains.
[5] F.-V. Raspail, *Appel à l'humanité* (Paris, n.d. [July 1848]).

doctors and other citizens to tend the wounded according to his methods.

Two "Almanacs" date from this period: one composed at Vincennes in 1848, and one at Doullens in 1849.[6] Many of the short pieces in these two volumes indicate that the prisoner's professional preoccupations were still medicine and politics. But he also kept turning to questions of veterinary practices and agriculture, interests that would stand him in good stead in exile. These concerns of course date back to his childhood in Vaucluse and to his botanical work at the Jardin des Plantes. In politics his aim was still reform: the *Almanac . . . for 1850* contains a detailed blueprint for revamping the French constitution. Many of the ideas expressed here were to reappear in Raspail's bills proposed to the national legislatures in 1869–1870 and 1876–1878. Indeed, the resumption of an active political career seems to have been an ever-present goal.[7]

And yet the almanacs contain nothing but fragments; the range of their contents is encyclopedic—the work of a dilletante. The prisoner evidently felt more and more cut off from the outside world. He summoned up his interest in all the far-flung areas of study that had arrested his attention in the past, in order to fill the empty hours with stimulating thought. He included a calendar; astronomic and meteorologic observations; tables of weights, measures, currencies, holidays; statistics. Anything, it would seem, that was of some interest to the prisoner and might be useful to the reader.[8]

[6] F.-V. Raspail, *La lunette du donjon de Vincennes. Almanach démocratique et social de L'Ami du peuple pour 1849* (Paris, 1848), and *La lunette de Doullens. Almanach démocratique et progressif de l'Ami du peuple pour 1850* (Paris, 1849).

[7] A "Letter" of 1849 to the electors at Lyons, e.g., counseling patience and unity, is signed "F.-V. Raspail, your representative through my son, and a citizen of your town by my gratitude." The terrain for his election from Lyons in 1869 was being prepared. F.-V. Raspail, *La lunette de Doullens,* 49.

[8] The faithful Benjamin even convinced the *Moniteur* to print his father's barometric and temperature readings at the time of a violent hailstorm and the appearance of a meteor, and to show how they agreed with the recordings made at the Paris Observatory, situated at the same longitude as Doullens. *Le Moniteur universel,* No. 213 (August 1, 1850), p. 2644, col. 1, and No. 220 (August 8, 1850), pp. 2760–61.

Au Dépôt: rue des Francs-Bourgeois-Saint-Michel, 5 (près l'Odéon).

LA LUNETTE DE DOULLENS.

ALMANACH

DÉMOCRATIQUE ET PROGRESSIF

DE L'AMI DU PEUPLE

POUR 1850,

PAR

F.-V. RASPAIL

PRIX : 50 centimes. - Par la poste : 75 centimes.

Poster advertising Raspail's *Almanac for 1850*
(Courtesy Archives du Département de la Seine)

While he was still at Vincennes, Madame Raspail brought his food every day, even though she had to walk five miles from her home at Montrouge. Occasionally patients came to consult Raspail. The Princesse de Canino, widow of Lucien Bonaparte, who was a faithful friend, sent letters from time to time through her son Pierre.[9] A lawyer evidently offered his services, since Raspail replied: ". . . I can only accept a proletarian to defend me, only an unlicensed lawyer. . . ."[10] Life was harsher at Doullens, where he was incarcerated in April 1849 as a convicted revolutionary. In his *Almanac . . . for 1850* Raspail described this gloomy fortress, which had been repaired and enlarged in the seventeenth century by Vauban, and where some hundred political prisoners

[9] G. Raspail, *La vie et l'oeuvre . . .* , 3.
When, twenty years later, Pierre Bonaparte committed his notorious murder of Victor Noir, his great past acts of kindness toward Raspail did not prevent the republican, then a member of the Legislative Body, to exert his influence in order to obtain a swift and stern sentence against the prince.

[10] Fonds Raspail, Archives du Département de la Seine, XXXIV.

were lodged. The six men sentenced at Bourges were housed in a separate brick building, twenty-four feet square, with two floors divided into eight rooms. They could not communicate with the other inmates.[11]

Exercise and some gardening was made possible, however, in a small enclosure surrounded by a wall twenty-five feet high. Despite the consequent lack of sunshine, roses apparently flourished in the prison yard, as well as dahlias, tulips, and carnations. Space was carefully apportioned to leave room for raspberries, strawberries and grapes. Every year, disputes arose: should the flowers be offered to lady visitors or remain on the bush?[12] In the narrow world of prison life, the details of everyday existence took the place of vital issues in the world outside, beyond the inmates' horizon.

The mail, if approved by the inspector, was let through. Numerous letters from patients were addressed to Raspail's son Camille— a medical student from 1852 on—who answered queries as best he could.[13] One letter to Raspail from his ten-year-old son Xavier has been preserved. It reads:

28 January 1850

Beloved papa:

On your birthday, I am happy to convey to you my feelings of love and gratitude. . . . My special wishes concern a speedy end of your sufferings, your continued happiness and long life. . . .[14]

The child seems to address a father whose existence is but legendary. Indeed, Raspail had been led away when Xavier was eight, and

[11] F.-V. Raspail, "Notice sur la prison de Doullens," *Lunette de Doullens,* 33–36, *passim.*

[12] M. Bernard, *Dix ans de prison au Mont-Saint-Michel et à la citadelle de Doullens* (Paris, 1861), 262–63.

[13] Fonds Raspail, Archives du Département de la Seine, LXXXV. One came from a poor woman, to judge by its tone and spelling, to whom Raspail had shown kindness; it is addressed to Camille: ". . . je viens donc vous pryer vous supplyer monsieur d'être assé bon de venir me voir je nai pas l'honneur d'être connu de vous mais bien de monsieur votre père et de madame votre mère. Car tout le temps qu'il à resté à Vincenne il ma toujour donné des consultations madamme votre mère a vait la bonté de me raporté lordonnance que j'avais à suivre je puis dire que monsieur raspail à ù pour moi tout les égard posible vous orez sans doute entandu parlé de moi. . . ." *Ibid.*

[14] Autogr. ms. letter belonging to M. Jacques Raspail.

the boy saw him rarely, in prison.[15] Xavier, like all his siblings, was brought up in veneration of his martyred parent.

Although lonely, prison life was not peaceful, and Raspail did not even feel safe. On October 20, 1849, he wrote to the district attorney at Doullens and to the attorney general in Paris, accusing the prison director, Valette, of having confiscated all his notes, papers, and manuscripts in an early morning raid. No inventory was made; no reasons were given.[16] The complaint that a prison director had manhandled and despoiled an inmate so disturbed the district attorney that the matter was brought before the Minister of Justice.[17] But the Prefect of the Somme Department had got wind of the accusation and was eager to hush it up. He prevailed upon the Minister of the Interior, Odilon Barrot, to prevent any meddling with prison administration.[18] In a long, carefully worded letter of November 20, 1849, addressed to the Minister of Justice, Barrot argued that public opinion must not be made suspicious of the nation's prison directors and guards. Nor should the risk be run to undermine their morale by an investigation of their conduct. Barrot saw "nothing but difficulties and dangers ahead, if this question were to be pursued." [19] The question was indeed dropped, but not before raising a storm in the National Legislative Assembly.

In that Assembly, which first met on May 28, 1849, Raspail had a natural advocate to publicize his complaints and keep his name in the news: his son Benjamin, commonly referred to in the *Moniteur*

[15] In 1907, Xavier, then President of the French Zoologic Society, recalled that his father would give him an hour's lesson and then spend another hour reminiscing about the great events in his past. (X. Raspail, *Raspail et Pasteur* . . . , 384.)

The elder Raspail had not always been so solemn a father. In his autobiography he tells—how accurately we cannot know—that in his younger days, when difficult work was concluded, he would "roll with my sons on the only rug at the foot of the bed and play with them in the noisiest manner." F.-V. Raspail, *Histoire de ma vie et de mon siècle*, 286.

[16] In another letter, a year later, Raspail revealed that his fellow inmate, Huber, repeatedly attempted to assassinate him. (Autogr. ms. letter from F.-V. Raspail to the attorney general, dated Doullens, September 17, 1850, in the possession of M. Jacques Raspail.)

[17] See Archives nationales, Series BB[30], No. 359, dossier 1.

[18] This whole incident is reviewed in A. Lebey, "Blanqui et Raspail à Doullens," *La révolution de 1848*, VI (1910–1911), 181–95.

[19] *Ibid.*, 193.

Raspail's letter of protest, sent to the Public Prosecutor from Doullens prison on October 20, 1849   (Courtesy Archives nationales, Paris)

and elsewhere as "M. Raspail *fils*." On the occasion of the Doullens incident, Benjamin, a deputy from Lyons,[20] formally challenged A.J.S. Dufaure, then Minister of the Interior. But Benjamin drew only denials from the government.[21] The language of this twenty-six-year-old champion tended to be so violent, his arguments so irrational, his attacks so personal, and his castigations so inclusive[22] that the hecklers rarely gave him any peace. In one instance the President, backed by a majority of the Assembly, even forced him to leave the rostrum.[23] Benjamin's political life was thus evidently determined and absorbed by his relationship to Raspail. The end of Benjamin's parliamentary career under the Second Republic came in January 1852, when Louis Napoleon expelled him from France.[24] He went to Belgium and settled at Boitsfort near Brussels, little knowing that he was preparing a home for his father.

In the meantime, soon after Raspail's transfer to Doullens in April 1849, his wife had moved to this town and was visiting her husband as often as she could. Sometimes the children came as well.[25] After his papers had been seized in October, her visits were curtailed, confined to the parlor, and even more strictly supervised. Any food she brought was dug into with a spoon by the guard, a practice Raspail found disgusting. Benjamin complained to the Legislative Assembly that his mother was searched upon entering and leaving. The political pieces published in the *Almanac* in 1849 and 1850—obviously smuggled out—had alerted the prison

[20] On his election, see "Département du Rhône, Représentants à l'assemblée nationale législative, élus en 1849," Archives nationales, Series C 1333, Rhône.

[21] *Le Moniteur universel*, No. 216 (August 4, 1849), 2574–75. Raspail's letter, cited above, was written after this incident. It contained a reiterated complaint.

[22] Raspail had led a better life as a prisoner of the July Monarchy in 1831, Benjamin asserted for example, with unlimited visits from his family, with his papers and instruments, and thus able to complete two books. "Only the government of the ex-prisoner of Ham would think of torturing a scholar as well as a republican." *Ibid.*, 2574.

[23] *Ibid.*, No. 141 (May 21, 1851), 1433, col. 3.

[24] *Le Moniteur universel*, No. 10 (January 10, 1852), 45.

[25] F.-V. Raspail, to his niece, Madame Ay, in an autogr. ms. letter dated September 8, 1849, belonging to M. Ay at Gigondas, (Vaucluse), communicated by Mademoiselle Simone Raspail.

authorities to the need of preventing further inflammatory literature from leaving Doullens.

The petty vexations that prison life often entails were soon overshadowed by tragedy. Earlier, in July 1848, Madame Raspail had shared her husband's food prepared in the kitchen of Vincennes prison. On the way home she was seized by nausea and cramps. When Raspail heard of this he was convinced that the symptoms indicated arsenic poisoning. She was continually weak and suffering after that, and in 1852, at Doullens, he detected new and even more frightening signs of impending disaster.

Your aunt [he wrote to his nephew Eugène on December 14, 1852] came to see me in this citadel two months ago with all the symptoms of approaching death. She wanted to continue climbing up to the fortress, despite her exhaustion; unfortunately she had tried, the day before, to hold back Emile's hunting dog which the police would otherwise have captured; this caused a tear in the left lung where there had been adhesions. . . . I was aghast to see in her face the havoc wrought. I asked permission for her to stay with me, so I could care for her day and night. Loyola was unrelenting. My poor patient was shown out into the awful weather; she could hardly drag herself away. . . . You can imagine if I slept that night; but, thank God!, I had frequent news of her state of health, and have succeeded in restoring her. She can now drive up to see me. . . . She endured all with resignation, and her convalescence is progressing rapidly.[26]

She died on March 8, 1853. "My chains were for a moment lengthened [Raspail wrote in an open letter to *La Presse*] so that I could witness her dying gasp and close her eyes, in the presence of three of her children." [27] He asked the newspaper to print his letter so that members of the family and friends might attend the funeral in Paris. Emile, on his way to visit his parents in Doullens, arrived one day too late. He wrote to a friend:

I promised to write to you when I left; but I did not think that I would have such news to impart. My unfortunate mother is dead. . . . I was told the awful truth a short distance from Amiens. How painful it is

[26] Autogr. ms. letter to Eugène Raspail, dated December 14, 1852, in the possession of M. Ay.

[27] *La Presse*, March 11, 1853.

not to have kissed her good-bye. I suffered horribly. . . . When I heard that my father had been allowed to close her eyes, my strength began to return and I completed my journey knowing hardly where I was or what I was saying. . . .

I found only cold death. . . . At least I shall have the painful comfort of accompanying her to her last resting place; we are leaving tomorrow for Paris. . . .[28]

Raspail was not allowed into the capital to bury his wife. The ceremony turned into a mass demonstration. Fifteen to twenty thousand persons, according to the *Journal des Débats,* followed the coffin to the Père Lachaise cemetery on Sunday, March 13. The more liberal *Presse* estimated the number of mourners at thirty thousand. Gabrielle Raspail, no doubt following her husband Xavier's impression, describes an imposing funeral, with more than a hundred thousand marchers.[29]

In accordance with the widower's request no speeches were pronounced at the grave. The high police official who was present could see for himself that "order reigned." [30]

One would have to search far in the annals of popular funerals [commented *La Presse*], to find a procession similar to the one we witnessed. . . . The noble woman died at her post, on the threshold, so to speak, of what had practically been her husband's only home since he entered the world of politics: a prison.

Abnegation, devotion, humility, these three words express her whole life.[31]

[28] Autogr. ms. letter from Emile Raspail to Mme. Testard at Busingy [where he was then employed], dated Doullens, March 9, 1853, in the possession of M. Jacques Raspail.

[29] G. Raspail, *La vie et l'oeuvre* . . . , 100.

[30] *Journal des Débats,* March 15, 1853.

But the Minister of Police, C. E. de Maupas (1818–1888), was worried enough by this show of popular sympathy to issue orders against similar occurrences in the future.

". . . the socialist party seems to seek new means of agitation . . . especially at the time of funerals. . . ." The government wishes to "prevent such profanation, where the crowd pretends to pay its respects to a corpse it does not even know, in order to stage a political demonstration." This circular to the prefects, dated March 15, 1853, is found in Fonds Raspail, Archives du Département de la Seine, LXXXVI.

[31] *La Presse,* March 14, 1853. It can only have been small if any comfort for Raspail to read that Orfila, ex-Dean of the Medical Faculty and Raspail's arch-enemy among doctors, died five days after Madame Raspail.

A marble monument on the family grave, executed by the well-known sculptor Antoine Etex (1808–1888), portrays a woman wrapped in a shroud, clinging to prison bars, followed by a forlorn young girl.[32]

Artist's sketch for Raspail's grave, showing Madame Raspail and her daughter Marie Apolline, outside a prison window   (Courtesy Hospice Raspail, Cachan, Seine)

"She suffered . . . with a stoicism worthy of antiquity."

F.-V. Raspail

On hearing of these tragic events, Napoleon III commuted the remainder of Raspail's sentence into two years of banishment.[33]

[32] Benjamin wrote to his brothers: "Nothing can be cut into the stone without the authorization of the Police Prefect." Raspail decided on all the details of the monument, including the flowers on the stone wreath. Fonds Raspail, Archives du Département de la Seine, LXXXVI.

Antoine Etex tells in his *Memoirs* that he was summoned to St. Cloud at that time, to call on the Emperor. Camille Raspail came to see him two days before that visit, expressing his father's worries that the police might interfere with the unveiling of his mother's tombstone. Should he mention the monument to the Emperor?, Etex asked. Camille gratefully assented. When he spoke of Madame Raspail's tombstone to Napoleon III, Etex relates, "the Emperor said: 'Oh yes, let's see your sketch.'—As I was explaining the drawing [Etex continues], which was lying quite close to him, he suddenly touched something hard, maybe my thick sketchbook. He jumped back three steps. . . . From that moment onward he was less friendly, less gay, and much less lively. . . . Never again did he pronounce my name nor mention this interview." A. Etex, *Les souvenirs d'un artiste* (Paris, 1877), 269–71.

[33] Napoleon's order was dated April 12, 1853. A letter from the district attorney at Doullens to the Minister of Justice, dated April 23, reads in part: "M. Raspail has expressed the desire to go to Brussels; he has received a passport for

Informed of the Emperor's decision, the prisoner protested: he did not wish to leave his country. Nevertheless, on the urging of his children, he traveled with Marie to Belgium. Benjamin, who had already lived there for one year, was eager to make his father welcome and comfortable. But Raspail's awesome reputation had preceded him: King Leopold I did not wish to admit the dangerous radical. Fortunately, the president of the Belgian Chamber of Deputies intervened in Raspail's favor. This was Viscount Charles Vilain XIIII,[34] an experienced diplomat, a Catholic and a con-

---

that city and has left this night for Arras . . ." Archives nationales, Series BB²¹, 566, dossier 5872, S 52.

The records of the ministry of justice show that two previous petitions for a pardon of Raspail's sentence had been rejected by the government, one, dated November 8, 1852, from a M. L. J. Dejaer, in Belgium (probably a friend of Benjamin's) "in the name of the venerated Emperor Napoleon I," the other originated with the Prefect of the Somme Department, on November 20, 1852. The prison director's report, appended to this petition, would have surprised Raspail. It reads: "His conduct is good, but his relations with the administration have always been difficult. He lives alone. He dislikes his comrades, and they do not like him. He is uncommunicative. He works, and waits patiently for the hour of his liberation. If he were to be pardoned by His Imperial Highness, since he has a large family (five children), there is every reason to believe that he would pursue his chemical work and would no longer engage in politics."

The attorney general, E. de Royer, however, was not as favorably disposed. He wrote: ". . . Raspail's part in the crime of May 15, 1848, was very serious and premeditated. . . . When the High Court of Justice limited the penalty to the legal minimum, it acted, I think, with extreme indulgence.

"The personality of the condemned, as revealed in the debates of the High Court, offers no guarantee of his sincerity. This man seeks to mask his violent thoughts with a false goodnaturedness. In court, he was eager to distort the most clearly established facts in order to provoke miserable incidents. It is difficult to believe that his chemical work would save him from renewed aberrations, since he has always abandoned his work without hesitation whenever politics seemed to offer some bait to his ambition. . . . True, his family is large, but, from the political point of view, it deserves little confidence or even interest. His eldest son, a representative in the Legislative Assembly, was among those . . . expelled . . . in January 1852. . . ."

And the Minister of Police, De Maupas, thought a release dangerous: "Like the attorney general, I do not believe that the time has come to be indulgent toward . . . Raspail. His political antecedents . . . would render an act of clemency dangerous and inopportune. Such a pardon, at the moment when the Empire will be inaugurated, might worry the well-intentioned citizens and awaken unwelcome hopes." Archives nationales, *ibid.*

³⁴ Charles-Ghislain-Guillaume, Viscount Vilain XIIII (1803–1878), belonged to a Belgian family tracing its ancestry back to the ninth century. Its odd-sounding name and the strange way its numeral is written seem to stem from

servative . . . who had been Raspail's student at the Institution Stadler in the 1820s. He brought the foreign rebel into the immunity of his home and prevailed upon his king to grant political asylum.[35] Raspail would stay in Belgium for nine years, much longer than his term of banishment. "I finally met M. Vilain XIIII," Benjamin wrote to his father ten years later; "when we began reminiscing, he was surprised to feel tears in his eyes. . . . His kind heart is unchanged. . . ." [36]

In 1856, three years after Raspail's arrival, Belgian hospitality toward all French political refugees was threatened by diplomatic pressure from France. French prestige had risen high, owing to the successful conclusion of the Crimean War, and the French Foreign Minister, Count Walewski, felt emboldened to demand, at a plenary meeting of the Congress of Paris, that Belgium restrict the freedom of speech of the French exiles, whose writings were said openly to preach "revolt and murder." [37] Walewski was, in fact, asking for a change in the Belgian constitution. "In Belgium, feeling ran high. National pride, coupled with an absolute cult of freedom, rebelled against Walewski's pretensions." [38] The Belgian Minister of Foreign Affairs, none other than Raspail's protector Count Vilain XIIII, undertook a quick trip to Paris to see Walewski and even Napoleon III. When publicly challenged in the Belgian Chamber on May 7, 1856, and asked whether the government intended to change the constitution, Vilain answered in terms that have remained famous in Belgian history: ". . . The Belgian government would answer 'Never!' This peremptory declaration caused a sensation and was enthusiastically applauded." [39]

---

an heraldic play on words, "Verdien en hoop" meaning both "Earn in hope" and "Fourteen in hops," indicating the money-crop from which the family derived its wealth.

[35] F. Van Kalken, *Biographie nationale . . . de Belgique* (Bruxelles, 1936–1938), XXVI, 734.

[36] Autogr. ms. letter from Benjamin to his father, dated May 4, 1863, in the possession of M. Jacques Raspail.

[37] These were the words of V.-F. Barrot (1806–1883), the French envoy in Brussels. F. Van Kalken, *Biographie nationale . . .* , 734.

[38] *Ibid.*, 735.

[39] *Ibid.*

And the French refugees remained safe from persecution. Count Vilain's biographer wrote:

The refugees and exiles considered the Minister of Foreign Affairs as their protector. They did not forget that Raspail, threatened with expulsion . . . had found an inviolable asylum in Viscount Vilain XIIII's home. Nor did the viscount hide his feelings of deep pity and respectful sympathy for the exiles who suffered from what he considered the greatest misfortune that could ever befall a man.

After becoming minister, M. Vilain XIIII managed to conciliate his sympathies with the duties of his high position. He explained his attitude to several of the refugees, asking them to inform their compatriots of his words. He told them frankly what his conduct toward them would be. He said that neither their names, nor their political antecedents before their entry into Belgium would ever harm them in the eyes of the government and he guaranteed that they would never be molested for deeds preceding their arrival in that country. But he declared that, if they committed acts in Belgium which would tend to interfere with the good relations which Belgium must maintain with foreign powers, he would act against them with the greatest firmness and vigor, and immediately expel them.[40]

During the nine years Raspail spent in Belgium, he seems to have led a peaceful and fairly contented life. Happiness was no longer possible, without his wife, and far from home. He first resided in the little town of Watermael-Boitsfort, which had about 4,000 inhabitants, and after four years moved, on May 12, 1857, to Stalle-sous-Uccle, a somewhat larger township.[41] In both cases he was lodged in the midst of fields, gardens, and pleasant woods, full of picturesque old castles and churches, and only four or five miles from Brussels.

As the biographer of the exiled colony of Frenchmen writes: "Silent, anxious to pass unnoticed, F.-V. Raspail had made a calm, solitary retreat for himself, first at Boitsfort, then at Uccle, far from the world and its noise. There, surrounded by his family, he devoted to scientific work the hours which politics could no longer

[40] Th. Juste, *Le vicomte Charles Vilain XIIII, ministre d'état, ancien membre du congrès national et ancien ministre des affaires étrangères* (Brussels, 1875), 26–27.

[41] Articles "Boitsfort" and "Uccle" in E. De Seyn, ed., *Dictionnaire historique et géographique des communes belges* (Turnhout, 1923), 2 vols.

Raspail's home in exile at Boitsfort, Belgium
(Courtesy Archives du Département de la Seine)
Signed "M.R.," doubtless sketched by Marie Apol-
line Raspail.

"In patria carcer, laurus in exilio."   *F.-V. Raspail*

claim." [42] Only Marie and Benjamin actually lived with him. The
sentences of exile punished only Benjamin and his father. It
is significant that Camille, Emile, and Xavier felt comfortable
enough in Napoleon III's France to pursue their careers at home.
Emile was a student at the Central School in Paris until 1856.
He then held various jobs to gain some practical experience, and
in 1858 opened the *Pharmacie complémentaire de la méthode*

[42] A. Saint-Ferréol, *Les proscrits français en Belgique ou la Belgique contemporaine vue à travers l'exil,* I, 328.

Raspail, 14, rue du Temple, in Paris. The correspondence between Benjamin and Emile is filled with details regarding the shape and color of bottles and labels, the prices of medicines and other pharmaceutical products, the cost of labor, publicity, and rent, the printing of books, pamphlets, covers, posters, illustrations—some of which they printed in Belgium—and, most serious, passages concerning the constant attacks and litigation regarding the illegal practice of pharmacy. Raspail was consulted about every detail, and was obeyed in everything by his sons. He wrote very few letters himself.

Camille had also remained in Paris. He gave up his job with the publisher Meilhac in 1852, having decided to study medicine. He graduated in 1856, and opened a dispensary, 11, rue Carnot (later called rue Bara). He also helped with the family printing shop which was transferred in 1857 from the rue Francs-Bourgeois St. Michel, near the Odéon, to 14, rue du Temple.

Xavier, born in 1840, was still a schoolboy at the Lycée Henri IV. These three sons came to visit their father in Belgium whenever time and money permitted. While the family was separated they exchanged almost daily letters, bearing witness to their concern about each other's health and comfort, and their common involvement in commercial, financial, legal, domestic, medical, and political issues concerning any one of them. They were a closely knit, dedicated clan—especially as long as they were apart.[43] In a way, Raspail's exile was thus only partial, since three of his sons lived in Paris and two of them engaged in work which was an extension of his own. They consulted him almost daily, printed his writings, sold his medications, practiced his method,[44] and also

---

[43] A rare note of discord was sounded when Benjamin wrote to his father on January 25, 1863: "Emile is very unhappy to be kept so isolated from the family. This is really due to his own weakness and kindheartedness. When I think about this dispersion, I admit that it is not what I dreamt of twelve years ago! Well, let us see in a while whether there is no remedy and whether everyone will not sooner or later understand that, especially in our position, unity makes strong." And, two days later to Emile: "You complain of your isolation; you could put an immediate end to it." Both autogr. ms. letters in the possession of M. Jacques Raspail.

[44] A case in point was a variety of orthopedic braces and other apparatus, some even using electric current, designed for therapeutic purposes, devised by Raspail *père,* drawn by Benjamin, advertised by Camille, and sold by Emile. See

sent him the money to finance his exile, making it much more pleasant than that of most members of the large colony of French political refugees.[45]

This group, about eight hundred strong, had all the characteristics of refugee colonies so sadly familiar in the agitated twentieth century. The exiles had little in common except their poverty and their scorn for the illegal, inhumane methods by which Louis Napoleon Bonaparte had seized power. They had chosen Belgium because it was French-speaking and close to home. Actually England and Switzerland were more liberal than Belgium in their attitude toward refugees. "In England these men encountered complete freedom and general indifference," writes Saint-Ferréol, "[Switzerland] . . . cordially welcomed citizens who . . . had sought a free country where they could live." [46] Jean-Louis Greppo[47] confirmed this view[48] when he wrote to Benjamin Raspail from England on April 30, 1852:

The number of exiles is growing daily. . . . Here, as in Brussels, there are various factions which get along more or less well. . . . First there are the rich, who do not associate with the lower classes, then the different sects, each with its private cult. We fight, but we tolerate each other—that's the state of mind in London. . . .[49]

Belgium, it seems, was harboring the "bourgeois" refugees, both Orleanist and republican, because

the workers, the peasants, those refugees who had no recommendation, and neither parents nor friends in Belgium, or arrived without papers

---

C. Raspail, *Notice théorique et pratique sur les appareils orthopédiques de la méthode Raspail* (Paris, 1862).

[45] The above information results from the perusal of hundreds of letters to and from Benjamin, Camille, Emile and some of Xavier's, all in the possession of M. Jacques Raspail.

[46] A. Saint-Ferréol, *Les proscrits français en Belgique* . . . , I, 35.

[47] Jean-Louis Greppo (1810–1888) was a weaver from Lyons and an ardent republican active in the 1830, 1832, and 1834 political uprisings. He served in the Constituent and Legislative Assemblies under the Second Republic, was exiled in 1852 when he fled to Belgium, then to England. He returned home after the 1859 amnesty and plunged once again into political activity.

[48] See also A. Zavaès "Les proscrits français en 1848 et 1851 à Londres," *La révolution de 1848*, XX (March 1923–Feb. 1924), 343–75; and XXI (March 1924–Feb. 1925), 94–114.

[49] Autogr. ms. letter, Fonds Raspail, Archives du Département de la Seine, LXXXVI.

legalized by the Belgian embassy in Paris, who could not prove that they had money enough to live on without working, or who declared their intention of exercising their profession, were expelled without pity. They were the majority. . . . This is why Belgium became the great highway into exile even more than a major center for exiled Frenchmen.[50]

Tolerated rather than welcome,[51] the exiles had to register every week at police headquarters, and could not leave their residences without permission.[52]

The Belgian government [wrote a historian], was forced, for family reasons, to be correct toward its unwanted guests of the Orleanist party. It took its revenge against the *Reds*. . . .

Even the climate made them unwelcome; the low, grey sky, the drizzling, monotonous rains, the sharp north wind, caused sore throats, bronchitis, and consumption in old men, children, and young girls. Soon some died.[53]

The exiles had no leaders, although some deference was paid to its two senior members, Edgar Quinet (1803–1875), the distinguished historian and essayist, and Etienne Arago (1802–1892), the well-known playwright and director of the Vaudeville in Paris, whose reputations were securely established in France. Others in the group would become famous later, either as members of republican legislatures or as political commentators and essayists. Some would combine the two careers—for example Paul Challemel-Lacour (1827–1896), the philosopher who served as deputy, senator, ambassador, and foreign minister under the Third Republic, and Emile Deschanel (1819–1904), a prolific historian and writer,

[50] A. Saint-Ferréol, *Les proscrits français en Belgique* . . . , I, 69.

[51] "We knew very few Belgians; after the amnesty they grew more hospitable." Madame Edgar Quinet, *Edgar Quinet depuis l'exil* (Paris, 1889), 46.

[52] A medical certificate issued to Benjamin in March, 1852, attested that he was too unwell to be removed from Brussels "in order to be interned in a less salubrious part of Belgium. This might expose him to depression because he would be isolated from his fellow exiles." Fonds Raspail, Archives du Département de la Seine, LXXXVI.

After a serious sickness, Edgar Quinet was allowed a rest cure at Blankenberghe, but only after deliberation in the Belgian Council of Ministers. A. Valès, *Edgar Quinet, sa vie et son oeuvre* (Ligugé, 1936), 203.

[53] *Ibid.*, 203 and 212.

professor of modern literature at the Collège de France from 1881, deputy and senator in the 1870s and 1880s.

A convenient roster of the talents represented in the group is afforded by their projected "Collège de France à l'éŧanger." With Victor Hugo as rector and Edgar Quinet as dean, it was to offer tuition in the military arts (General Juchault de Lamoricière), medicine (F.-V. Raspail), the theatre (Etienne Arago), eloquence (N. F. A. Madier de Montjau), law (Marc Dufraisse), literature (Emile Deschanel), and philosophy (Paul Challemel-Lacour).[54] While this ambitious project never materialized, some French exiles did hold teaching posts in Belgium or at least lectured to the general public.[55] In fact, it is claimed that they created a new "genre," the political conference.

The conference, this child of exile, was to grow fast, and soon travel all over the world. It was applauded from the moment of its birth by

[54] E. Krakowski, *La naissance de la troisième république: Challemel-Lacour, le philosophe et l'homme d'état* (Paris, 1932), 118–19.

[55] Désiré Bancel (1823–1871) taught at the Université libre at Brussels. Emile Deschanel lectured to the public in the Belgian capital.

Head by Antoine Etex (Plaster)   (Courtesy Musée Carnavalet, Paris) Photo Bulloz

the best known Belgian political and literary men and by most exiles from many countries living in Brussels. Its godfathers had been Victor Hugo, Edgar Quinet, David d'Angers, Michel de Bourges, and Alexandre Dumas.[56]

Quinet's biographer adds that these conferences "proved that the exiles' eloquence matched their convictions. In these monarchist strongholds where they were at first received with misgivings, almost with horror, they showed, by their example, how much the authors of the coup d'état had slandered them by depicting them as men prone to violence."[57] Many exiles wrote books, on history, literature, philosophy, and politics.[58]

So did Raspail, whose work was mainly concerned with questions of health.[59] The reader will easily recognize three Raspaillian variations in the books he completed in exile. The *Health Annual* was a continuation of the manual issued almost every year since 1845. The third, revised, and expanded edition of the *Natural History of Health* proved laborious, but was completed in 1860. And the *Appeal* represents an effort to awaken the social conscience of some industrialists. The *Review* and the *New Studies* were two more compendia, filled with a great variety of scientific observations, some biographical sketches (among them a notable one of Jean-

[56] A. Saint-Ferréol, *Les proscrits français en Belgique* . . . , I, 193–94.

[57] A. Valès, *Edgar Quinet* . . . , 210.

[58] A complete list of their writings would be long indeed. Some representative books are:

Etienne Arago, *Une voix de l'exil* (Geneva, 1860)

F. D. Bancel, *Histoire des révolutions de l'esprit français* (Paris, 1878)

V. Borie, *Travaux des champs* (Paris, 1857)

Lt. Colonel J. B. A. Charras, *Histoire de la campagne de 1815* (Brussels, 1857)

M. Dufraisse, *Le 2 décembre devant le code pénal* (Madrid, 1853)

P. Duprat, *Les révolutions* (Paris, 1869)

P. Joigneaux, *Dictionnaire d'agriculture pratique* (Paris, 1855)

E. Quinet, *Livre de l'exilé* (Paris, 1875).

[59] F.-V. Raspail, *Appel urgent au concours des hommes éclairés de toutes les professions contre les empoisonnements industriels* (Paris, 1863).

F.-V. Raspail, *Manuel-annuaire de la santé,* published every year from 1854 to 1864.

F.-V. Raspail, *Nouvelles études scientifiques et philologiques* (Paris, 1864).

F.-V. Raspail, *Revue complémentaire des sciences appliquées à la médecine et pharmacie, à l'agriculture, aux arts et à l'industrie* (Paris, 1854–1860), 6 vols.

Paul Marat), and reminiscences with which prison and exile forced him to fill his time.

My father really boasts an iron constitution [Benjamin wrote somewhat enviously to his aunt, Madame Camille Bellier, in 1858], he is thus able to accomplish a herculean amount of labor. Apart from his daily studies, he was for a while able to work on the *Manual* for 1858, the *Complementary Review,* and the third edition of the *Natural History.* . . ." [60]

Restless and ingenious even at sixty, Raspail soon acquired a new reading public and clientèle: he decided to cure animals since men were, for the moment, almost entirely beyond his reach. The many printings and translations of his *Farmer as Veterinary* attest to his success in this new undertaking.[61]

Raspail knew that the Belgian physicians would never have forgiven him for restoring their patients' health, without a Belgian diploma, and that the Jesuits, always the enemies of researchers and thinkers, were waiting for a favorable occasion to have him expelled. Therefore he would see only persons whom he trusted entirely and would grant consultations only to foreigners who came to see him with a valid passport.[62]

During these nine years of exile, Raspail's writings kept his name before the French public: ". . . his *Health Annual,* his *Complementary Review* were distributed throughout France where, despite the author's name, each new book arrived without being seized at the border, since it contained only pure science." [63] Letters continued to reach him from all over the world (as they did until the end of his life), although he replied rarely,

[60] Fonds Raspail, Archives du Département de la Seine, LXXXVI.

[61] F.-V. Raspail, *Le fermier vétérinaire ou méthode aussi économique que facile de préserver et de guérir les animaux domestiques et même les végétaux cultivés du plus grand nombre de leurs maladies* (Paris, 1854). This book was reprinted in 1855, 1856, 1858, 1862, 1864, 1869, 1871, 1873, and 1882. It was translated into Italian (Turin, 1856), Spanish (Lima, 1856), (Madrid, 1896), and German (Bern, 1885).

[62] A. Saint-Ferréol, *Les proscrits français en Belgique* . . . , I, 328.

[63] *Ibid.,* I, 328.

and then only to persons he knew.[64] At times someone would write to communicate scientific information; at other times someone would ask for permission to practice or propagate the "Raspail method," or simply thank its originator for having devised useful remedies.[65]

In this manner, throughout the 1850s and early 1860s, Raspail maintained his place as a "party leader."

[These party leaders gave rise to] what may be called a "popular legend" which, varying with place and shade of doctrine, imagined these leaders according to newspaper reports, and to those lithographed portraits which all democrats collected . . . [and which] though hardly flattering, . . . were nevertheless welcomed, carefully framed and given the place of honor in proletarian dwellings. . . .

The workers saw in Raspail the people's friend and the healer of all their ills. In the wine-growing regions of central France they still call *"vin Raspail"* the free-flowing light, inexpensive wine which was drunk after the February Revolution at fraternal banquets and which was poured on liberty trees.[66]

Meanwhile Raspail maintained a pleasant relationship with his neighbors at Boitsfort and Uccle. He tells how the villagers of Boitsfort came to serenade him before his departure and offer him a laurel tree, which he planted at his new abode in a specially carved stone vase engraved with the words: *"In patria carcer, laurus in exilio."* [67] How active a social life he led, we can only surmise, although several years later he reminisced: "Those were the ten best years of my life. Numerous were my visitors and the distinctions I received." [68] His daughter-in-law alludes to many

[64] "My father [Benjamin wrote on September 4, 1867], has let it be known for years that he was no longer replying to letters." Fonds Raspail, Archives du Département de la Seine, LXXXVI.

[65] See, e.g., letters from M. Bisson, Henderson City, Minnesota, about a very large tick, unknown in Europe; from Benjamin King, M.D., of 151 Great Portland Street, London, on September 15, 1867; and from Patterson, New Jersey, dated April 3, 1876, thanking for many years of successful use of Raspail medicines. Fonds Raspail, Archives du Département de la Seine, vols. II, VIII, XVII, respectively.

[66] A. Saint-Ferréol, *Les proscrits français en Belgique* . . . , I, 325–26.

[67] G. Raspail, *La vie et l'oeuvre* . . . , 102–6.

[68] X. Raspail, *Procès de l'almanach Raspail* . . . , 130.

connections with highly placed and wealthy Belgians, but her wish is the most likely source of these facts.[69]

One more aspect of Raspail's Belgian exile deserves mention and invites speculation: when he returned home in 1862, he brought a library of 2,500 books and a collection of paintings which included a Van Dyck, a Rubens, and three Breughels, to mention the most striking.[70] He was obviously well off, but what could be the source of this affluence? Two explanations seem possible, and perhaps both of them apply. First, Emile Raspail, now a chemical engineer, had patented the camphorated medicines and the liqueur, and was producing them most profitably at Arcueil. Quite likely Raspail claimed a share of Emile's earnings, although in later years the business became Emile's entirely. Second, Benjamin may have reached affluence in 1863 through matrimony. At any rate, from the 1860s on, Raspail's income must have been of bourgeois proportions.

[69] Gabrielle Raspail wrote: "Familiar faces he enjoyed seeing at his table were: Count Vilain XIIII, President of the Chamber, Charles de Brouckere, senator, Minister of the Interior, and Burgomaster of Brussels, General Chazal, Minister of War, the Marnix family whose head, Count de Marnix, was a senator and minister, Count and Countess de Marneffe, the great banker Oppenheim and his family, M. Pesez, one of the biggest silk merchants in Brussels, an enlightened art connoisseur and the owner of a beautiful collection of paintings, finally Dr. de Preter, a gentle and philosophic humanitarian who was Raspail's best and most devoted friend." *La vie et l'oeuvre* . . . , 106.

[70] Benjamin had collected these paintings and paid for them with "family funds." He was quite a successful artist himself, having exhibited oil paintings —mostly still lives—at Mons, Ostende, Antwerp, The Hague, Malines, Ghent, and Courtrais. He had tracked down the paintings he acquired "by rummaging in second-hand shops, flea markets, and castle attics. . . . By retouching and remounting old paintings that he had found buried under dust . . . he had managed to compose an amateur gallery that included several masterpieces." A. Saint-Ferréol, *Les proscrits français en Belgique* . . . , I, 258. Before leaving Belgium, he sold a large part of the collection.

[I "discovered" these paintings in a hanger at Cachan in 1957. They had been left by Benjamin to the Seine Department. An attempt to sell them was blocked by the timely intervention of Mademoiselle Simone Raspail. They are still in the hands of the Seine Department which replied to an inquiry, in June 4, 1965, that "litigation has been going on for years between the representatives of the Raspail family and the Seine Department with regard to these paintings. They are now in the safeguard of a ministerial officer in a room where they cannot be seen."]

Personal wealth had never been a preoccupation with Raspail,[71] and when he returned home, at seventy, he was not likely to deviate from the proud poverty of a lifetime. Yet, although his wants were few, he appreciated money and valuable possessions as did his sons. All four were now adults, and their father was aging. Naturally the family's finances were increasingly managed by the younger men. Thus Raspail, who had no intention of resigning as head of the family, found himself drawn into the realistic world of industry, investments, and banking. There is even some indication that his personal reputation may have suffered because of the money-mindedness of some members of his family.[72]

Some insight into Raspail's financial affairs is afforded by his will, first written in 1867.[73] It reveals him as the owner of several houses and fields at Cachan, an apartment house in Paris (rue Carnot), 175,000 francs in mortgages, at least 40,000 francs in cash, an

[71] Benjamin had written to Camille and Emile on October 9, 1857, shortly after the move from Boitsfort to Uccle: "Because of his work, our Father has never been able to worry about our expenses. The other night, when we discussed our budget, he seemed very surprised at the cost of our move, and of the presents we have had to offer this year." Autogr. ms. letter, in the possession of M. Jacques Raspail.

A little notebook in which Raspail recorded his expenses seems to indicate that he spent a good deal on books and equipment. It also shows that maids and gardeners never lasted very long. Fonds Raspail, Archives du Département de la Seine, XL.

[72] The complaints of Gustave Lefrançais (1826–1901) may not be trustworthy because he was an embittered revolutionary, prone to denouncing capitalism in any guise. Yet, since he keeps referring to "what everyone expects of the Raspails," and "what everyone says of them," the remarks seem worth quoting.

In 1856, Lefrançais rented an apartment in the house where Camille had his dispensary. The building belonged to Raspail, then in exile. Unable to pay the rent, Lefrançais was threatened with eviction. The intercession of a socialist friend proved of no avail.

"The Raspails never give away anything . . . on principle," wrote the indignant lodger.

"No one would have the right to object to their conduct, were it not for all their talk about their devotion to the people and to science, and for the presence of their father's bronze bust, which reigns over the dispensary—crowned with thorns. Maybe it's a camphor branch. . . ." G. Lefrançais, *Souvenirs d'un révolutionnaire* (Bruxelles, n.d.), 233.

"This whole brood of 'Friends of the people' should be called 'Rapacious' not 'Raspail.' *Ibid.,* 252.

[73] F.-V. Raspail, *Mes dernières volontés,* autogr. ms. No. 2405, Folios 557–61, Bibliothèque Inguimbertine, Carpentras, Vaucluse.

annual income from his books, a sizable library, and collections of paintings, fossils, drugs, and scientific instruments. The will also sheds light on Raspail's feelings toward his children. Benjamin, the eldest son, his father's colleague in the National Assembly and companion in Belgium, was specially mentioned in the will in connection with the paintings and the family publishing house. The picture gallery was to be Benjamin's special concern; the will empowered him to sell it, but one-third of the proceeds would have to go to his siblings. In addition, since Benjamin had served as head of the Maison d'édition Raspail, 14, rue du Temple, since his return to Paris in May, 1863, with his Belgian bride,[74] he was to be paid retroactively a salary of 6,000 francs per annum.[75]

The "Etablissements Raspail" at Arcueil belonged entirely to Emile. No special gifts are recorded for him in the will or its codicils. Raspail seems to have felt that Emile, thoroughly bourgeois, respectable, and wealthy, could fend for himself. Hence the following paragraph: ". . . if Emile's fortune should be four times as big as his part of the inheritance, he shall only take one quarter of his share, in recognition of the fact that I turned over to him my part of the profits derived from the commercial enterprise for which he used my name and which I have supervised daily." [76] In a codicil of September 1877, Raspail returned to this theme, thus indicating that he feared trouble between the four young Raspail households over money matters. The codicil reads in part: ". . . I do hope that Emile will share my part [of his fortune] with his three brothers . . ." [77] And, in a postscript: "After my death, the houses at Cachan and rue Carnot belong to my three

[74] He took over from Camille at that time, thus permitting the doctor to devote more time to his patients. See *supra*, p. 146 n. 35 and p. 242.

[75] Benjamin continued to pursue his father's politics in the Chamber where he served until 1889. At his death he left the house at Cachan to the Seine Department, on condition that it be turned into an old people's home. That is the present purpose of the Hospice Raspail at Cachan. He also left a million and a half francs to French workers' cooperatives, with the stipulation that the money be used to make loans at low interest rates. See D. W. Brogan, *France under the Republic* (New York, 1940), 292. His surviving brother Xavier was furious not to have inherited more. See autogr. ms. letter from Xavier to Julien Raspail, dated 28 September 1899, in the possession of M. Jacques Raspail.

[76] F.-V. Raspail, *Mes dernières volontés*, autogr. ms. No. 2405, Folio 559, Bibliothèque Inguimbertine, Carpentras, Vaucluse.

[77] *Ibid.*, Folio 560.

sons Benjamin, Camille, and Xavier. Emile owns enough and should not ask for a share in this real estate." [78] (Emile's signature is conspicuously absent from this document.)

No special mention is made of Camille and Xavier in the will. Marie Apolline, on the other hand, was the object of loving provisions.

My daughter Marie Apolline Raspail [he wrote in 1867], has since her childhood served her father with a sublime and disinterested devotion rare in our history. In school she would suffer rather than disavow her father's convictions. She has followed me wherever the winds of persecution have thrown me—into prison, exile, solitude. Everywhere she has been my sweet and pure consolation.[79]

Marie Apolline was to receive all the silver, linen, and household equipment at Cachan, as well as 25,000 francs of remuneration, before the inheritance was divided up. He had also saved for her, he wrote, a fee of 2,000 francs received in 1845 from his old friend Suzanne de Bréauté. Marie was to be paid 5% annual interest on this gift, retroactively from 1845. Lastly, she was to be the guardian of a "box containing the materials for my memoirs." [80]

While the detailed arrangements in this will were worked out after Raspail's return to France, the feelings that inspired them gradually asserted themselves during his nine years' exile in Belgium. Without Benjamin and Marie, this long drawn-out stay abroad would have been unbearable. He was deeply grateful to them. Once the amnesty of 1859 had been proclaimed, he felt the attraction of France more and more strongly. He had prolonged his stay seven years beyond the penalty imposed by the High Court of Bourges. Doubtless he had judged the political climate in Paris too unfavorable. At last, on May 27, 1862, he returned home.

Camille, who was at Uccle at the time, informed Emile of their father's impending return and asked him to meet Raspail and Marie at the railroad station with a cab and take them straight to Cachan. He in turn would take the baggage to his home in Paris and bring it the next day. ". . . in this manner you can arrive without being seen by anyone." [81] Raspail's hasty departure from

---

[78] *Ibid.,* Folio 561.   [79] *Ibid.,* Folio 558.   [80] *Ibid.*

[81] Autogr. ms. letter, dated May 26, 1862, in the possession of M. Jacques Raspail.

Belgium was occasioned by an indisposition he blamed on impure (poisoned?) camphor. Benjamin was left behind, and for a whole year labored grudgingly, packing and shipping cases of books, seeing the 1863 *Annual* through the press, and saying goodbye to friends and protectors. In his haste Raspail had not even paid a visit to Viscount Vilain XIIII before he left. Benjamin wrote to Camille:

Our dear Father would do well to write immediately to M. Vilain XIIII who came four days ago, asked for me as well, but I was not home. When [the maid] told him that our Father was leaving the country, was, in fact, gone, he seemed dumbfounded. Oh, he said, that's impossible, he is gone and did not write to me? He left a magnificent volume of portraits from his father's library, as a present for our Father.

I shall pay him a visit very soon; I could then bring him the letter.[82]

Three weeks later Raspail had not yet written.

Upon Raspail's return, he found France in a political frame of mind much more congenial to his views than when he had left.[83] Hostility to the Empire was growing (although it was not until 1868 that newspapers were allowed to print the attacks of opposition leaders). New antagonists had joined the socialists, republicans, Orléanists, and legitimists who had opposed the Empire from the start. In addition, the Emperor's Italian policy had alienated many Catholics who feared a curtailment of the pope's temporal power. In the elections of 1869, votes for the government's official candidates declined sharply. Even among Napoleon's friends many had come to doubt and criticize.

But Napoleon's foes were not united—not even his opponents on the Left. Raspail, for example, competed for election to the Legislative Body in 1869 against two other critics of the Emperor, Louis-Antoine Garnier-Pagès (1803–1878) and Jules Favre (1809–1880), both of whom had served in the imperial legislature.[84]

---

[82] Autogr. ms. letter, dated March 5, 1863, in the possession of M. Jacques Raspail.

[83] See F.-V. Raspail, *Appel urgent . . .* , 8.

[84] In Paris, in the 5th voting district, Garnier-Pagès won on May 22, with 19,500 votes to Raspail's 14,500. But in Lyons, Raspail beat Favre by a margin of 10,000 votes. See infra, 257.

Raspail's home at Cachan, Seine   (Courtesy Hospice Raspail)

Raspail won in Lyons,[85] together with Désiré Bancel, his companion in Belgian exile.[86] He wrote that when he visited Lyons, "Men, women, and children threw themselves into my arms and covered me with flowers. I told them, like Voltaire: 'Do you want

[85] His numerous publications and his camphorated medicines had kept his name alive among the working class. Still, now and then, merchants had been condemned for selling pictures of Raspail, on posters, kerchiefs, or pamphlets. See the condemnation of Mathias Meyer of Courbevoie (Seine) for selling kerchiefs picturing heroes of "The Mountain" on April 11, 1853. Archives nationales, Series BB[21], 4538, S 53.

[86] See G. Duveau, Raspail, 59. See also "Département du Rhône; Député au corps législatif élu le 24 mai 1869," Archives nationales, Series C 1372, document No. 224, where he called himself a "physician" by profession for the first time in an official document. Usually he had put down "writer" or "chemist."

Raspail at the age of sixty-eight. Photograph taken by his son Emile (Courtesy Archives du Département de la Seine)

me to die of happiness?'—'You are our father,' they replied; 'our children learn your name as soon as they can talk.' " [87] An admiring critic confirmed that on this occasion "the whole city turned out to welcome him, unhitch the horses from his carriage and cover him with flowers and acclamations, in touching expression of a gratitude which still lasts [1891] and is far from dying." [88]

Lyons was on the far Left in the French political spectrum under the Liberal Empire, and Raspail was not necessarily in agreement with his constituents on all issues. His exact place within the opposition can be best defined by his votes and actions in the two subsequent years. Although highly critical of the Empire, he nevertheless consented to take the loyalty oath in order to assume office

[87] Fonds Raspail, Archives du Département de la Seine, LXXXVI.
[88] E. Spuller, "Raspail," in *Figures disparues: portraits contemporains politiques et littéraires* (Paris, 1891), 3 vols., II, 61.

—a gesture that more intransigent men, his former comrade Louis-Charles Delescluze,[89] for example, refused. But once elected, he asked for abolition of the oath.[90]

Raspail was assisted in the Chamber by Henri Rochefort, the future Boulangist and anti-Dreyfusard [91] about whom Raspail wrote to his constituents: ". . . my young friend, citizen Rochefort, continues to assist me with his acute mind, and his highly articulate support. I think that, despite the resistance of the majority in such a chamber, we two will be able significantly to further human progress." [92] On the floor of the Chamber Raspail objected to the cost of the imperial régime[93] and to its foreign expeditions, including the war with Prussia against which he cast his vote. Once that war was declared, however, the patriot within him prevailed: he urged that all valid Frenchmen, including seminarists, should be

[89] Louis-Charles Delescluze (1809–1871) was a Jacobin journalist who had fought in 1830 and joined several secret societies under the July Monarchy. Repeatedly arrested and exiled for subversive newspaper articles, he spent long years in Belgium, England, and Cayenne. In 1870 he was elected to the National Assembly and subsequently to the Commune. He helped lead the military resistance of Paris against Versailles and when, on May 25, 1871, the situation appeared hopeless, he deliberately sought death on the barricades.

[90] Jan. 10, 1870. See *France, Annales . . . du corps législatif,* 1870 (I, 13) in *France, Annales du sénat et du corps législatif,* 1869–1870. See also Archives nationales, Series C 1147, document No. 293.

[91] Victor-Henri, Marquis de Rochefort-Luçay (1830–1913), was a radical pamphleteer and politician. He was editor of the *Figaro* (1863) and founded two anti-imperial journals, *La Lanterne* (1868) and *La Marseillaise* (1869). He supported the Commune and was exiled to New Caledonia from where he escaped and returned to France after the general amnesty of 1880. He then started the *Intransigeant,* supported General Boulanger, and fought actively against Dreyfus.

[92] Fonds Raspail, Archives du Département de la Seine, LXXXVII.

[93] He demanded an investigation of Baron Haussmann's personal fortune, asking how one could save millions from a salary of 50,000 francs. (*France. Annales . . . du corps législatif,* 1870, I, 13.) When the national budget was being discussed, Raspail demanded drastic economies: ministers' salaries should be cut by two thirds; expense accounts for official entertainment should be abolished; a ceiling of twenty thousand francs should be put on all government salaries; cumulation of offices should be forbidden. *Ibid.,* July 8, 1870 (V, 529).

He was, at the same time, generous in supporting republican and lay causes, e.g. when he sent a check for 5,000 francs to the Society for Free and Lay Teaching, in April 1869, to support the founding and expenses of a school. "These are my father's economies from his deputy's salary," wrote Benjamin. Fonds Raspail, Archives du Département de la Seine, LXXXVI.

5ᵉ Circonscription électorale de la Seine

CANDIDATURE DE LA DÉMOCRATIE RADICALE

F.-V. RASPAIL

Mes chers Concitoyens,

Merci du nombre imposant de suffrages que vous m'avez accordés, malgré l'hostilité et la conspiration du silence de presque toute la presse.

La lutte va recommencer.

On vous dit aujourd'hui : le citoyen Raspail est nommé à Lyon, pourquoi n'abandonne-t-il pas sa candidature à Paris?

Non, il ne l'abandonne pas,

Parce que la Démocratie radicale triomphante à Lyon, à Paris dans plusieurs circonscriptions, à Marseille, à Saint-Étienne, etc., ne doit pas être vaincue dans cette 5ᵉ circonscription qui a été son principal berceau en **1848**.

Citoyens, vous avez à juger entre M. Garnier-Pagès, l'orléaniste qui a joué un si triste rôle surtout pendant les fratricides journées de juin **1848**, et F.-V. Raspail, le démocrate radical.

Choisissez !

Si votre choix porte sur M. Garnier-Pagès, c'est la démocratie que vous reniez, et, dès ce moment, vous abandonnez votre cause.

En me nommant, au contraire, vous réservez, après l'option, l'entrée au Corps législatif d'un démocrate digne de vos suffrages.

F.-V. RASPAIL.

Poster used during Raspail's candidacy for the Legislative Body, 1869 (Courtesy Archives du Département de la Seine)

drafted.[94] Remembering his socialist convictions, he asked the

[94] *France. Annales . . . du corps législatif . . .*, August 10 and 18, 1870 (VII, 40 and 152). This demand seems logical, given his anti-Catholic convictions. It gains deeper personal meaning in the light of the fact that Raspail himself had once escaped the draft, being a seminarist—a circumstance which he possibly later regretted.

legislature for a moratorium on workers' rents.[95] He also defended the International Workingmen's Association's right to meet[96]—although he did not join it: his old-fashioned patriotism precluded a militant internationalist attitude. He welcomed Napoleon III's fall.[97] Although not present at the Hôtel de Ville on September 4, he supported the Government of National Defense, while at the same time sympathizing with its socialist critics. He was proud that, in the war with Prussia, Camille and Xavier served in the army as medical men, and Emile as an engineer. Raspail himself spent the winter of 1870–1871 in Paris, sharing the Parisians' privations and suffering. He was still, at seventy-five, capable of stoic firmness. He took no part in the Commune, which he condemned for its fratricidal bloodshed, but his sympathies were definitely with Paris, against Versailles.

In his official life, Raspail became a symbol of the romantic republicanism of bygone days.[98] His voice, like those of Victor Hugo and Louis Blanc, was charged with the authority but muted by the remoteness of the past. Ignoring the petty realities of party politics, he reminded the deputies of promises that a republican government must fulfill. None of Raspail's major objectives were reached in his lifetime, although most of them became law within two generations after his death. His efforts were fruitless in some areas, while in others he was instrumental in promoting reform. Many of his arguments as a legislator were based on his belief in the citizen's right to good health. They will be discussed in the context of his general ideas on public health and social medicine.[99] His convictions also involved him in many political incidents dur-

[95] *Ibid.*, August 14, 1870 (117). See also Archives nationales, Series C 1163, document No. 57.

[96] *France. Annales . . . du corps législatif . . .* , V, 479–82.

[97] *Ibid.*, September 4, 1870 (VII, 365). Having been absent from the Legislative Body when the Empire was declared defunct, he made a point of asking that his name be added to the list of deputies who welcomed the imperial régime's demise.

[98] When André Billy described Ste.-Beuve's funeral in Paris in 1869, he wrote: "The white mane of the elder Dumas could be spotted next to George Sand who was leaning on the arm of Dumas *fils*. . . . Flaubert . . . Taine. The numerous bystanders, two deep, respectfully doffed their hats before these famous men, especially before the aged Raspail." A. Billy, *Sainte-Beuve . . .* , II, 362.

[99] See *infra*, chapter X.

Portrait of Raspail at the age of eighty, by Mirallès (Courtesy Musée Carnavalet, Paris) Photo Bulloz

ing the last ten years of his life—incidents occasioned by his partisan pronouncements, his writings, and his family.

Raspail's role in the legislature was thus predetermined by his lifelong convictions, his personality, and his advanced age. Soon he was embroiled in public controversy. Shortly after the overwhelming victory for Napoleon III in the plebiscite of May 8, 1870, three medical students, about to graduate from the Ecole de santé militaire at Strasbourg, were dismissed for having voted "no." "Is there no political freedom?" Raspail demanded of the Minister of War, Marshal Le Boeuf.[100] He obtained little satisfaction. Soon he was reminiscing before the Legislative Body:

Yes, I have experienced unhappiness: that is how I learned to sympathize with the unfortunate. I am the first to feel the suffering I observe, and I have never inflicted pain on anyone. If I had remained a military man, which I was for a short while, I would never have punished anyone . . . ; it is hideous to inflict pain. Those who suffer point an accusing finger at their tormentors. . . . [101]

But the members of the legislature were hardly in the mood for the reminiscences of an octogenarian rebel. Jeers and laughter drowned out the feeble voice with its unmistakable Provençal accent.

Less than ever was Raspail able to dissociate his own life experience from public issues. This was evident when the scandalous murder of Victor Noir by Prince Pierre Bonaparte shocked the nation and aroused the legislature. The prince, summoned to fight a duel, had turned on his opponent's second and shot him dead. The issue before the Legislative Body was the nature of the court that should try the prince. A criminal court, with a jury, seemed to guarantee a fair trial far better than a high court of justice, which was preferred by the government. Raspail rose to speak. Remembering his own trial before the High Court of Bourges, he argued that such an extraordinary tribunal would never be impartial. It would acquit a prince just as surely as it had condemned

---

[100] "Demande d'interpellation de M. Raspail," Archives nationales, Series C 1136, document No. 41.
[101] *Annales . . . du corps législatif,* IV, 367.

a republican. His premonitions were justified. The high court acquitted Pierre Bonaparte of murder.[102] Raspail firmly believed that a republican régime would have dealt more justly with this incident. Yet his faith in the Third Republic was soon to be severely tested. The possibility of an undemocratic republic was still inconceivable for him. Unfortunately he was to feel its fist, as he had in 1848.

Raspail's major collision with the government of the Third Republic concerned his *Sailor's and Farmer's Almanac and Meteorologic Calendar,* published annually after 1865.[103] At first the publication was filled mainly with meteorology and astronomy, his pastimes in prison.[104] Eventually, however, its usefulness for political propaganda occurred to Raspail. In 1869, once censorship was lifted, he began to add, in chronological order, "Notes on famous men and events." On December 29, 1873, the police (now republican) confiscated the manuscript of the 1874 *Almanac,* asserting that the booklet would "disturb the peace and excite the citizens to hate and despise each other." [105] At the trial on February 12, 1874, the so-called "government of moral order" was more specific: Raspail had "attacked the army and its leaders," had praised the Commune and especially Delescluze, and had condoned the murder, by the Communards, of Generals Thomas and Lecomte on March 19, 1871. Furthermore, it was asserted, Raspail had repeatedly attacked the Jesuits. The prosecutor recalled that

[102] *Ibid.,* Jan. 11, 1870 (I, 28).

[103] Raspail's writings during this final epoch of his life comprise (1) one major work on social reform; (2) a variety of minor publications, two of them annual, with the characteristic mixture of science, medicine, and politics.

(1) *Réformes sociales* (Paris, 1872); [discussed in Chapter X].

(2) Annual publications: *Manuel-annuaire de la santé,* published every year, 1864–1878; *Prévision du temps; Almanach et calendrier météorologique, suivi d'un traité succinct sur l'art de prognostiquer le temps avec une certaine probabilité, à l'usage de l'homme des mers et de l'homme des champs,* published 1865 to 1877, except 1871; one or several editions of: *Le choléra en 1865–1866* (Paris, 1866); *Peu de chose, mais quelque chose* (Paris, 1873, 1874, 1875).

[104] Professional meteorologists and astronomers seemed to take a rather dim view of his theories and of some unsubstantiated assertions. See A. Hermant, "De la prévision rationnelle du temps—Les astronomes et les astrologues," *Revue contemporaine,* 2ème série, XLVIII (Nov.–Dec. 1865), 753–73.

[105] X. Raspail, *Procès de l'almanach Raspail . . . ,* 8.

Raspail had participated ". . . in all the plots which, from 1814 to 1830, caused disorder and scandal. . . ." [106] The government's lawyer then enumerated all the prison sentences and fines that Raspail had incurred. It was a long list.

The arguments of the accusation were, in fact, just as biased as Raspail's own. To charge him with anti-patriotism because he had criticized the army's conduct in the Franco-Prussian war was unfair. To accuse him of anti-Christian feelings because he attacked the Jesuits was equally unfounded. But in the political atmosphere of Paris after the Commune, equanimity seems to have been impossible. "Gentlemen of the jury [the prosecutor cried], . . . help us prevent such books from continuing to infect the population, corrupt the teaching of our young, and incite them to hatred. . . ." [107] Evidently the octogenarian rebel seemed so dangerous that the republican government wished to jail him. His politically biased *Farmer's Almanac* was expected to be so widely read and so subversive as to warrant a stern sentence.[108]

Despite an impassioned defense by Raspail [109] and by his lawyer, Maître Forest, he was condemned to two years in jail and to a fine of 1000 francs. Xavier, the co-editor, was sentenced to six months' imprisonment and a fine of 500 francs. Protests poured in against this harsh treatment of a republican by a republic. One Frenchman wrote: ". . . to imprison the dean, the father of democracy, at such an advanced age . . . makes one shudder." [110] Maître Forest

[106] *Ibid.,* 41.

[107] *Ibid.,* 114.

[108] Once again the French government provided Raspail with free publicity: his defense lawyer quoted a communication from the police officer of Le Creuzot (Saône-et-Loire) who had searched the local stores: "The widow Martin says she has sold over one hundred copies of this *Almanac* since the *Petit Moniteur* announced its seizure [in Paris]—this is a sign of the times and of the workers' state of mind." *Ibid.,* 150.

[109] This defense, largely a recapitulation of his life, did not reassure the jury. See, e.g., his questionable interpretation of universal suffrage as on-the-spot-plebiscite in his account of the events of February 25, 1848: "The provisional government was deliberating to decide whether a regency should be proclaimed. I consulted my men. . . . I consulted them, because universal suffrage is a principle for me. I wanted to know public opinion. . . . I asked them 'What do you want? Do you want a regency?' They all said: 'No, we want a republic.' They were unanimous. Not a vote against." *Ibid.,* 122–23. See *supra,* pp. 201–2.

[110] Fonds Raspail, Archives du Département de la Seine, XXXIX.

informed the Court of Appeals that "English, Belgian, and American newspapers have commented on this condemnation, judging the penalty excessive, unheard of. . . . Some persons in the U.S.A. . . . have expressed their regret that M. Raspail, at his age, with his personal history and his humanitarian ideas, should be condemned to . . . jail." [111]

A Court of Appeals halved Raspail's prison sentence and permitted him, because of ill health, to serve it at a rest home at Bellevue. And so the old man returned to prison, accompanied, this time, by his daughter Marie who nursed him. "Our dear Father," Marie wrote to her brothers on July 15, 1874, "endures his fate with admirable resignation." [112] After his release, Marie fell ill with tuberculosis. Since the siege of Paris and so many privations she had never regained her strength. Sent to Monaco for a rest cure, she died there in 1876.

Once again the workingman's Paris and socialist France mourned Raspail's loss of a beloved woman. This time he buried her himself, next to his wife. "All of Paris participated in this solemn funeral," wrote Alfred Deberle in *Le Ralliement;* "Marie Raspail was mourned as no other woman in the world has ever been. The number of persons following her coffin and those lining the streets, was estimated at three hundred thousand." [113] The rightist newspaper *L'Ordre* callously commented: "The whole radical clan was full of joy yesterday. There was an occasion for a little demonstration around a corpse—that of Mademoiselle Raspail." [114] The newspaper *Le Rappel* published lengthy sympathetic comments, explaining Marie's lifelong dedication: " 'Promise me [Marie's mother demanded on her deathbed, when the girl was seventeen], that you will continue to surround your father with the devotion I have always shown him and, to achieve this task, stay single.' Marie promised. Neither her family's urging, nor marriage proposals could induce her to alter her promise. . . ." [115]

[111] X. Raspail, *Procès de l'almanach Raspail* . . . , 212.
[112] Fonds Raspail, Archives du Département de la Seine, XC.
[113] Quoted in F.-V. Raspail. "Avertissement," *Manuel-annuaire de la santé* (Paris, 1877), VI.
[114] December 19, 1876.
[115] *Le Rappel,* December 15, 1876.

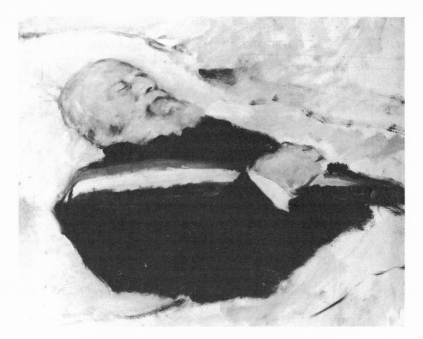

Deputy Raspail on his deathbed　(Courtesy Musée
Carnavalet, Paris) Photo Bulloz

Raspail was crushed.[116] In sorrow he added a codicil to his will:
"There are eleven thousand gold francs in the lower right-hand

[116] He composed this "Prayer to My Daughter in the Heavens," dated December 17, 1876, signed "F.-V. Raspail, microscopist":

". . . Oh, my daughter, model of a child. Even the skies shed tender tears at
the moment when one hundred thousand souls confine your honored remains
to the tomb.

"Don't forget me in the heavens, you who in the forty years of your short existence have never left me for one moment and have never lost sight of the mission with which your dying mother entrusted you.

"You have more than accomplished this mission. You never stopped holding
the hand of the old man who was your father.

"Your memory will replace your presence. I was advancing, under your auspices, toward the reform of humanity. I shall continue the struggle which I have
waged for sixty years against monarchy and for the triumph of the republic, the
government of the people, the government of all.

"For the republic is the voice of God, since it is the voice of the people. . .

"Farewell, my daughter in the heavens!

"I kneel on your tomb and raise my eyes heavenward."

(Original in the possession of M. Jacques Raspail.)

drawer of my desk (at Emile's house). . . . This sum is to be used for a life-size oil painting and a marble bust of my angel of a daughter, Marie Apolline Raspail." [117] Only a clay model of the bust was ever completed. Raspail moved to Emile's house, finding Cachan unbearable; and there he died, of pneumonia, on January 7, 1878, surrounded by his sons.

His death brought varied comments from the press. "Looking like an inspired dervish," wrote *Le Pays* on January 10, "father Raspail was a cunning and skillful tradesman. His successes in pharmacy made up for his political miscalculations." *Le Français* agreed and characterized Raspail as "this medical and political charlatan skilled in exploiting both democracy and camphor. . . ." [118] Jean de Nivelle, writing in *Le Soleil* on January 11, went so far as to declare that "No one . . . has more successfully exploited human credulity, nor covered his determination to grow rich with louder philanthropic oratory. One might call him the father of publicity. His every action, in politics and in science, was conceived and designed for the purpose of publicity." An article by "A. L." in the January 11 *Assemblée nationale* denounced "this race of men [who] are the shame and death of society. Even if an old man, dead at eighty-four, popularized camphor, that's no excuse for having been, during sixty years, the enemy of law and a rebel against men and God."

The democratic and socialist press sounded quite different: *La république française* praised

the good [Raspail's] system has done for the large mass of workers. His books contain excellent hygienic advice, wise encouragement toward domestic peace, self-respect, social responsibility, strict habits of orderliness, punctuality, and cleanliness, all of them important half-virtues. F.-V. Raspail has been the people's professor of morality, of a morality which is tender, humane, simple and effective. . . . The Raspail *Manual* has brought comfort to many a garret . . . it is a really popular book for which its author better deserves the people's blessings than for all his sufferings. . . . It is the untarrying source of a popularity which sometimes approaches idolatry. . . . [119]

[117] F.-V. Raspail, *Mes dernières volontés,* autogr. ms. No. 2405, Folio 560, Bibliothèque Inguimbertine, Carpentras, Vaucluse.
[118] January 10.
[119] January 10.

Letters, poems, flowers, and telegrams poured into Arcueil-Cachan from all over France and abroad. Socialist, republican, masonic groups, and labor unions sent telegrams; there was one from the "Medical circle, Raspail System, Brussels", and from Louis Blanc, Garibaldi, and Karl Marx. The newspaper *Le Figaro* commented on the "quasi-homeric epoch" now drawing to a close.

The funeral, delayed until Sunday, January 13, so that workers, provincial delegates, senators, and deputies could attend, was that of a great national leader. It brought over 100,000 persons to Arcueil to honor "democracy's veteran, the people's friend . . ." the *Manual* for 1878 reports. Sympathetic newspapers estimated the participants at 500,000. ". . . they represented towns, democratic organizations, labor unions, chambers of commerce and of arbitration, and many masonic lodges." [120]

Louis Blanc spoke at his old comrade's grave, as did deputies from the Departments of Bouches-du-Rhône and from Vaucluse. The latter, Dr. Alfred Naquet (1834–1916), was a physician from Carpentras whose political convictions agreed with Raspail's. He recalled a recent occurrence at the Chamber of Deputies which had been the crowning moment in Raspail's life. Having been elected a deputy from Marseilles in 1876 and re-elected in 1877,[121] Raspail was then the oldest deputy, whose solemn prerogative it was to open the session. On March 8, 1876, at Versailles, he slowly approached the National Assembly, walking between two rows of soldiers who presented arms. "It is the first time they don't lead me to prison," he remarked.[122] He walked up to the presidential chair and turned to face an assembly whose very existence was to him the symbol of political freedom. All his self control was needed to

[120] X. Raspail, ed., "Avertissement," *Manuel-annuaire pour 1878*.

[121] In 1873 he declined to run for office, probably because of ill health. But in 1876 he agreed and was elected on the second ballot, by a plurality of 5,280 votes out of 12,601. In 1877, he was re-elected at Marseilles, this time by a majority of 9,672 out of 17,556 votes, without having undertaken a trip that Benjamin urged upon him when he wrote: ". . . When are you leaving for Marseilles where, I am told daily, *they count on seeing you soon* . . . you must arrange your trip with Emile. Maybe Camille could come with you. As for me, I am too busy in my own district to think of accompanying you. P.S.: Tomorrow, Monday, we have a meeting at Louis Blanc's house. (Autogr. ms. letter, September 23, 1877, owned by M. Jacques Raspail.)

[122] G. Raspail, *La vie et l'oeuvre* . . . , 112, n. 1.

maintain his composure. In a short speech he extolled mutual confidence and cooperation as the wellspring of a democracy.[123] This indeed was the message the eighty-year-old fighter wished to leave with the younger generation—that in a democracy conscious of its social responsibility, the burden of the effort toward moral, physical, and political health rests with the individual. This was Raspail's legacy.

[123] *France, Assemblée nationale. Annales de la chambre des députés* in *Annales du sénat et de la chambre des députés.* 1870. I, 3–4.

Jamais il ne s'est démenti,
jamais il ne s'est repenti.

Eugène Spuller

X

PUBLIC HEALTH

AND THE

RIGHTS OF MAN

THE NOTION OF HEALTH was the pivot of Raspail's thought. He envisaged the healthy man as a happy man, an active worker, a good provider, a responsible citizen. In Hippocratic terms, he saw health as harmony—as a salutary adaptation to the environment, an equilibrium reflecting the satisfactory interplay of body and mind. The environment played a major role in this view, since health needs to be safeguarded and promoted—and could be endangered—by surrounding conditions, especially in the opinion of a convinced contagionist. Although specific microbes were not identified as the carriers of disease until late in Raspail's life, this democratic reformer had long urged an unprepared society and an unheeding state to enter the fields of preventive and "environmental" medicine, mainly because he believed that the citizen's right to health entailed programs, expenditures, and regulations that the community must shoulder and enforce. The notion of health thus furnished the focus of Raspail's thought, the goal for his work, and the sting for prodding his adepts and laggard fellow legislators. During his long career he devised many programs for drastic changes in politics, religion, and education. The citizen's health was his special concern when he demanded a revision of the penal code, prison reform, the abolition of penal colonies, and total political amnesty. He urged doctors and lawyers to listen to their consciences and professional codes and offer the unique social service that their competence enabled them to give.

Raspail's audience, initially composed of subscribers to the *Reformer* and members in democratic clubs, grew to national proportions after his political and medical lawsuits, his medical and hygienic publications, the success of his therapy, the publicity surrounding his forays into politics in 1848, and his remarkable service as a legislator in 1869–1870 and 1876–1878. He himself felt that his multiple reform proposals constituted the essence of life-long efforts, for in 1872 he reissued many of his earlier writings in a volume entitled *Social Reforms*. Long excerpts are reprinted from the *Reformer* of 1835 and from the *Letters on Parisian Prisons*.[1] A chapter deals with each social field that he deemed in need of change. This book thus serves as a convenient guide to the reformer's work in politics and public health as he himself envisaged it toward the end of his life. His lasting achievement was that he helped create a receptive attitude toward health measures among a wide French audience. He accustomed them to the view that health and hygiene, private and public, were but one aspect of their inalienable rights.

Georges Duveau, the social historian and expert on Raspail, supports the above view in his *Vie ouvrière en France sous le second empire*. Discussing the workers' need for literacy and education, Duveau points out that the well-meant efforts of a Victor Duruy (1811–1894), Minister of Education, and of a Jules Simon (1814–1896), humanitarian democrat and deputy, often failed to move the worker, who did not really understand these gentlemen's language.

[1] See *infra*, pp. 279–83.

The worker, however, had other guides who led him toward school: Greppo,[2] Joigneaux,[3] Perdiguier,[4] Raspail, who had an admirable knowledge of the people's feelings. . . . The brochures written by these old militants found their way into the farthest hamlets, into the darkest alleys. They expressed the worker's hopes in clear language. Having read these, he could easily understand the noble style and the actions of a Victor Duruy, a Jules Simon. The call to education was launched in a stubborn and skilfull manner by the very men to whom the workers listened most readily.[5]

In viewing the right to good health as a facet of the right to equality, Raspail placed himself among those leaders who gave a liberal interpretation to the democratic credo. Within his lifetime this tradition reached back to the Duc de La Rochefoucauld-Liancourt (1747–1827) and his *Comité de mendicité* which, under the Constituent Assembly, tried to free medical assistance from the humiliating notion of charity, and to establish the right of certain categories of citizens—veterans, for example—to national gratitude and help. This tradition was continued, among Raspail's French contemporaries, by politically active physicians such as Ulysse Trélat (1795–1879) and Jules Guérin (1801–1886), and it eventually led to the establishment of a national scheme for public assistance (1849) and a Ministry of Public Health (1930),[6] although not yet a national program for social medicine.

As a socialist who wrote on problems of public health, Raspail did not stand alone. The Saint-Simonians paid heed to medicine, as did Etienne Cabet in whose ideal community, *Icaria*, all citizens

[2] On Greppo, see *supra*, p. 243, n. 47.

[3] Pierre Joigneaux (1815–1892) graduated from Central School as an agronomist. In 1834 he published some articles in *L'Homme libre* which earned him four years in jail. He became a popularizer of democratic reform ideas. He served in the Constituent Assembly of 1848, and was forced into exile in Belgium in 1852. He wrote prolifically. Two representative publications are: *Dictionnaire d'agriculture pratique* (1855) and *Livre de la ferme et des maisons de campagne* (1860). From 1871 to 1889 he was a deputy, then a senator.

[4] On Perdiguier, see *supra*, p. 206, n. 21.

[5] G. Duveau, *La vie ouvrière en France sous le second empire* (Paris, 1946), 448–49. In a footnote, Duveau adds: "The booklets of Joigneaux, of Raspail were found, for example, in the library of a shoemaker of Saint-Ouen de Pont-cheuil (Eure) [during a search made by the police in 1852]."

[6] *Ministère de la santé publique et de la population.*

received free medical care while all doctors were trained at state expense and served proudly as civil servants.[7] Some socialists who were also physicians theorized on public health. These included not only Ulysse Trélat, a founder of the French carbonari and the author of *Précis élémentaire d'hygiène* (1826), but also P. J. B. Buchez, in his young days a Saint-Simonian, co-author with Trélat of *Eléments d'hygiène, ou manuel de santé pour toutes les conditions et pour tous les âges* (1826).

French doctors in the first three or four decades of the nineteenth century—even if their politics were hostile to socialism— also showed interest in a wide spectrum of questions pertaining to hygiene, sanitation, preventive, environmental, and social medicine.[8] None of these concerns were entirely new to them, for significant progress and change had occurred in France since the eve of the Great Revolution.

A perusal of the first forty volumes of a representative publication, the *Annales d'hygiène publique et de médecine légale* (1829–1848), reveals active involvement in these issues on the part of many French doctors, scientists, lawyers, legislators, and statisticians. They studied the purity of food and drugs,[9] the physical and moral welfare of children, patients, prisoners, and soldiers;[10] the sanitary conditions in factories;[11] street lighting;[12] sewerage, epidemics and quarantines; the illegal practice of pharmacy and medicine; and the causes and circumstances of suicides and mur-

[7] See H. Hausheer, "Icarian Medicine: Etienne Cabet's Utopia and Its French Medical Background," *Bulletin of the History of Medicine*, IX (1941), 294–310; 401–35; 515–29.

[8] For an informative study and a rich bibliography, see E. H. Ackerknecht, "Hygiene in France, 1814–1848," *Ibid.*, XII (1948), 117–55.

[9] See, e.g., G. Andral, "Rapport fait au conseil de salubrité sur le danger qui peut résulter de l'emploi des bonbons coloriés," *Annales d'hygiène publique et de médecine légale*, III (1830), 48–51.

[10] See, e.g., A. Bouchardat, "Mémoire sur l'hygiène des hôpitaux et hospices civils de Paris," *Ibid.*, XVIII (1837), 37–73; 296–351; and E. Ducpétiaux, "Questions relatives à l'hygiène des prisons et des établissements de bienfaisance," *Ibid.*, VII (1833), 272–95.

[11] See, e.g., L. F. Benoiston de Chateauneuf, "De l'influence de certaines professions sur le développement de la phthisie pulmonaire," *Ibid.*, VI (1831), 5–48.

[12] See, e.g., A. Trébuchet, "Recherches sur l'éclairage public à Paris," *Ibid.*, XXXI (1844), 103–30.

ders. They published statistical studies on the life expectancy of the rich and poor, scholars and writers;[13] on the relative heights of city dwellers and peasants;[14] on mortality in the various boroughs of Paris;[15] and on the health of workers in the cotton, wool, silk, lead, tobacco, or rubber industries.[16]

The *Annales d'hygiène* reviewed for its readers relevant debates and reports from the Academies of Medicine and of Sciences, legislative measures, court proceedings, and foreign books. Professional men could therefore keep abreast of new developments in public health through this excellent journal.

Contrary to the widespread notion that the literate French public lacked an interest in this field,[17] Garrison, in his classic *Introduction to the History of Medicine,* asserts that "the subject was extensively cultivated in France," [18] while Ackerknecht claims:

The hygiene movement probably reached an all-time peak in France in the years between the Napoleonic wars and 1848; and France, which was known as the leader of Western clinical medicine (and in many other fields of science and the humanities) for these years, might well be credited with the same leadership in hygiene (preventive medicine) for the period under discussion.[19]

[13] See, e.g., L. F. Benoiston de Chateauneuf, "De la durée de la vie chez le riche et chez le pauvre," *Ibid.,* III (1830), 5–15; and "De la durée de la vie chez les savants et chez les gens de lettres," *Ibid.,* XXV (1841), 241–68.

[14] See, e.g., L. A. J. Quételet, "Sur la taille moyenne de l'homme dans les villes et dans les campagnes et sur l'âge où la croissance est complètement achevée," *Ibid.,* III (1830), 24–26.

[15] See, e.g., L. Villermé, "De la mortalité dans les divers quartiers de la ville de Paris et des causes qui la rendent très différente de plusieurs d'entre eux, ainsi que dans les divers quartiers de beaucoup de grandes villes," *Ibid.,* III (1830), 294–341.

[16] See, L. Villermé, "De la santé des ouvriers employés dans les fabriques de soie, de coton, et de laine," *Ibid.,* XXI (1839), 338–420; and F. Mélier, "De la santé des ouvriers employés dans les manufactures de tabac," *Ibid.,* XXXIV (1845), 241–300.

[17] France is usually not even mentioned in discussions of public health during the days before Pasteur. This applies to such surveys of the problem as C.-E.-A. Winslow, *The Evolution and Significance of the Modern Public Health Campaign* (New Haven, 1923), or Sir Arthur Newsholme's *Evolution of Preventive Medicine* (Baltimore, 1927). A welcome exception is G. Rosen, *A History of Public Health* (New York, 1958).

[18] F. H. Garrison, *Introduction to the History of Medicine* (Philadelphia, 1929, 11th ed.), 659.

[19] E. H. Ackerknecht, "Hygiene in France, 1814–1848," *Bulletin of the History of Medicine,* IX, 118.

This authoritative scholar goes further still and asserts that French achievement was outstanding in the practical as well as in the theoretical realm. "France," he writes, "was a pioneer in labor legislation in 1810, and in voluntary health insurance, having one hundred and twenty *Sociétés de prévention* in 1822." [20] He adds that ". . . occupation with hygiene almost became a fashion" [21] and that France could boast more practical achievement than either England or Germany.

The initiative leading to such practical achievement was taken by the French government and by various professional groups. The *Conseil de salubrité de Paris,* for example, set up by Napoleon in 1802 at the suggestion of the great pharmacist Cadet de Gassicourt (1769–1821), applied its powers of inspection and denunciation to an ever-widening range of public and commercial places, goods, utilities, and professions. Many other cities emulated the capital. Professional groups chartered their own societies for mutual help, especially in case of accident, sickness, or death. Soon these groups, such as the *Association de prévoyance et de secours mutuels des médecins de Paris,*[22] took on wider powers of professional vigilance and control. Public health was a concern familiar to many.

Among the public at large, certain feelings militated against cooperation with efforts initiated by the government or by professional groups such as doctors or lawyers. Anti-democratic governments had done nothing to earn popular trust. Even deeper than this diffidence went the distaste of the poor for compliance with any measures that smacked of charity. Their right to medical help, with the purpose of safeguarding the general health, was by no means established—they were even denied a vote in the conduct of their political fortunes. Medical aid had for many centuries been doled out by the rich or the Church. There was little enthusiasm for more of this among the French working classes.

Raspail thus satisfied an acute need: the unique combination of

[20] *Ibid.,* 121.

[21] *Ibid.,* 140. The official and popular interest in hygiene—i.e. preventive medicine—contrasted with skepticism toward therapy—i.e. curative medicine. See *supra,* pp. 137–39.

[22] See *supra,* p. 156, n. 64 and p. 195, n. 102.

humane empathy with medical success and political liberalism earned him a special place in the French workers' pantheon. His advocacy of hygiene was aimed primarily at the thousands of French men and women living in straitened circumstances. For them he emphasized the importance of cleanliness, diet, regularity of habits, adequate clothing, and attention to health in the management of the home. He urged them to procure street cleaning, sewage disposal, wider streets with trees to control air pollution, and houses with better ventilation.

The air of our towns [he wrote in 1843], with our narrow streets, our tall houses, our low and small apartments and our crowded population is a slow poison which the inhabitant breathes from the cradle and which shortens his life. Once streets are transformed into boulevards, life in town will be as healthy as life in the country.[23]

Beyond hygiene he counseled preventive measures. These were predicated on his belief in contagion and on his conviction that "infinitely small" parasites were the cause of many illnesses. His experience with camphor engendered a belief in its outstanding qualities as a vermifuge. His lifelong promotion of camphorated preparations was the well-known consequence. It led him far, for he wished to cleanse body, clothes, home, and food of these parasites. He urged, for example, that

confectioners . . . conspire with us . . . and transform every piece of candy into a vermifuge. The problem can be solved by offering for sale candied angelica, orange and lemon peels, and by concealing the bitter taste of camphor under a sugar coating flavored with vanilla, rose water, lemon or orange. . . .[24]

His enthusiastic attitude toward health prompted a concern for industrial plants and factories and for the disposal of harmful waste products. In 1862, for example, alerted by painful symptoms, he traced the camphor (which he took every night) to its industrial source.[25] He found that the drug was being refined in a factory where the same employees handled corrosive sublimate and arsenicals as well as camphor. Sanitary precautions were entirely insuffi-

[23] F.-V. Raspail, *Histoire naturelle de la santé* . . . , II, 365.
[24] *Ibid.*, 379.
[25] See *supra*, pp. 252–53.

cient. In *An Urgent Appeal for Help Against Industrial Poison-
ings, Addressed to Enlightened Men of All Professions,* Raspail
attempted to arouse the public. He rebuked manufacturers whose
greed permitted unsanitary working conditions. He demanded not
government interference, but "sanitation societies," which should
be formed in each department, their mission being the "preserva-
tion and protection" of the workers' health and the "fraternal and
preventive supervision" of working conditions.[26] His warning
reached the Paris Council for Public Health and Hygiene and he
eventually received a respectful letter from its vice-president, Du-
chesne, inviting him to collaborate with the Council on this problem.[27]

Following the pattern of his life's work Raspail made single-
handed efforts in line with the most advanced contemporary developments while ignoring the work of others. Believing the cholera
epidemic of 1865 to be caused by some "putrid fermentation" that
would yield to careful cleanliness and anti-contagionist measures,
he wrote with some pride:

Today, not even the smallest French village lacks some adept of the
Manual able to combat cholera or its pseudonym: at the first symptom
of its appearance, someone exists everywhere who can serve as nurse
and put at the disposal of his brothers a small pharmacy of the new
system . . . the sickness usually yields as if by magic and stops at the
earliest symptoms.[28]

The "small pharmacy of the new system" was hardly the answer
to cholera. How much more effective he might have been had he
abandoned his self-imposed isolation and collaborated with like-
minded persons! He was a gallant fighter in the face of opposition
to public health efforts, as, for example, when in June 1870 he
proposed in the legislature that the government sponsor an investigation of smallpox. His suggestion was greeted with laughter.
"Legislators are poor law-makers [he commented], if they see no
connection between the law and medicine."[29]

[26] F.-V. Raspail, *Appel urgent au concours des hommes éclairés de toutes les
professions contre les empoisonnements industriels* (Paris, 1863), 97.

[27] Fonds Raspail, Archives du Département de la Seine, III.

[28] F.-V. Raspail, *Le choléra en 1865 et 1866* (Paris, 1866), 8.

[29] *Annales du . . . corps législatif,* June 2, 1870 (IV, 237).

While concern for public health was always with him, his political objectives were of course much broader. And yet one can discern the unifying theme of the citizen's health in every one of Raspail's protests and projects as a legislator. Health symbolized for Raspail a man's dignity; the state's attention to the citizen's health symbolized the respect due to his opinions. And so, whether Raspail campaigned for increased franchise, for freedom of speech, assembly, religion, and education, or for national health, accident, and pension schemes, the citizen's health and dignity were his fundamental concern. In the legislature, under the Liberal Empire as under the Third Republic, despite old age and fatigue, he often rose to speak. He urged administrative decentralization[30] to foster voluntary, local action. Already in the *Reformer* he had spoken of "cooperative labor" [*"corvées réciproques"*] to raise grain production.[31] Always eager to tax the rich and aid the poor, he proposed a bill for a single, progressive income tax.[32] And he did not tire of inveighing against the expensive and wasteful imperial régime.

Fundamental change was needed, he held, in education, religion, the military, medicine, and law. Free, lay, compulsory, elementary education ought to exclude teaching priests and nuns and "be entrusted to married persons only." Religion in the schools ". . . should not transgress its proper limits. It should deal with what is demonstrable and not with the suppositions or dreams of spiritualists and similar illuminati." [33] He would even abolish the Ministry of Religion. Let each cult pay its priests, and ban public processions: "The street does not belong to any religion; no ceremony may be held outside the temple." [34] A Ministry of War seemed unnecessary in peacetime: Raspail proposed universal military training for men from the ages of twenty to fifty, but saw no need

[30] E.g., in a discussion in the corps législatif, December 8, 1869. See also Archives nationales, Series C 1144, dossier 253. His bill, co-sponsored by Henri de Rochefort, was rejected. Xavier Raspail points out that it corresponds almost verbatim to Article 3 of the Law of April 5, 1884. (X. Raspail, *Raspail et Pasteur* . . . , 272.)

[31] F.-V. Raspail, *Réformes sociales*, 200.

[32] *Annales du . . . corps législatif,* July 8, 1870 (V, 529).

[33] *Ibid.,* 532.

[34] *Ibid.* The aim of this proposal was of course achieved in the Law of 1905, separating church and state.

Messieurs,
Merci, Merci de votre sympathie; je m'efforcerai de la mériter tout
le restant de ma longue vie
F. V. Raspail,
juin
1869

A mes concitoyens Marseillais.

Mes électeurs,

En vous redemandant vos voix pour
la nouvelle chambre des députés, je me
trouve forcé de vous faire mes excuses.

C'est la première fois de ma vie que
je manque de parole à d'honnêtes et
braves citoyens.

La faute en est à ma vieillesse qui
ne permet à un homme de 84 ans de
voyager seul et sans l'aide de ses
enfants.

C'est dans l'intérêt de notre cause
commune que l'un d'eux cette fois
doit s'abstenir d'accompagner son
vieux Père auprès de vous.

Cependant j'avais juré de mourir
sur la brèche, je retire de vous
cet honneur qui ne se refuse à
aucun vétéran d'une armée qui veut
l'emporter dans l'immortalité: mort
au Champ d'honneur.

Après la paix notre champ d'honneur n'est plus que là.

L'ennemi que nous allons attaquer
est reconstitué: La Royauté, la San-
glante Royauté, la hideuse Royauté
ose vous demander de réimposer
les abus qu'avait foulé aux pieds 89.
Fermons lui la bouche aujourd'hui
et que je sois un de ces Spartiates.

Dans notre dernière session, la
chambre des députés a achevé de
démontrer, en dépit des trois
tyrannies qui se disputent si vainement
le pays, que la République seule peut
donner à la France la paix Source
de la fortune et de la liberté, de
la moralité et de la Science, qui un
jour formeront la Religion de ce
monde, Religion qui remplacera
la pénalité par l'amélioration du
Coupable et la réparation du mal
qu'il a commis; tandis que notre
Code pénal et notre Code d'instruction
criminelle n'améliorent nullement
le coupable et ne restituent rien au
lésé ou à ses parents.

La République cherche à Réhabiliter
tous les faillis et à les rendre à l'honneur
et au Commerce.

C'est pour développer ces grands,
principes à la Chambre que je
vous demande vos voix:

amélioration
du Coupable,
et
abolition
de la
pénalité.

Arcueil
30 Sept
1877

F. V. Raspail

Samples of Raspail's handwriting, 1869 and 1877 (Courtesy Archives
du Département de la Seine)

for barracks or uniforms. Drills could be held on Sundays in the soldiers' home towns. The recruits should dress "at their own expense, in the simplest way, which suits every purse; courage ennobles any costume." [35]

The medical profession, he believed, should be in the forefront of this struggle for public health. He was appalled by the low medical standards, the traditionalism, the clannishness, the disregard for hygiene, the waste of human lives, the lack of experimentation with new drugs and procedures. The teaching of medicine should be free from academic censorship, he argued, and depend only on talent. Amphitheatres and laboratories must be provided free of charge. New treatments and remedies should be discussed in an official bulletin, and a medical council should act as a tribunal for all questions of public health.[36]

He advocated that the state pay all doctors and assign medical students to be their assistants. Physicians would report every night to a district committee on the condition of their patients.[37] "We want this medical corps," he wrote, "which is torn and corrupted with anarchy, to become a great and vast magistracy . . . responsible, at state expense, for safeguarding public and private health. . . ." [38] This was his thought as early as 1843. Five years later, under the Second Republic, he pressed on, proposing the founding of a "Free School of Popular Medication" which would train men and married or widowed women in his hygienic method. A certificate would recommend them "to the people's confidence"; they would agree to care for the poor without remuneration and accept no more than two francs from the rich. They would be called "Nurses of fraternity." [39] Public health and democracy would then really be dispensed together by this Raspaillian Red Cross organization.

Raspail also pleaded that hospitals be "ennobled by public opinion," and changed from "gutters of misery into temples of health." "The taxpayer," he wrote, "whom his money entitles to breathe pure air and to sleep without the fear of being robbed, has an equal

[35] *Ibid.*, 534.
[36] F.-V. Raspail, *Histoire naturelle de la santé* . . . , LV–LVI.
[37] *Ibid.*
[38] *Ibid.*, XL.
[39] F.-V. Raspail, *L'Ami du peuple en 1848*, No. XXI, 2.

right to be defended against illness which is often caused by society itself." [40] This apostle of "socialized medicine" was anxious to see the state shoulder the responsibilities and the cost for all those health problems that the constituents could not assume alone.

If doctors seemed to Raspail negligent of their social duties, lawyers were downright corrupt—and expendable. He was highly critical of the codes sponsored by his hero Napoleon, and although his condemnation was too general, his criticisms were not unfounded and some of his proposals had considerable merit. Of course he went too far. He demanded that the Chamber of Deputies "throw the Penal Code into the fire, because it bristles with torture, and burn the Code of Criminal Instruction, because it abounds in lies; and that it substitute a cantonal jury for the old magistracy which is trained merely to uphold these [obsolete] laws and this inextricable jurisprudence. . . ." [41] He would submit as many disputes as possible to voluntary local arbitration, certain that reasonable and cheap settlements could thus be obtained, and all lawyers, judges, and even the Ministry of Justice eventually be rendered obsolete. [42]

In a less categoric vein, Raspail leveled specific criticisms at the handling of suspects, the role of technical experts in criminal cases, and the jury system. His thoughts on these matters are most conveniently found in his *Letters on Parisian Prisons,* written in jail and smuggled out to his friend, Guillard de Kersausie. [43] The *Letters* contain a detailed examination of the manner in which arrests were then carried out. Although, in theory, a prisoner had to be informed of the charges against him soon after arraignment, the practice was far different. Raspail distinguished among four different warrants: an injunction to accompany the officer of the law immediately; a subpoena for a fixed day; a warrant for preventive custody at the will of the magistrate; and confinement until trial. Raspail took exception to the last two, and especially to preventive custody. Too often had he been held in jail ignorant of the ac-

[40] F.-V. Raspail, *Nouveau système de chimie organique* . . . , LII.

[41] *Annales* . . . *de la chambre des députés,* 1876, III, 100.

[42] *Ibid.,* 1870, V, 531.

[43] F.-V. Raspail, *Réforme pénitentiaire. Lettres sur les prisons de Paris* (Paris, 1839). This book was dedicated to Kersausie's sister, the Comtesse de Pontavice. It reflects the strong contemporary interest in prison reform.

cusations against him, at the mercy of a judge. When he was inter-rogated, the clerk would take notes, not of the interview, but of the questions and answers as dictated by the magistrate.[44] This biased version would then constitute the official record.

The function of experts who testify in court hearings was a problem to which Raspail often reverted. Only too well did he remember his role as an expert chemist who crossed the path of the all powerful Orfila. Specialists in any field should be liable to court duty, Raspail proposed; each discipline should set up its own rules for the choice of these men.[45]

The jury system was another subject of his concern. He objected to a law of 1827 that left the selection of jurors to the prefects. Jurors were chosen from the ranks of public officials, doctors and professors, members of the Institute, lawyers, responsible citizens who requested jury duty, and members of the electoral colleges. Substantial, politically conservative citizens only were called upon. Raspail condemned this law as reactionary, charging that each prefect kept a "red book" that listed the reading habits, religious conformity, and general political reliability of all potential jurors.[46] He called for liberal reform.

[44] He had often publicly protested against this practice which resulted in mis-leading verbatim records of the testimony of witnesses and defendants. See F.-V. Raspail, *Procès et défense* . . . , 17.

[45] F.-V. Raspail, *Accusation d'empoisonnement* . . . , 136. It is worth noting that the availability and role of technical experts in the courtroom is still a largely unsettled problem. On this same point, see C. P. Collard de Martigny, "Commentaire sur les articles 43 et 44 du code d'instruction criminelle en ma-tière d'expertise médico-légale," *Annales d'hygiène publique*, VII (1832), 160–72; and "Mémoire adressé à l'Académie des sciences morales et politiques; De l'instruction des faits de médecine légale devant le jury, de son insuffisance, de ses dangers, et de sa réforme," *Ibid.*, X (1833), 115–25.

[46] F.-V. Raspail, *Réforme pénitentiaire* . . . , II, 232. He had already attacked the political criteria which determined the choice of jurors in his defense of the Society of the Friends of the People (Jan. 10–12, 1832) of which he was then president. (See *supra*, pp. 170–71.) Very cleverly he had pointed out that the public seemed always to accept the jury's verdict in criminal cases and protest against its verdict in political cases. ". . . Agree that we have [in France . . .] an aristocracy of the jury [he challenged the jurors], and save us the trouble of defending ourselves." (F.-V. Raspail, *Défense et allocution* . . . , 4). The ver-dict was "not guilty."

Some documents preserved in the Archives nationales prove how founded was this criticism. A letter from Adolphe Thiers, then Minister of the Interior, to the attorney general, dated December 21, 1832, deplores the imminent

Raspail's tireless attack on contemporary institutions in the context of his quest for health gives special meaning to his campaign for prison reform and to his fight for the abolition of penal colonies. The poignancy of his arguments stems from his experiences as a prisoner, corroborated by information he received from political friends. Indeed, Raspail argued that society might have the right to put a man under lock and key, but surely not to imprison him in an environment that will make him incurably sick. The French prisons and penal colonies, such as they existed in Raspail's time, were therefore, he argued, immoral.

Imprisonment as a form of punishment was being widely criticized in Western countries at that time, on humanitarian, sanitary, psychological, and even economic grounds. Raspail had read many books on prison reform—there are over forty titles on his annotated reading list—including the famous works of Beccaria, Howard, and Tocqueville.[47] England, Belgium, and Switzerland had already introduced reform, and agitation for improvements in France was widespread and well publicized. Doubts about the justification for imprisonment were thus being raised at a time when unprecedented numbers of Frenchmen were being jailed for political reasons. Conservative estimates give the figure for June 1848 as 4,000, and 26,000 for December, 1851.[48] No prison facilities were available for such crowds. The problem was pressing, and any debate in the Chamber was sure to provoke heated reaction.

"scandal" of a victory banquet uniting the jurors with the defendants—members of the Society of the Friends of the People—whom they had just acquitted. The police prefect of Paris could and should have ascertained the political opinions of the prospective jurors. In fact, the prefect had offered his services to the attorney general when he wrote: "The practice has always been that before the opening of a court session where political crimes . . . were to be judged, my prefecture would be asked for information about the political opinions of the prospective jurors. . . . I have always been eager to respond to such requests, since I appreciate their importance. It seems to me that magistrates should always follow this course, in the interest of the government and of civil peace. . . . If my conjectures are correct, and if you should find it useful and relevant to obtain complete information, you know, Mr. Attorney General, that I shall be more anxious to assist you. . . ." (Archives nationales, Series BB[18], 1212 dossier 8291.) He added that the prosecutor at the trial could then challenge the competence of any juror whose republican, bonapartist, or legitimist opinions were known to the police.

[47] Fonds Raspail, Archives du Département de la Seine, CXIL.

[48] Ch. Seignobos, *La révolution de 1848* . . . , 220.

On the subject of prisons Raspail had the undoubted advantage of intimate and extensive inside knowledge, since he had spent a total of seven-and-a-half years at Sainte-Pélagie, Versailles, Vincennes, and Doullens. His personal experience rendered his writings and his arguments in the legislature concrete and vivid. He provoked compassion among readers and listeners. But with his tone of injured innocence and the very violence of his protests, he overshot the mark. He failed to induce the legislators to support his sweeping proposals.

The inmates of these prisons and the treatment inflicted upon them are vividly described in Raspail's *Letters on Parisian Prisons* of 1839. Sainte-Pélagie was filled, during his stay, with political prisoners, criminals, and debtors—one third each. "Debt and crime would carry on conversations with politics through the windows." [49] Debtors could buy food, drink, luxurious furnishings, and the company of friends, anything short of freedom. The political prisoners were usually too poor to afford such privileges, yet even they had to pay for the simple comforts of a mattress and sheets. [50] Raspail depicts scenes of filth, stench, beating, drunkenness, rotten food, and polluted water. "The bread is of abominable quality; it is darker than rye bread, so dark that it looks burnt and crumbles in your hands like sawdust. It is prickly to swallow and excruciating to digest." [51] While in prison he was permitted to perform the microscopic analysis of bread and water. He used all his experience and ingenuity as a microscopist in analyzing the various kinds of flour, but concluded that the substance furnished him for analysis was of much better quality than what must have gone into the

[49] F.-V. Raspail, *Réforme pénitentiaire* . . . , II, 316.

[50] Neither the dignity nor the discipline was exemplary or rigid in all cases. In 1832, the poet Gérard de Nerval once spent a night at Sainte-Pélagie, after a group of artists had mingled with a revolutionary crowd and those "with the longest hair and the longest beards" got arrested. Having arrived late at night, he was pushed into a dormitory for political prisoners. These soon returned from a walk in the courtyards. They sang the *Marseillaise,* the *Ça ira,* the *Chant du départ,* and then performed charades re-enacting the Revolution of 1830. The tableaux showed Charles X and his ministers, the storming of the Hôtel de Ville, and ended with a battle on the barricades. Beds and mattresses were overturned, pillows used for ammunition. At 1 a.m. it all ended with another *Marseillaise.* G. de Nerval, "Mes prisons," in *La Bohême galante* (Paris, 1927), 153–68.

[51] F.-V. Raspail, *Réforme pénitentiaire* . . . , II, 248.

baking of prison bread.[52] He found the water full of germs. He spoke to the prison doctor, but "it seems that the doctor can only deal with sickness and not with health; he cares for patients and practices medicine; health measures are up to the jailers . . ."[53] He deplored the presence, in the same jail, of hundreds of vagrant boys, who were bereft of care and education. Their only teachers were social misfits and criminals. He tried to give them some lessons—one wonders with what results. The *Letters on Parisian Prisons,* even though unfinished, bear witness to Raspail's capacity for putting his own painful experiences to use in promoting social reform.[54] He was, in fact, prepared to make a major effort in his legislative career to bring about drastic changes in the practice of imprisonment on political ground.

The fate of political prisoners was a touchy problem for French governments of the mid-nineteenth century. Six changes of rulers during the preceding fifty years had awakened many Frenchmen— even the respectable, substantial middle class—to the frightening

[52] F.-V. Raspail, "Essai d'analyse microscopique sur le pain des prisons de Paris, par un homme qui en a mangé," *Le Lycée, Journal des sciences et des sociétés savantes,* 5ème année, No. 28 (December 4, 1831), 118.

[53] F.-V. Raspail, *Réforme pénitentiaire* . . . , 248–49.

[54] One particularly touching response to his concern for the plight of French prisoners reached him from the well-known poetess Marceline Desbordes-Valmore (1786–1859) who became his friend and admirer for life. She dedicated to him a poem entitled "Prisons and Prayers," written when he was serving a long sentence at Doullens. The first two stanzas might read in English as follows:

"Oh let us weep and tell the names of France's banished
Those from whose choking hearts all hope has not yet vanished
And let the mourning palm do homage to their plight
A law has banished all but jailers from their sight.
We pass: our pious hands are bare of might or sword
Nor do our hearts conceal a fratricidal word;
As women we but bring our tears and our orataion
For these are dear to God, the God of all our nation."

Poésies choisies (Paris, 1935), 181.

Sainte-Beuve greatly admired Madame Desbordes-Valmore, and felt that her friendship with Raspail stemmed from "human, plebian, and truly fraternal feelings."—"Raspail's deep patriotism found expression in one of his letters addressed to her from Belgium: 'Oh, how beautiful my country is! A land rich in miracles, even in its moments of turmoil and partial madness! Here, one passes; there, where you are, one lives, one loves, one enjoys, understands, and respects one another, even after death.'" Quoted in C.-A. Sainte-Beuve, *Nouveaux lundis* (Paris, 1878), XII, 251.

realization that they might be victims of the next political purge. And if implicated in subversion, they might find themselves in prison or in exile. More than one member of the Legislative Assembly in 1849—nay, the President of the Republic himself—were former jailbirds. No wonder they were unusually sensitive to complaints on this subject.

In fact, the fate of the political prisoner may have been worse under the Second Republic than either before or after. Earlier in the century such prisoners—Blanqui, Barbès, Huber, or Raspail, for example—were usually confined to ancient fortresses, like Vincennes, Belle-Isle, or Doullens, or to special sections in all-purpose prisons such as Sainte-Pélagie, La Force, or Versailles, separate from debtors, thieves, and convicted felons sentenced to forced labor. But then, the abolition of the death penalty for political crimes in 1848 increased the sentences to life imprisonment—thus swelling the ranks of prisoners. During the reforms of the early 1850s, when new accommodations had to be found for the vast numbers of political detainees, these men were to make the ever closer acquaintance of convicted criminals.

The major change decided upon between 1852–1854[55] was to close the pontoons, relics of the days when convicted criminals were used as rowers on galleys, chained to their benches and driven by the whip. The pontoon, which had replaced the galley in the mid-eighteenth century meant hardly any improvement, since the prison was now a dismantled battleship anchored in stagnant waters. Forced inaction was barely preferable to hard work. Toulon, Brest, Rochefort had been endowed with pontoons in the mid-eighteenth century, and the French Revolution added those of Lorient, Nice, Le Havre, and Cherbourg. As soon as humanitarian considerations emerged, it was clear that these festering graves for the living must be closed.[56]

The English example of penal colonies far removed from the mother country then caught the French imagination. It would be wise to transport convicts to distant lands—humane and profitable

---

[55] Decrees of February 21 and March 27, 1852, April 2, 1853, and Law of May 30, 1854.

[56] See articles "bagne," and "ponton," in the *Grande encyclopédie Larousse du 19ème siècle.*

to let them work there in comparative freedom. But France lacked a colony (such as Australia) where Europeans would find the climate congenial. Only tropical possessions could be used. Disregarding considerations of health, the Legislative Assembly decided on June 8, 1850, to transport criminals and political prisoners to Lambessa in North Africa, to the Marquises Islands, or to French Guiana.

The penal colony in Lambessa was advertised as having a cultural purpose: the uncovering of Roman ruins. In 1851 political prisoners began to dig these out. Neither accommodations nor even bread had been provided for. After December 2, 1851, more "workers" arrived, and again after Orsini's attempt on Napoleon III's life in 1858. After 1860 only thieves, arsonists, and murderers were sent there.

The Marquises Islands were just as ill-fated a penal colony, and the penitentiary in New Caledonia served only from 1864 to 1896, mainly to house the 7,500 Communards condemned to deportation. Eventually only Cayenne remained. Conditions on Devil's Island were dramatically brought to world attention at the time of the Dreyfus case. Not until the end of the Second World War was this place of detention closed.

Where, in the early 1850s, while the government deliberated and experimented, where did the prisoners go? Those of the June Days of 1848, of the June 13, 1849 revolt, of the December 1851 coup d'état? Most of those not immediately sent to Algeria were kept on the pontoons, with the felons, awaiting transportation. On the frigates *Canada, Mogador,* and *Duguesclin,* thousands of Frenchmen suffered deprivation and degradation. Among the prisoners were former representatives, physicians, even a prefect. Raspail was comparatively lucky, for at the time of Louis Napoleon's coup d'état he was jailed at Doullens.

Raspail raised the problem of penal reform as soon as he became a member of the legislature. On June 17, 1870, he presented a bill with the ultimate aim of "abolishing pain as a legal form of punishment." [57] The attitude of society toward offenders must change, he argued. Even criminals must not be treated punitively, but with a view toward their rehabilitation through socially mean-

[57] *Annales du . . . corps législatif,* June 17, 1870 (IV, 533–34). See also Archives nationales, Series c 1142, document No. 134.

ingful work. They are sick rather than wicked, he believed, unless corrupted by life in prison. "All means of inflicting pain, moral or physical, must be completely abandoned." [58] Houses of detention should be closed, hard labor and the death penalty abolished. "The day will come," he predicted, "when men will blush to read that their brothers were once condemned to suffer for four years, for two years, even for three months, in silence and isolation, where intelligence and morality perish." [59] Felons susceptible of rehabilitation should be sent to "one of our salubrious, arable, and exploitable islands" with their families. If the wife refused to go along, divorce should be allowed.[60]

The rapporteur of Raspail's bill seemed intent on killing it fast. He stressed that Raspail had "lived in a state of perpetual hostility to the institutions and laws of his country," and concluded that "his proposal could not properly be called a bill." [61] The legislature seemed relieved and passed on to the next item on the agenda.

In the meantime Raspail pressed on with the major and most successful legislative effort of his life: total amnesty for political prisoners. The issue had been close to his heart ever since his repeated jail sentences of the 1830s. In the *Reformer* of 1835 he had already demanded the abolition of this penalty for political opponents. In the *Friend of the People* of 1848, he persisted. Had he been free to take his seat in the Constituent Assembly in the fall of 1848, he would have been a sponsor of a bill aiming at complete amnesty. This bill, introduced on October 14, 1848, was co-sponsored by fifty-nine convinced republicans, among them Eugène Raspail, Ledru-Rollin, and Demosthène Ollivier. It failed. So did four others.[62] In the people's mind, Raspail's name was from then on connected with the amnesty issue. Witness, for example, a newspaper article in *Le peuple souverain* of Lyons where, on May 18, 1849, Benjamin Raspail and eleven other democrats were

[58] F.-V. Raspail, *Réformes sociales*, 445.
[59] *Annales du . . . corps législatif*, July 8, 1869 (IV, 204).
[60] F.-V. Raspail, *Réformes sociales*, 443–44.
[61] *Annales du . . . corps législatif*, June 17, 1870 (IV, 533–34).
[62] For an excellent discussion of the amnesty issue, see J. T. Joughin, *The Paris Commune in French Politics 1871–1880* (Baltimore, 1955). This reference is to p. 60.

nominated to the National Assembly. "Each of these [twelve] names was greeted with enthusiastic applause; Raspail's name was accompanied with the unanimous shout, rising from all hearts 'Amnesty; Amnesty!' May the echo reach Doullens and soften the rigors of a captivity which our triumph will terminate at last." [63]

In May 1876 Raspail was at last able to raise the amnesty issue in the Chamber of Deputies.[64] He spoke with passion of the patriotism and honesty of the thousands of exiles: "Believe me, let them come home, those men who now enrich foreign countries with our national industry, just like the Protestant refugees in 1685 . . ." [65] He appealed to noble sentiments: "In case of civil war, amnesty . . . is the duty of the winner; it means that injuries are forgotten, that the strong have forgiven the disarmed." [66] He rejected any offer of a pardon, because it "implied crime." [67] If his bill were defeated, he warned that the fight for a total amnesty would go on: "Every three months, according to your rules, we shall fulfill the same act of humanity toward our suffering fellow citizens." [68]

His language was inflammatory, but his voice was low. He was heckled and interrupted. Some bored and angry deputies called for closure. Others objected. Benjamin Raspail tried to quiet the general turmoil by speaking from the rostrum. Finally, with order restored,

[63] Quoted in S. Commissaire, *Mémoires et souvenirs*, I, 219.

[64] *Annales* . . . *de la chambre des députés*, 1876 (I, 151 ff. and II, 95 ff.). See also X. Raspail, *De la nécessité de l'amnistie* (Paris, 1876).

[65] *Annales* . . . *de la chambre des députés*, May 18, 1876 (II, 97).

[66] *Ibid.*, 96.

[67] *Ibid.*, 95.

[68] *Ibid.*, 98. The "Raspail bill" read as follows: "This amnesty shall apply to all those condemned for actions pertaining to the events of March, April, and May 1871. Prosecution connected with these events is and remains void. This full and total amnesty includes all crimes and misdemeanors relating to politics or to the press, and to all convictions concerning political events since the last amnesty of 1870."

It was greeted with shouts of "That means the Pantheon for the murderers." It was signed, among others, by Raspail and his son, by Georges Clémenceau and Edouard Lockroy, both of whom spoke at length in support of the bill, by Louis Blanc, by Raspail's fellow-exiles in Belgium, Greppo and Madier-Montjau, by Dr. Naquet who would shortly eulogize the dead Raspail.

It evidently created a stir abroad, since it was translated into German. See F. Rohleder, *Die Pariser Kommune vor der Deputiertenkammer in Versailles; Generaldebatte über die Amnestieanträge und Rede Raspail's (Vater) vom 16–18. Mai 1876* (Braunschweig, 1876).

the Assembly voted to reject the amnesty bill 392 to 50. Victor Hugo's bill in the Senate, identical to Raspail's in the Chamber, was not even discussed, but died in committee.

The "Raspail bill" failed, but the issue now moved into the forefront of socialist objectives. On January 20, 1878, two weeks after Raspail's death, the proposal was made at a socialist rally in Paris that Raspail's vacant seat in the legislature be used to dramatize the amnesty issue: Auguste Blanqui would be the socialist candidate, although he was ill, seventy-five years old, and serving a life sentence in Clairvaux prison. For every subsequent vacancy, Blanqui was the socialist candidate. In March, nearly fifteen hundred persons at a socialist rally in Paris voted to press for the amnesty—and to deposit a wreath on Raspail's grave with the inscription: "To Raspail, from the Friends of Amnesty." [69]

At last on July 11, 1880, the bill was passed. And just in time for a celebration on July 14, which had recently been consecrated as a national holiday on the motion of a deputy from the Seine, Benjamin Raspail. The eldest son thus helped honor his late father's major legislative achievement.

[69] J. T. Joughin, *The Paris Commune* . . . , 166–67.

CONCLUSION

LOOKING BACK ON HIS CAREER, Raspail saw a constancy of purpose and direction that filled him with pride. And indeed, judged by his own criteria, Raspail's life was a success. Had he not, as a youngster, dreamt of achieving greatness in medicine, science, or law? He had contributed original work to science—to microscopy and histochemistry; and, through the "Raspail system of medicine" (although it lacked experimental proof) he had encouraged the masses to comply with hygienic and preventive precautions, thus preparing them to cope with public health measures. He could also derive well-deserved satisfaction from the memories of the suffering he had stoically borne in defense of his ideals. In terms of his own goals, Raspail was justified in seeing his life as a success.

From a more objective point of view, what was Raspail's role in French science, medicine, politics? The scientists have surely made amends for ignoring his work of the 1820s. The doctors still scorn him; even the fact that he emphasized contagion and prepared the ground for Pasteur does not count with them. Public health and sanitation mixed with socialist politics has not yet found favor with the French medical profession. In politics, Raspail left a

289

mark, but his popularity lay with the masses rather than the leaders; he was stronger as a symbol after his death than during his lifetime.

A critical observer might point out that, although his philosophy and his language remained that of a scientist and a democrat, yet, with every political revolution he changed his role and, indeed, his profession. He turned tutor, experimental scientist, republican organizer, orator, author, medical practitioner, scientific popularizer, presidental candidate, and deputy, as the occasion warranted. To Raspail these multifarious activities appeared as the single-minded efforts of a lifetime to lead France toward social and political democracy. To him, as to many others, political and social equality were but two facets of the same ideal. Observers as different as Alexis de Tocqueville and Karl Marx had agreed on that. But even science was democracy's ally in the pursuit of equality—or so it seemed to many of Raspail's contemporaries. Indeed, politicians and social scientists from the Utopian Socialists (at the beginning of Raspail's life) to the Social Darwinists (near its close), did not hesitate to infer and deduce political and social dogmas from scientific data nor did they hesitate to use "science" in their pursuit of democracy.

The complexity and contradictions inherent in these views arise from the many meanings that can be given to the term "science" and the meaning that Raspail himself gave to the concept. His own efforts evolved from experimental laboratory technique to medical therapy and eventually to advocacy of governmental involvement in science and health. True, experiment, therapy, and government programs can all pursue and subserve science, but the role of any one man changes according to the function he fulfills in the advance toward his scientific objective. To Raspail they were all equally valid and, somehow, identical.

In fact, he did not serve his ideal in a scientific manner, at least not after the Revolution of 1830. Had his passion for science been the same in 1835 as in 1830, he would again have worked alone, with makeshift equipment and sparse supplies, as under the Restoration. When, in 1835, he returned to the laboratory, he was unable to keep his mind on pure research. More than that, after 1835 his democratic passion affected his approach to biology and to medicine. It would seem as if his long involvement in political struggles determined his very concept of life: that instead of seeing nature, in particular the human body, as the scene of multiple interactions and interrelationships, he ended by perceiving a vast battlefield where health and disease vied for the possession of all living creatures. He would have been delighted with the military terminology of a later age—which he indeed foreshadowed—with "bodily defenses," "toxins" and "anti-toxins." He turned into a passionate fighter for the health of individuals and of society. He had lost the taste and the detachment needed for "pure" research.

More and more Raspail assumed the attitude of an evangelist and of a preacher. And one soon detects the revered image of the Abbé Esseyric and his Jansenist teaching in Raspail's devotion to science. The role that Esseyric's religious and intellectual convictions suggested—the role of leader for a persecuted minority—suited Raspail well. As a child he chose this man as his mentor, for reasons that lie buried, of course, in the history of his own emotional and academic development, in the history of revolutionary Carpentras and of the Raspail family—his jovial father's mysterious death not the least of them. The persecuted minority, convinced that it is morally and intellectually superior—that is the group to which Raspail felt he belonged. How else to explain his failure to seek proper training in science, medicine, or law? his espousal of the microscope, a tool favored in Germany in the 1820s, but not in France? his conspicuous alliance with the carbonari, his ostentatious rebuffs to the July Monarchy, his eagerness to tangle with lawyers and judges, his illegal acts, even under the Second and Third Republics?

He chose a role as leader of the oppressed, as their teacher, guide, and adviser. It is true, as one obituary pointed out, that Raspail "practiced medical charity and preached cleanliness as if it were a religion" [1] and also that "a religious faith in humanity" [2] was one of his characteristic traits. But when Pierre Mauriac called Raspail "the Don Quixote of medicine," [3] he understood the combative, idealistic, uncompromising character of the man, but failed to perceive the nature of the windmills. For Raspail was not tilting at phantoms, nor was his Dulcinea a lowly creature. Rather, his ac-

[1] A. Scholl, *L'Evènement*, June 3, 1878.
[2] I. Tchernoff, *Le parti républicain sous la monarchie de juillet. Formation et évolution de la doctrine républicaine*, 252.
[3] P. Mauriac, *La médecine et l'intelligence* (1840–1940), (Paris, 1949), 53.

tivities on behalf of social medicine put him in the broad democratic and humanitarian tradition stemming from the French Revolution, that of the Duc de la Rochefoucault-Liancourd's *Comité de mendi-cité*,[4] of the Marquis de Condorcet's concept of the "social art," [5] and of the idealistic "forty-eighter" so aptly characterized by Jean Cassou as searching for "true Christianity," for "a humanism . . . a synthesis." [6]

And when Octave Aubry described Raspail in 1870 as a "ghost from the dead past," [7] he focused on the man's white hair, not on his message. For this past, the "spirit of 1789" as interpreted by socialist democracy, was very much alive in late nineteenth-century France. And it was Raspail who had significantly helped broaden the meaning of the republican ideal of equality by insisting that an equal right to the protection and promotion of good health was every citizen's due. Public health and preventive medicine, he taught, must become the active concern of every democratic government.

[4] See the forthcoming book by David Brandenburg.

[5] H. Guerlac, "Science as a Social and Historical Phenomenon: Some Aspects of Science during the French Revolution," *The Scientific Monthly*, LXXX, 93–101.

[6] J. Cassou, *Le Quarante-huitard* (Paris, 1948), 20, 40–41.

[7] O. Aubry, *The Second Empire* (New York, 1940), 456.

BIBLIOGRAPHY

Manuscript sources other than those in private hands

Archives du Département de la Seine et de la Ville de Paris. Fonds Raspail.

Archives nationales, Paris. Dossier Raspail. Entrée No. 1684. Also particularly useful: Series BB [18] and BB [21].

Bibliothèque de la Chaux-de-Fonds, Switzerland. Fonds Berner. Family papers of Xavier Raspail, left to his friend, M. Berner.

Bibliothèque historique de la Ville de Paris. Dossier Raspail. Série biographique.

Bibliothèque Inguimbertine, Carpentras, Vaucluse. MS 2191, F.-V. Raspail, "Ebauche de traduction d'Anacréon"; MS 2157, "En l'honneur de la Sainte Vierge"; MS 1248, "Sur la non-infallibilité du pape"; MS 2405, Lettres; MS Carpentras. Séances du conseil municipal de la Ville de Carpentras. 1803.

Bibliothèque du Muséum d'histoire naturelle de Paris. Fonds Raspail. MS 2388.

Musée Calvet, Avignon, Vaucluse. MS 1679, Correspondance de Mgr. Périer, évêque d'Avignon, avec le ministre des cultes et les préfets de Vaucluse et du Gard.

293

Periodicals and Journals Consulted

Académie de médecine, Paris. *Mémoires*, 1828 ff.; *Bulletin*, 1836 ff.

Académie des sciences. *Comptes-rendus hebdomadaires des séances.* 1835 ff.

Annales d'histochimie. 1956 ff.

Annales d'hygiène publique et de médecine légale. 1829 ff.

Asmodée: Revue des journaux, ouvrages de médecine, chimie, pharmacie et sciences accessoires. Oct. 1845–Jan. 1846.

Bulletin of the History of Medicine. 1933 ff.

Bulletin de la société française d'histoire de la médecine. 1902 ff.

Le Droit. Journal des tribunaux de la jurisprudence, des débats judiciaires et de la législation. 1835 ff.

Esculape. Journal des spécialités médico-chirurgicales. Paris: 1839–1841, 3 vols. in 1.

L'Expérience. Journal de médecine et de chirurgie. 1837–1844, 14 vols.

France. Annales du Sénat et du Corps Législatif. 1869–1870.

France. Assemblée nationale. Annales du Sénat et de la Chambre. 1876–1878.

La France médicale. 1854–1914, 61 vols.

Gazette des hôpitaux, see *La Lancette française.*

Gazette médicale de Paris. 1830–1916, 87 vols.

Isis. An International Review Devoted to the History of Science and Its Cultural Influences. 1912 ff.

Journal de chimie médicale, de pharmacie, de toxicologie. 1825–1876, 52 vols.

Journal des Débats. 1814–1864, 50 vols.

Journal général de médecine, de chirurgie et de pharmacie. 1796–1830, 111 vols.

Journal of the History of Medicine and Allied Sciences. 1946 ff.

Journal de médecine, chirurgie, pharmacie. 1801–1817, 40 vols.

Journal de pharmacie et des sciences accessoires contenant le bulletin de la Société de pharmacie de Paris. 1815–1841, 27 vols.

La Lancette française: Gazette des hôpitaux civils et militaires. 1828 ff.

Le Lycée: Journal des sciences et des sociétés savantes.

Le Moniteur universel. Journal officiel de la république française. 1848–1852.

Muséum d'histoire naturelle. *Mémoires.* 1815–1832, 20 vols.

Le National. 1830.

Némésis médicale illustrée, A.-F.-H. Fabre, ed., 1840.

Paris médical. 1875–1891, 16 vols.; 1910–1951, 41 vols.

La Presse médicale. 1893 ff.

La révolution de 1848. 1904 ff.

La Revue des Deux Mondes. 1831 ff.

Revue d'histoire de Lyon. 1902–1914, 13 vols.

Revue d'histoire moderne et contemporaine. 1953 ff.

Société d'histoire naturelle de Paris. *Mémoires.* 1823–1834, 5 vols.

Société philomathique de Paris. *Nouveau bulletin.* 1825–1832.

Books and articles by raspail*

Almanach et calendrier météorologique pour 1873 and *Almanach et calendrier météorologique pour 1874* (Paris: chez l'éditeur de M. Raspail, 1872, 1873).

L'Ami du peuple en 1848, An Ier de la république reconquise, Feb. 27–May 4, 1848 (Paris: Au bureau du journal).

With J.-F. Saigey: *Annales des sciences d'observation, comprenant l'astronomie, la physique, la chimie, la minéralogie, la géologie, la physiologie, et l'anatomie des deux règnes, la botanique, la zoologie, les théories mathématiques et les principales applications de toutes ces sciences à la météorologie, à l'agriculture, aux arts et à la médecine* (Paris: Baudouin, 1829–1830, 4 vols.).

"Appareils pour l'emploi du camphre en poudre et des cigarettes de camphre," *La Lancette française: Gazette des hôpitaux civils et militaires,* November 17, 1838.

Appel à l'humanité (Paris: Raffin, n.d. [1848]).

Appel urgent au concours des hommes éclairés de toutes les profes-

---

* The profusion of almanacs, pamphlets, manuals, posters, and the like emanating from Raspail's pen makes the customary division of his writings into "books" and "articles" rather useless. All his writings have therefore been listed under this heading, except for his scientific articles, which will be found in the succeeding category.

sions contre les empoisonnements industriels (Paris: chez l'éditeur de M. Raspail, 1863).

Aux citoyens-électeurs de la Seine, Merci! (Paris: Imprimerie Courlet, 1848).

Aux citoyens-électeurs des 4 et 5 juin (Paris: Imprimerie Schneider, 1848).

Aux citoyens-électeurs du Rhône (Paris: Imprimerie Schneider, 1848).

Le choléra en 1865 (Paris: chez l'éditeur de M. Raspail, 1865).

Le choléra en 1865 et 1866 (Paris: chez l'éditeur de M. Raspail, 1866).

Cigarettes de camphre et camphatières hygiéniques; contre une foule de maux lents à guérir ou même incurables et chroniques qui ne réclament pas immédiatement ou ne réclament plus la présence du médecin, ou bien enfin qu'on est condamné à soulager en son absence (Paris: Collas, 1839).

Conclusions pour M. F.-V. Raspail, homme de lettres, contre (1) Les sieurs Levavasseur, Lacour et Leriche, associés en participation; (2) Les sieurs Lefrançais et Didier, syndics de la faillite Leriche; (3) Les sieurs Lecou, Danvin, Laîné, Nicolas, Gabriel, Delente, Labitte, Mulot, libraires détaillants [Tribunal de police correctionnelle de la Seine, 8ème chambre, présidence M. d'Herbelot, 20 mars 1847] (Paris: Schneider, 1847).

Cours élémentaire d'agriculture et d'économie rurale à l'usage des écoles primaires (Paris: Hachette, 1832).

Défense et allocution du citoyen Raspail, président de la Société des amis du peuple, aux assises des 10, 11, et 12 janvier 1832 (Paris: Auguste Mie, 1832).

De la Pologne sur les bords de la Vistule et dans l'émigration (Paris: Imprimerie de Bourgogne, 1839); tr. into Polish (Poitiers, 1840).

Départ des prisonniers de Vincennes, leurs adieux au peuple; les dernières paroles des citoyens Barbès, Raspail, Blanqui, et Huber adressées au Président de la république, Louis Napoléon (Paris: N. Chaix, 1849).

Discours . . . dans l'assemblée générale de l'Association républicaine pour la liberté de la presse et reproduit pour sa défense devant la cour d'assises qui l'a acquitté (Paris: Publications du Populaire, 1834).

Discours de M. Ledru-Rollin prononcé au banquet du Châtelet le 22 septembre 1848 suivi des remerciements de F.-V. Raspail (Paris: Dairnvall, 1849).

Discours prononcé par M. Raspail sur la tombe de Ludwig Börne le 15 février 1837 (Paris: Renouard, 1837).

Domestic Medicine; or Plain Instructions in the Art of Preserving and Restoring Health by Simple and Efficient Means, G. L. Strauss, ed. (London: John Weale, 1853).

"Essai d'analyse microscopique sur le pain des prisons de Paris par un homme qui en a mangé," *Le Lycée: Journal des sciences et des sociétés savantes*, 5ème année, No. 28 (Dec. 4, 1831), 117–19.

Le fermier vétérinaire ou Méthode aussi économique que facile de préserver et de guérir les animaux domestiques et même les végétaux cultivés du plus grand nombre de leurs maladies (Paris: chez l'éditeur de M. Raspail, 1854; 2nd ed., 1864; 3rd ed., by Xavier Raspail, 1882; tr. into Italian: Turin, 1856; Spanish: Lima, 1856, Madrid, 1896; German: Bern, 1885).

Histoire naturelle de la santé et de la maladie chez les végétaux et chez les animaux en général et en particulier chez l'homme, suivie du formulaire pour une nouvelle méthode de traitement hygiénique et curatif (Paris: A. Levavasseur, 1843, 2 vols.; 2nd ed., A. Levavasseur, 1845, 2 vols.; 3rd ed., Paris and Brussels: chez l'éditeur de M. Raspail, 1860, 3 vols.).

Lettre à Bravard (Paris: [?], 1840).

Lettre à un ami médecin (Paris: [?], March 30, 1847).

Lettre adressée à la Société libre de secours mutuels des blanchisseuses, repasseuses et adhérentes de la Ville de Lyon (Paris: [?], n.d. [1870]).

Lettre de M. J. J. Coste à M. Raspail et Réponse à M. Coste (Paris: Bureau du Réformateur, [1835]).

La lunette du donjon de Vincennes. Almanach démocratique et social de l'Ami du peuple pour 1849 (Paris: chez l'éditeur de M. Raspail, 1848).

La Lunette de Doullens. Almanach démocratique et progressif de l'Ami du peuple (Paris: chez l'éditeur de M. Raspail, 1849).

Manuel-annuaire de la santé (Paris: chez l'éditeur de M. Raspail, 1845; published every year of Raspail's life except 1848, 1853; and annually after his death until 1935). Adaptations: London, 1846, 1853; New Orleans, 1846. Tr. into Swedish: 7th ed., Stockholm, 1886; Spanish: Mexico City, 1850, Lima, 1856, Madrid, 1857, 1862, 1896, Barcelona, 1929; Portuguese: Lisbon, 1850).

Mémoire à consulter à l'appui du pourvoi en cassation de Dame Marie Cappelle, Veuve Lafarge, sur les moyens de nullité que présente l'expertise chimique (Paris: Bureau de la Gazette des Hôpitaux, 1840).

Mémoire à consulter. Pourvoi en cassation contre un arrêt rendu le 10 juillet 1856 par la chambre d'appel de police correctionnelle du Département de la Seine (présidence de M. Zangiacomi) au sujet du pro-

cès en contrefaçon de bois artificiel dit charbon de Paris (Bruxelles: Vanderauwera, 1856).

Mémoire comparatif sur l'histoire naturelle de l'insecte de la gale (Paris: Bureau du Bulletin général de thérapeutique, 1834).

Mémoire présenté à la section criminelle de la cour de cassation (Paris: Baudouin, 1835).

[pseudonym Lutrin]: *Les missionnaires en opposition avec les bonnes moeurs et avec les lois de la religion* (Paris: chez les marchands de nouveautés, 1821).

[**Dr. Raspail's**] *Neues Heilverfahren, oder theoretische und praktische Anweisung zur Selbstbehandlung der meisten heilbaren Krankheiten und zur Selbstbereitung der einfachen und bewährten Heilmittel der neuen Schule* (Leipzig: Bruno Hinze, n.d.).

Nouveaux coups de fouet scientifiques (Paris: Meilhac, 1831).

Nouveau système de chimie organique (Paris: Baillière, 1833; 2nd ed., Paris: Baillière, 1838, 3 vols.; 3rd ed., Bruxelles: Société encyclographique des sciences médicales, 1840, 2 vols.-in-1 and Atlas.)

Nouveau système de physiologie végétale et de botanique, fondé sur les méthodes d'observation qui ont été développées dans le Nouveau système de chimie organique accompagné d'un Atlas de 60 planches (Bruxelles: Haussmann Cattoir, 1837 and 1840).

Nouvelle défense et nouvelle condamnation de F.-V. Raspail à 15,000 francs de dommages-intérêts pour avoir demandé, le 8 novembre 1845, et obtenu, le 30 décembre 1847, la dissolution de la société par lui formée avec le pharmacien-droguiste [Morel] du No. 14 de la rue des Lombards (Paris: chez l'éditeur de M. Raspail, 1848).

Nouvelles études scientifiques et philologiques (Paris: chez l'éditeur de M. Raspail, 1864).

Opinion du citoyen F.-V. Raspail au sujet du plébiscite. Manifeste de F.-V. Raspail (Paris: Imprimerie Dupont, 1870).

Peu de chose, mais quelque chose (Paris: chez l'éditeur de M. Raspail, 1873, 1874, 1875, 3 vols. in 1).

Pharmacie portative et de voyage pour la méthode de traitement publiée dans l'Histoire naturelle de la santé (Paris: Collas, 1843).

Procès et défense de F.-V. Raspail poursuivi le 19 mai 1846 en exercice illégal de la médecine devant la 8ème chambre (police correctionnelle) à la requête du ministère public, et sur la dénonciation formelle des sieurs Fouquier, médecin du roi, et Orfila, doyen de la Faculté de médecine de Paris, agissant comme vice-président et président d'une association anonyme de médecins (Paris: Schneider, 1846).

Procès perdu, gageure gagnée, ou Mon dernier procès (Paris: chez l'éditeur de M. Raspail, 1857).

Propagande électorale: Prêtres et socialistes (Paris: Desoye, n.d. [1848]).

Le Réformateur: Journal quotidien des nouveaux intérêts matériels et moraux, industriels et politiques, littéraires et scientifiques (Paris: Oct. 8, 1834–Oct. 27, 1835).

Réforme pénitentiaire: Lettres sur les prisons de Paris (Paris: Tamisey et Champion, 1839, 2 vols.).

Réformes sociales (Paris: chez l'éditeur de M. Raspail, 1872).

Réponse de M. Raspail à l'avis de MM. Pelletier, Payen, Gaultier de Claubry. Affaire Elkington contre MM. Bédier et Simon, le 15 décembre 1836 (Paris: Imprimerie de Bourgogne, 1836).

Résumé par ordre de dates des moyens présentés à la cour le 1er et 8 décembre 1847 par F.-V. Raspail, appelant d'une sentence arbitrale qui le condamne à 50,000 francs de dommages-intérêts envers le Sieur Morel, pharmacien-droguiste, rue des Lombards, 14 (Paris: Schneider, 1848).

Revue complémentaire des sciences appliquées à la médecine et pharmacie, à l'agriculture, aux arts et à l' industrie (Paris: chez l'éditeur de M. Raspail et Bruxelles: Librairie nouvelle, 1854–1860, 6 vols.).

Revue élémentaire de médecine et de pharmacie domestiques ainsi que des sciences accessoires et usuelles mises à la portée de tout le monde (Paris: chez l'éditeur de M. Raspail, 1847–1849, 2 vols.).

Sainte Liberté! ton nom n'est pas un blasphème. Discours prononcé à la loge d'adoption des amis bienfaisans, samedi 16 mars 1822 (Paris: Corréard, 1822).

SCIENTIFIC ARTICLES BY RASPAIL*

Botany

"Mémoire sur la formation de l'embryon dans les graminées," *Annales des sciences naturelles,* IV (1824), 271–319.

"Essai d'une classification générale des graminées, fondée sur l'étude

---

* The articles in each category appear in chronological order. No mention is made of condensed versions of papers given *in extenso* in other journals, or of the numerous brief review articles written by Raspail between 1826 and 1830, or of brief polemic pieces. Most of the last two groups of papers can be found in *Bulletin universel des sciences et de l'industrie,* Sections 1 and 2, 1825–1828, and in *Annales des sciences d'observation,* 1829–1830.

physiologique de cette famille," *Ibid.,* IV (1824), 423–51; V (1825), 287–311, 433–60.

"Réponse à la Note sur les graminées de M. J. J. C. de la Harpe," *Ibid.,* VIII (1826), 76–89.

"Note sur les accidents morbides auxquels la semence des Stipa pennata et capillata expose les troupeaux," *Ibid.,* IX (1826), 82–84.

"Mémoire concernant l'ouverture que Grew a décrite le premier sur le test des graines, suivi d'une notice sur le genre Pontederia," *Mémoires du Muséum d'histoire naturelle,* XIV (1827), 131–71.

"Notice sur la détermination spécifique des céréales trouvées par M. Passalacqua dans un tombeau égyptien et sur le mode de préparation qu'on leur a fait subir," *Ibid.,* XV (1827), 145–56.

"Observations et expériences propres à démontrer que les granules qui sortent pendant l'explosion du grain de pollen, bien loin d'être les analogues des animalcules spermatiques, comme Gleichen l'avait pensé le premier, ne sont pas même des corps organisés," *Mémoires de la Société d'histoire naturelle de Paris,* IV (1828), 347–61.

"Note sur le développement par stolons du Conoplea cylindrica," *Ibid.,* 238–45.

"Essai d'expériences et d'observations sur l'espèce végétale en général et en particulier sur la valeur des caractères spécifiques des graminées," *Annales des sciences d'observation,* I (1829), 406–38.

"Monographie de deux espèces de Panicum qu'une erreur d'observation avait érigées en genre sous le nom de Monachne, accompagnée de considérations relatives à quelques autres genres fondés sur des caractères tout aussi illusoires," *Ibid.,* I (1829), 438–51.

"Sur le genre Hierochloe et ses analogues et sur les analogies du Festuca flabellata Lamck.," *Ibid.,* II (1829), 70–90.

"Déviations physiologiques et métamorphoses réelles du Lolium," *Ibid.,* 233–44.

"Revue analytique de quelques-unes des espèces Cynodon Rasp. qui constituaient l'ancien genre Arundo," *Ibid.,* III (1830), 99–113.

"Sur le Centaurea Myacantha D.C.," *Ibid.,* 113–16.

"Les arborisations des calcédoines et des agates mousseuses proviennent-elles, en certains cas, de la présence de Conferves fossiles," *Ibid.,* 243–51.

"Examen critique des recherches chimiques que M. H. Braconnot vient de publier sur le pollen du Typha latifolia," *Ibid.,* 386–97.

"Etudes agrostographiques," *Ibid.,* IV (1830), 274–80.

"Histoire de la théorie de la structure de la fleur," *Ibid.*, 280–85.

Zoology

"Histoire naturelle de l'Alcyonelle fluviatile et de tous les genres voisins, considérés, soit sous le rapport de leur organisation et de leur identité spécifique, soit sous le rapport physiologique de leurs tentacules avec les branchies des mollusques et des animalcules ou infusoires ou sperma- tiques," *Mémoires de la Société d'histoire naturelle de Paris,* IV (1828), 75–165.

"Note sur la parturition vivipare des bivalves, adressée à l'Académie des sciences le 14 juillet 1828," *Annales des sciences d'observation,* I (1829), 122–27.

"Histoire naturelle des bélemnites accompagnée de la description et de la classification des espèces que M. Eméric, de Castellane, a recueillies dans les Basses-Alpes de Provence," *Ibid.*, 271–331.

"Additions au mémoire sur les bélemnites," *Ibid.*, II (1829), 65–70.

"Anatomie comparée de deux espèces de Strongylus qui vivent dans le Delphinum phocena," *Ibid.*, 244–54.

"La gale humaine est-elle le produit d'un insecte?," *Ibid.*, 446–58.

"Note sur les bélemnites," *Ibid.*, III (1830), 86–88.

"Recherches sur l'insecte parasite de la gale du cheval," *La Lancette française: Gazette des hôpitaux civils et militaires,* V, No. 34 (August 15, 1831), 135.

Microscopic Anatomy and Physiology

"Recherches physiologiques sur les graisses et le tissu adipeux," *Réper- toire général d'anatomie et de physiologie pathologiques et de clinique chirurgicale,* III (1827), 165–82.

"Premier mémoire sur la structure intime des tissus de nature animale," *Ibid.*, IV (1827), 148–61.

"Anatomie microscopique des nerfs, pour démontrer leur structure intime et l'absence de canaux contenant un fluide et pouvant après la mort être injectés," *Ibid.*, 185–92 [signed by both Raspail and G. Breschet].

"Anatomie microscopique des flocons du chorion de l'oeuf humain," *Ibid.*, V (1828), 211–16 [signed by both Raspail and Breschet].

Microscopic Chemistry

"Tableau comparatif des charactères physiques des diverses fécules," *Bulletin des sciences mathématiques, physiques et chimiques,* Section I of *Bulletin universel des sciences et de l'industrie,* VI (1826), 333–39.

"Nouveau réactif propre dans les expériences de chimie microscopique à faire distinguer le sucre, l'huile, l'albumine et la résine," *Annales des sciences d'observation*, I (1829), 72–93.

"Description d'un goniomètre microscopique," *Ibid.*, 228–30.

"Réaction singulière de l'acide sulfurique sur l'albumine de l'oeuf de poule," *Ibid.*, II (1829), 287–90.

"Essai de chimie microscopique appliquée à la physiologie, ou L'art de transporter le laboratoire sur le porte-objet, dans l'étude des corps organisés," *Ibid.*, II (1829), 430–45; III (1830), 65–82, 216–28, 368–86; IV (1830), 65–81, 225–51.

Paleontology

"Note sur le rôle qu'on a fait jouer aux fossiles dans la détermination de l'ancienneté relative des couches qui composent la croûte du globe," *Annales des sciences d'observation*, III (1830), 408–13.

Forensic Medicine

"Sur les moyens, soit chimiques, soit microscopiques, qu'on a tout récemment proposés, pour reconnaître les taches de sang en médecine légale," *Journal général de médecine, de chirurgie et de pharmacie*, CII (1828), 335–50.

"Polémique à ce sujet," *Ibid.*, 362–72, 373–84.

"Médecine légale. Examen critique des recherches que M. Barruel vient de publier sur les moyens de distinguer le sang des animaux," *Annales des sciences d'observation*, II (1829), 133–43.

Botany and Chemistry

"Développement de la fécule dans les organes de la fructification des céréales et analyse microscopique de la fécule, suivie d'expériences propres à en expliquer la conversion en gomme," *Annales des sciences naturelles*, VI (1825), 224–39, 384–427.

"Additions au Mémoire sur l'analyse microscopique de la fécule," *Ibid.*, VII (1826), 325–35.

"Note sur une fécule singulière, extraite des tiges souterraines du Typha angustifolia," *Bulletin des sciences mathématiques, astronomiques, physiques et chimiques*, Section I of *Bulletin universel des sciences et de l'industrie*, VIII (1827), 264–67.

"Mémoire sur l'hordéïne et le gluten, et sur la difficulté d'isoler, par les procédés en grand, les différents principes dont se compose une farine," *Mémoires du Muséum d'histoire naturelle*, XVI (1828), 253–94.

"Nouvelles observations sur les cristaux calcaires qu'on trouve dans les tissues végétaux vivants," *Mémoires de la société d'histoire naturelle de Paris,* IV (1828), 413–22.

"Analyse microscopique du suc qui circule dans les tubes des Chara," *Annales des sciences d'observation,* I (1829), 396–429.

Botany, Chemistry, and Zoology

"Recherches chimiques et physiologiques destinées à expliquer non seulement la structure et le développement de la feuille, du tronc, ainsi que les organes qui n'en sont qu'une transformation, mais encore la structure et le développement des tissus animaux," *Mémoires de la société d'histoire naturelle de Paris,* III (1827), 17–88, 209–313.

"Expériences de chimie microscopique, ayant pour but de démontrer l'analogie qui existe entre la disposition qu'affecte la silice, dans les Spongilles et dans certaines Eponges, et celle qu'affecte l'oxalate de chaux dans les végétaux; accompagnées de l'anatomie microscopique des Spongilles," *Ibid.,* IV (1828), 204–37.

"Expériences chimiques et physiologiques ayant pour objet de déterminer le mécanisme de la circulation dans les entre-noeuds de Chara et dans le système vasculaire des animaux," *Annales des sciences d'observation,* II (1829), 396–429.

BOOKS AND ARTICLES ABOUT RASPAIL

Anfos-Martin, A., "Raspail," in *Grandes figures vauclusiennes* (Avignon: Rullière, 1936).

Aubert, A., "Raspail," in *Les vauclusiens ou Dictionnaire biographique spécial du département de Vaucluse* (Avignon: Seguin, 1890).

Bengolea, A. J., *Raspail: Historia de una conciencia* (Buenos Aires: Futura, 1946).

Blanchard, R., "Notices biographiques: François-Vincent Raspail," *Archives de parasitologie,* VIII (1903–1904), 5–87.

Bossu, J., *Raspail: sa vie ardente et chevaleresque* (Paris: Editions de l'idée libre, n.d.).

Breton, C.-A., *F.-V. Raspail: sa méthode et ses oeuvres, ses détracteurs et ses partisans* (Marseille: Lebon, 1868).

Capmal, P., [pseud. Jean St. Martin], *F.-V. Raspail* (Paris: Dentu, 1877).

Castel, H., *Les bienfaits de la méthode Raspail à Roubaix* (Roubaix: A. Lesguillon, 1875).

Angrand, P., *Etienne Cabet et la république de 1848* (Paris: Presses universitaires de France, 1948).

Aubry, O., *The Second Empire* (New York: Knopf, 1940).

Aulard, A., *L'état de la France en l'An VIII et an l'An IX* (Paris: Société de l'histoire de la révolution française, 1897). *Napoléon Ier et le monopole universitaire* (Paris: Colin, 1911).

Babaud-Laribière, F.-S.-L., *Histoire de l'assemblée nationale constituante* (Paris: M. Lévy, 1850, 2 vols.).

Barjavel, C.-F.-H., *Dictionnaire historique, biographique et bibliographique du Département de Vaucluse* (Carpentras: L. Devillario, 1841, 2 vols.).

Barret, Abbé, *Vie de l'abbé Sollier, vicaire général du diocèse d'Avignon* (Avignon: Aubanel, 1843).

Baunard, Mgr. *L'Episcopat français, 1802–1905* (Paris: Librairie des Saints- Pères, 1907).

Bernard, M., *Dix ans de prison au Mont-St.-Michel et à la citadelle de Doullens* (Paris: C. Joubert, 1851).

Bertier de Sauvigny, G. de, *La restauration* (Paris: Flammarion, 1955).

Billy, A., *Sainte-Beuve: sa vie et son temps* (Paris: Flammarion, 1952, 2 vols.).

Blanc, L., *History of Ten Years, 1830–1840* (London: Chapman & Hall, 1844, 2 vols.). *Pages d'histoire de la révolution de février 1848* (Paris: au bureau du "Nouveau Monde," 1850).

Blanc, L., Blanqui, Ledru-Rollin, Lamennais, Raspail, et al., *Almanach républicain démocratique pour 1850* (Paris: [?], n.d.).

Boissard, M., *Trois siécles d'histoire* (Paris: Compagnie de St. Sulpice, 1962, 3 vols.).

Brogan, D. W., *France under the Republic* (New York: Harper, 1940).

Bruhat, J., *Les journées de février 1848* (Paris: Presses universitaires de France, 1948).

Calman, A. R., *Ledru-Rollin and the Second French Republic* (New York: Columbia University Press, 1922).

Cameron, R. E., *France and the Economic Development of Europe* (Princeton: Princeton University Press, 1961).

Cassou, J., *Le quarante-huitard* (Paris: Presses universitaires de France, 1948).

Castelot, A., *Paris: The Turbulent City* (New York: Harper & Row, 1962).

Caussidière, M., *Mémoires de Caussidière, ex-préfet de police et re-présentant du peuple* (Paris: Michel Lévy, 1849, 3rd ed., 2 vols. in 1).

Charpenne, P., *Les grands épisodes de la révolution dans Avignon et le Comtat* (Avignon: Henri Guigou, 1901, 4 vols.).

Chevalier, A., *Les frères des écoles chrétiennes et l'enseignement primaire après la révolution* (1797–1830) (Paris: Poussielgue, 1887).

Chevalier, L., *Classes laborieuses et classes dangereuses* (Paris: Plon, 1958).

Commissaire, S., *Mémoires et souvenirs* (Paris: Garcet, 1888, 2 vols.).

Constantin, Abbé J.-M.-J., *Vie de Monsieur l'abbé Antoine-Anthime Frizet* (Carpentras: Tourette, n.d.).

Courtet, J., *Dictionnaire géographique, géologique, historique, archéologique et biographique des communes du Département de Vaucluse* (Avignon: Seguin, 1876).

Crémieux, A., *La Révolution de février. Etude critique* (Paris: Cornély, 1912).

Daudet, E., *La terreur blanche: épisodes et souvenirs* (Paris: Hachette, 1906).

Deries, L., *Les congrégations religieuses au temps de Napoléon* (Paris: Félix Alcan, 1929).

Desbordes-Valmore, M., *Poésies choisies* (Paris: Garnier, 1935).

De Seyn, E., ed., *Dictionnaire historique et géographique des communes belges* (Turnhout: Brepols, 1923, 2 vols.).

Deslandres, M., *Histoire constitutionnelle de la France de 1789 à 1870* (Paris: Sirey, 1932, 2 vols.).

Dolléans, E., and J.-L. Puech, *Proudhon et la révolution de 1848* (Paris: Presses universitaires de France, 1948).

Duquai, E., *Les grands procès politiques: les accusés du 15 mai 1848* (Paris: Chevalier, 1869).

Durand, Chanoine A., *Un prélat constitutionnel: Jean-François Périer,* (1740–1824) (Paris: Bloud, 1902).

Duruy, A., *L'instruction publique et la révolution* (Paris: Hachette, 1882).

Dutacq, F., *Histoire politique de Lyon pendant la révolution de 1848* (Paris: Cornély, 1910).

Duveau, G., *La vie ouvrière en France sous le second empire* (Paris: Gallimard, 1946).

Eliot, G., *Middlemarch* (London: Zodiac Press, 1950).

Etex, A., *Les souvenirs d'un artiste* (Paris: Dentu, 1877).

Flaubert, G., *Correspondance* (Paris: Conard, 1930, 9 vols.). *Bouvard et Pécuchet* (Paris: Conard, 1923).

Ford, F. L., *Robe and Sword: The Regrouping of the French Aristocracy after Louis XIV* (New York: Harper and Row, 1965).

Gallois, L., *Histoire de la révolution de 1848* (Paris: Naud & Gourju, 1849, 5 vols.).

Garnier, A., *Mgr. Frayssinous, son rôle dans l'université sous la restauration* (Paris: Picard, 1925).

Gerbod, P., *La condition universitaire en France au dix-neuvième siècle* (Paris: Presses universitaires de France, 1965).

Girard, L., *La garde nationale* (Paris, Plon, 1964).

Goncourt, E. and J., *Journal*, vol. VI: 1863–1864 (Monaco: Imprimerie nationale, 1956).

Granget, Abbé, *Histoire du diocèse d'Avignon et des anciens diocèses dont il est formé* (Avignon: Seguin, 1862, 2 vols.).

Hatin, E., *Bibliographie historique et critique de la presse périodique française* (Paris: Firmin Didot, 1866). *La presse sous la restauration*, vol. 8 of *Histoire politique et littéraire de la presse en France* (Paris: Poulet-Malassis et de Broise, 1859–1860, 8 vols.).

Heine, H., *Französische Zustände: Lutezia*, vol. 9 of *Sämmtliche Werke* (Hamburg: Hoffman & Campe, 1884).

Index librorum prohibitorum (Rome: Typographia Camera Apostolica, 1837).

Isaac, J., and Ch.-H. Pouthas, *Révolution, empire, première moitié du dix-neuvième siècle* (Paris: Hachette, 1929).

Jauffret, Count J., *Mémoires historiques sur les affaires écclésiastiques de France pendant les premières années du 19ème siècle* (Paris: Le Clerc, 1819–1824, 3 vols.).

Joughin, J. T., *The Paris Commune in French Politics, 1871–1880* (Baltimore, Johns Hopkins University Studies in Historical and Political Science, Series 73, No. 1, 1955, 2 vols.).

Juste, Th., *Le Vicomte Charles Vilain XIIII, ministre d'état, ancien membre du congrès national et ancien ministre des affaires étrangères* (Bruxelles: Muquardt, 1875).

Krakowski, E., *La naissance de la troisième république: Challemel-Lacour, le philosophe et l'homme d'état* (Paris: V. Attinger, 1932).

La Gorce, P. de, *Histoire de la seconde république française* (Paris: Plon-Nourrit, 1911).

Lamartine, A. de, *Histoire de la révolution de 1848* (Bruxelles: F. Michel, 1849, 2 vols.).

Latreille, A., *La période contemporaine,* vol. 3 of *Histoire du catholicisme en France* (Paris: Ed. Spes, 1962).

Lefèbvre, G., *La révolution française* (Paris: Presses universitaires de France, 1951).

Lefrançais, G., *Souvenirs d'un révolutionnaire* (Paris: Eds. Les Temps Nouveaux, 1886).

Le Play, F., *Les ouvriers européens,* vol. 5 of *Les ouvriers de l'occident* (Tours: Name & fils, 1878, 2nd ed.).

Liabastres, J., *Histoire de Carpentras* (Carpentras: Barrier, 1891).

Maurin, A., *Le terreur blanche* (Paris: Arnic L'aîné, 1850).

Mistler, J., *La Librairie Hachette de 1826 à nos jours* (Paris: Hachette, 1964).

Monier, S., *Blanqui* (Paris: Presses universitaires de France, 1948).

Monod, G., *La vie et la pensée de Jules Michelet, 1798–1852* (Paris: Champion, 1923, 2 vols.).

de Nerval, G. [pseud. of Gérard Labrunie], *La Bohême galante* (Paris: Le Divan, 1927).

Perdiguier, A., *Mémoires d'un compagnon* (Moulins: Eds. Cahiers du Centre, 1914).

Perreux, G., *La propagande républicaine au début de la monarchie de juillet* (Paris: Hachette, 1930).

Pic, P., *Traité élémentaire de législation industrielle: Les lois ouvrières* (Paris: Arthur Rousseau, 1922, 5th ed.).

Ponteil, F., *Histoire de l'enseignement en France, 1789–1964* (Paris: Sirey, 1966).

Portalis, J.-E.-M., *Discours, rapports et travaux inédits sur le Concordat de 1801* (Paris: Joubert, 1845).

Procès des accusés d'avril devant la Cour des Pairs (Paris: Paguerre, 1834–1835, 2 vols.).

Procès des accusés du 15 mai devant la Haute Cour de Bourges (Paris: Imprimerie de Beaulé et Maignand, 1849).

Procès du citoyen Huber devant la Haute Cour de Justice de Versailles (Paris: Ballard, 1849).

Procès du droit d'association, soutenu et gagné en décembre 1832 par la Société des amis du peuple (Paris: Rouanet, 1833).

Procès des vingt-sept, ou de la Société des droits de l'homme et des élèves de l'Ecole polytechnique (Paris: Riou, 1834).

Quicherat, J., *Histoire de Sainte-Barbe: collège, communauté, institution* (Paris: Hachette, 1864, 3 vols.).

Quinet, Mme. E., *Edgar Quinet depuis l'exil* (Paris: Calmann-Lévy, 1889).

Raspail, Xavier, *Catalogue de livres anciens ayant fait partie de la bibliothèque de F.-V. Raspail* (Paris: Ch. Berger, 1912). *De la nécessité de l'amnistie* (Paris: chez l'éditeur de M. Raspail, 1876). *Procès de l'almanach Raspail. 1874. Compte-rendu in extenso* (Paris: chez l'éditeur de M. Raspail, 1874).

Renard, G., *La république de 1848,* vol. 9 of *Histoire socialiste, 1789–1900,* J. Jaurès, ed. (Paris: l'auteur, 1906).

Resnick, D. P., *The White Terror and the Political Reaction after Waterloo* (Cambridge, Mass., Harvard University Press, 1966).

Rocquain, F., *L'état de la France au 18 brumaire d'après les rapports des conseillers d'état chargés d'un enquête sur la situation de la république* (Paris: Didier, 1874).

Rohleder, F., *Die Pariser Kommune vor der Deputiertenkammer in Versailles. Generaldebatte über die Amnestieanträge und Rede Raspail's (Vater) vom 16.–18. Mai 1876* (Braunschweig: Bracker, 1876).

Rouquette, J., *La terreur blanche* (Paris: Cinqualbre, n.d.).

Saint-Ferréol, A., *Les proscrits français en Belgique ou La Belgigue contemporaine vue à travers l'exil* (Bruxelles: Muquardt, 1870–1871, 2 vols.).

Sainte-Beuve, C.-A., *Chroniques parisiennes* (Paris: Calmann-Lévy, 1876). *Nouveaux lundis,* vol. XII (Paris: Calmann-Lévy, 1878).

Schnerb, R., *Ledru-Rollin* (Paris: Presses universitaires de France, 1948).

Seignobos, Ch., *La révolution de 1848—Le second empire,* vol. 6 of *Histoire de France contemporaine, depuis la Révolution jusqu'a la paix de 1919,* E. Lavisse, ed., (Paris: Hachette, 1921).

Spuller, E., *Histoire parlementaire de la seconde république* (Paris: Alcan, 1896).

Stern, D. *see* Agoult.

Tchernoff, I., *Le parti républicain sous la monarchie de juillet. Formation et évolution de la doctrine républicaine* (Paris: Pédoue, 1901).

Thompson, J. M., *Louis-Napoleon and the Second Empire* (New York: Noonday Press, 1955).

Tinayre, V., *Raspail, Michelet, enfants* (Paris: Kéva, 1881).

Tocqueville, A. de, *Recollections*, J. P. Mayer, ed. (New York: Columbia University Press, 1949).

Trollope, F., *Paris and the Parisians in 1835* (New York: Harper, 1836).

Troubat, J., *Le blason de la révolution* (Paris: Lemerre, 1883).

Valès, A., *Edgar Quinet, sa vie et son oeuvre* (Paris: "La Cause," 1839).

Van Kalken, F., *Biographie nationale . . . de Belgique* (Bruxelles: A. Bruylant, 1936–1938).

Vermeil de Conchard, P., *L'assassinat du Maréchal Brune; épisode de la terreur blanche* (Paris: Perrin, 1887).

Vidalenc, J., *Louis Blanc* (Paris: Presses universitaires de France, 1948).

Vignery, R. J., *The French Revolution and the Schools* (Madison: The State Historical Society of Wisconsin, 1965).

Weill, G., *Histoire du parti républicain en France, 1814–1870* (Paris: Alcan, 1928, nouv. ed.).

BACKGROUND READING: THE MEDICAL AND SCIENTIFIC SCENE

Books: Medicine, Science, Public Health, Pharmacy, and the Law

Ackerknecht, E. H., *Medicine at the Paris Hospital, 1794–1848* (Baltimore: The Johns Hopkins Press, 1967); and *Rudolf Virchow, Doctor, Statesman, Anthropologist* (Madison: Wisconsin University Press, 1953).

Administration générale de l'assistance publique à Paris, *Cent ans d'assistance publique à Paris* (Paris: n. publ., 1949).

André, L., *Madame Lafarge, voleuse de diamants* (Paris: Plon, 1914).

André-Pontier, L., *Histoire de la pharmacie* (Paris: O. Doin, 1900).

Auenbrugger, L., *Preliminary Experience with a Specific Remedy in a Specific Syndrome of Human Insanity* (Vienna: Trattner, 1776).

Baker, J. R., *Cytological Technique* (London: Methuen, 1950, 3rd ed.).

Balthazard, Dr., *Orfila et l'Affaire Lafarge* (Paris: Baillière, 1920).

Barse, J., *Manuel de la cour d'assises dans les questions d'empoisonnement à l'usage des magistrats, des avocats, des experts, des jurés et des témoins contenant des travaux inédits sur plusieurs points de la science par M. Orfila* (Paris: Labé, 1845).

Bass, G., *Die Gerichtsmedizin als Spezialfach in Paris von 1800 bis 1850* (Zürich: Juris-Verlag, 1964).

Beaudéant, J., et A. Pasturel, *Affaire Lafarge: Une réhabilitation qui s'impose. Etude juridique et psychologique d'une cause criminelle célèbre* (Paris: Maloine, 1913).

Belloni, L., *Le "contagium vivum" avant Pasteur* (Paris: Palais de la Découverte, 1961).

Benedetti-Pichler, A.-A., *Introduction to the Microtechnique of Inorganic Analysis* (New York: John Wiley & Sons, 1942).

Bichat, X., *Anatomie générale* (Paris: Chaude, 1830).

Boussoulade, J., *Moniales et hospitalières dans la tourmente révolutionnaire* (Paris: Letouzey et Ané, 1962).

Bouvet, M., *Histoire de la pharmacie en France des origines à nos jours* (Paris: Occitania, 1937).

Broca, P., *Correspondance, 1841–1857* (Paris: Paul Schmidt, 1886). *Traité des tumeurs* (Paris: P. Asselin, 1866, 2 vols.).

Cameron, G. R., *Pathology of the Cell* (London: Oliver & Boys, 1952).

Casper, J. L., *Charakteristik der französischen Medizin mit vergleichenden Hinblicken auf die englische* (Leipzig: Brockhaus, 1822).

Castiglioni, A., *A History of Medicine*, E. B. Krumbhaar, tr. (New York: Knopf, 1947).

Chauffard, M., *Andral. La médecine française de 1820 à 1830* (Paris: Baillière, 1877).

Chevalier, Ch., *Des microscopes et de leur usage* (Paris: chez l'auteur, 1839).

Church, J., *An Inaugural Dissertation on Camphor* (Philadelphia: Thompson, 1797).

Coleman, W., *Georges Cuvier, Zoologist* (Cambridge, Belknap Press, 1964).

Coulom, R., *L'Affaire Lafarge: une histoire vraie* (Paris: Breschi, 1938).

Crosland, M., *The Society of Arcueil—A View of French Science at the Time of Napoleon I* (London: Heinemann, 1967).

Cuvier, G., *Histoire des progrès des sciences naturelles depuis 1789 jusqu'à ce jour* (Paris: Baudouin, 1838, 2 vols.).

Daremberg, Ch., *Histoire des sciences médicales comprenant l'anatomie, la physiologie, la médecine, la chirurgie, et les doctrines de pathologie générale* (Paris: Baillière, 1870).

Daremberg, G., *Les grands médecins du 19ème siècle* (Paris: Masson & Cie, 1907).

Delasiauve, L. J., *De l'organisation médicale en France sous le triple rapport de la pratique, des établissements de bienfaisance, et de l'enseignement* (Paris: Fortin, Masson & Co., 1843).

Delaunay, J., *Contribution à l'étude du camphre depuis ses origines jusqu'à Raspail* (Paris: Faculty of Medicine. Thesis No. 1069, 1956).

Derouin, H., A. Gory, and F. Worms, *Traité théorique et pratique d'assistance publique* (Paris: Recueil Sirey, 1914, 3rd ed., 2 vols.).

Dubos, R. J., *Pasteur, Free Lance of Science* (Boston: Little Brown, 1950).

Fabre, F.-A.-H., *L'Orfilaïde* (Paris: chez l'auteur, 1836).

Fayol, A., *La vie et l'oeuvre d'Orfila* (Paris: Albin Michel, 1930).

Florkin, M., *Naissance et déviation de la théorie cellulaire dans l'oeuvre de Théodore Schwann* (Paris: Hermann, 1960).

Foissac, M., *Du camphre* (Paris: Faculty of Medicine. Thesis, 1866).

Friedman, R., *The Story of Scabies* (New York: Froben Press, 1947).

Frison, E., ed., *L'évolution de la partie optique du microscope au cours du 19ème siècle* (Leyden: Rijksmuseum voor de Geschiedenis der Natuurwetenschappen, 1954).

Galperin, L., *Les évènements de juillet 1830 au point de vue chirurgical dans les hôpitaux de Paris* (Paris: Marcel Vigué, 1930).

Gardel, M., *Camphre et sérum camphré* (Toulouse: Faculty of Medicine. Thesis, 1913–1914).

Garrison, F. H., *Introduction to the History of Medicine* (Philadelphia: Saunders, 1929, 11th ed.).

Geoffroy St.-Hilaire, E., *Notice sur Buffon* (Paris: F. D. Pillet, 1838).

Gomori, G., *Microscopic Histochemistry* (Chicago: University of Chicago Press, 1952).

Graffenhauer, J.-P., *Traité sur le camphre considéré dans ses rapports avec l'histoire naturelle, la physique, la chimie, et la médecine* (Paris & Strasbourg: Levrault, 1803).

Guiart, J., *Histoire de la médicine française, son passé, son présent, son avenir* (Paris: Nagel, 1947).

Gumpert, M., *Hahnemann: The Adventurous Career of a Medical Rebel* (New York: Fischer, 1945).

Haller, A. v., *Disputationes ad morborum historiam facientes* (Lausanne: M. M. Bousquet, 1757).

Henle, J., *Allgemeine Anatomie* (Leipzig: Leopold Voss, 1841).

Hertwig, O., *The Cell: Outline of General Anatomy and Physiology* (New York: Macmillan, 1895).

Hughes, A., *A History of Cytology* (New York: Abelard-Schumann, 1959).

Jordan, H. E., *A Textbook of Histology* (New York: Appleton-Century-Crofts, 1947, 8th ed.).

King, L., *The Growth of Medical Thought* (Chicago: University of Chicago Press, 1963).

Klein, M., *Histoire des origines de la théorie cellulaire* (Paris: Hermann, 1936).

Krause, R., *A Course in Normal Histology* (New York: Rebman, 1913, 2 vols.).

Kremers, E., and G. Urdang, *History of Pharmacy* (Philadelphia: Lippincott, 1963, 3rd ed.).

Lafarge, Marie Cappelle, Veuve, *Mémoires* (Brussels: Caus & Co., 1841–1843, 4 vols.).

Laignel-Lavastine, M., ed., *Histoire générale de la médecine, de la pharmacie, de l'art dentaire, et de l'art vétérinaire* (Paris: A. Michel, 1936–1949, 3 vols.).

Leclerc, H., *En marge du codex* (Paris: Masson, 1924).

Le Roy de Méricourt, A., *Rapport sur le progrès de l'hygiène navale* (Paris: Imprimerie impériale, 1876).

Lévy, M., *Rapport sur les progrès de l'hygiène militaire* (Paris: Imprimerie impériale, 1876).

Lillie, R. D., *Histopathologic Technic and Practical Histochemistry* (New York: Blakiston, 1954).

Lison, L., *Histochimie animale* (Paris: Gauthier-Villars, 1936).

Long, E. R., *A History of Pathology* (Baltimore: Williams & Wilkins, 1928).

Magne, J. H., *Rapport sur les progrès de la médecine vétérinaire depuis vingt-cinq ans* (Paris: Imprimerie impériale, 1876).

Mauriac, P., *La médecine et l'intelligence* (1840–1940) (Paris: Delmas, 1949).

Meding, H., *Paris médical: Vade-mecum des médecins étrangers* (Paris: Baillière, 1852).

Newsholme, Sir A., *The Evolution of Preventive Medicine* (Baltimore: Williams & Wilkins, 1927). *International Studies on the Relation between the Private and Official Practice of Medicine with Special*

Reference to the Prevention of Disease (Baltimore: Williams & Wilkins, 1931, 3 vols.).

Nicolson, M. H., *Science and Imagination* (Ithaca: Cornell University Press, 1956).

Nutting, M. A. and L. L. Dock, *A History of Nursing* (New York: Putnam's, 1907–1912, 4 vols.).

Oken, L., *Lehrbuch der Naturphilosophie* (Jena: Frommann, 1809).

Orfila, J.-M.-B., *Traité de médecine légale* (Paris: Labé, 1848, 3 vols.).

Pearse, A. G. E., *Histochemistry Theoretical and Applied* (Boston: Little Brown, 1953).

Picard, E., et al., *Histoire des sciences en France*, vols. XIV and XV of *Histoire de la nation française*, G. Hanotaux, ed. (Paris: Plon & Nourrit, 1920–1929).

Picavet, F., *Les idéologues: Essai sur l'histoire des idées et des théories scientifiques, philosophiques, religieuses, etc., en France depuis 1789* (Paris: F. Alcan, 1891).

Policard, A., *La méthode de la microincinération* (Paris: Hermann & Cie, 1938).

Prater, H., *On the Injurious Effects of Mineral Poisons in the Practice of Medicine; Comprising an Epitome and Commentary on . . . the New System of Medicine of F.-V. Raspail: Every Man His Own Physician.* (London: Sherwood & Co., 1846).

Raspail, Benjamin, *Une première campagne contre l'administration de l'assistance publique* (Paris: chez l'éditeur de M. Raspail, 1875).

Raspail, Camille, *Notice théorique et pratique sur les appareils orthopédiques de la méthode Raspail* (Paris: chez l'éditeur de M. Raspail, 1862). *Le choléra. Ses causes, ses effets, son traitement préventif et curatif, basés sur la théorie parasitaire publiée en 1843 par F.-V. Raspail* (Paris: chez l'éditeur de M. Raspail, 1884).

Raspail, Emile, *Des odeurs de Paris* (Paris: chez l'éditeur de M. Raspail, 1880).

Raspail, François, *Nouvelle thérapeutique des plaies et ulcérations par l'aéro-thermo-balsamogène et la camphénine* (Paris: A. Joanin, 1906).

Raspail, François, and Désirée Séhé, *L'éducation physique dans la famille; ouvrage précédé de "Conseils aux mères de famille" par Mad. Juliette François Raspail* (Paris: Delagrave, 1921).

Raspail, Julien, *La rôle pathogène des helminthes en général et en particulier dans les maladies infectieuses* (Paris: Imprimerie de la Cour d'appel, 1906).

Raspail, Xavier, *Hygiène d'enfants en bas âge fondée sur les principes du système médical de F.-V. Raspail* (Paris: Vigot, 1905). *Raspail et Pasteur: Trente ans de critiques médicales et scientifiques 1884–1914* (Paris: Vigot, 1916).

Rognetta, F., *Procès de Dijon. Consultation médico-légale sur un cas de mort attribué à l'empoisonnement par l'arsenic* (Paris: Bureau de la Gazette des Hôpitaux, 1839).

Romeis, B., *Mikroskopische Technik* (München: Leibnitz, 1948).

Rosen, G., *A History of Public Health* (New York: M. D. Publications, 1958).

Sassani, L., *Les précurseurs français de Schleiden et de Schwann* (Paris: Michalon, 1907).

Schwann, Th., *Mikroskopische Untersuchungen über die Übereinstimmung in der Struktur und dem Wachstum der Thiere und der Pflanzen* (Berlin: Reimer, 1839).

La science française (Paris: Ministère de l'Instruction publique et des Beaux-Arts, 1915, 2 vols.).

Shryock, R. H., *The Development of Modern Medicine* (New York: Knopf, 1947).

Simmons, J. S., ed., *Public Health in the World Today* (Cambridge: Harvard University Press, 1949).

Simon, H. J., *Attenuated Infection: The Germ Theory in Contemporary Perspective* (Philadelphia: J. B. Lippincott, 1960).

Singer, Ch., *A History of Biology* (New York: H. Schuman, 1931).

Tissot, M. D., *Avis au peuple sur sa santé* (Paris: Didot, 1772, 2 vols. in 1, 5th ed.).

Trébuchet, A., *Jurisprudence de la médecine, de la chirurgie, et de la pharmacie en France* (Paris: Baillière, 1834).

Underwood, E. A., ed., *Science, Medicine, and History: Essays on the Evolution of Scientific Thought and Medical Practice Written in Honor of Charles Singer* (London: Oxford University Press, 1953).

Valéry-Radot, P., *La Faculté de médecine de Paris: ses origines, ses richesses artistiques* (Paris: Masson, 1944).

Virville, A. Davy de, *Histoire de la botanique en France* (Paris: Société d'édition de l'enseignement supérieur, 1954).

Winslow, C.-E.-A., *The Evolution and Significance of the Modern Public Health Campaign* (New Haven: Yale University Press, 1923).

Wolf, A., *A History of Science, Technology and Philosophy in the 18th Century* (New York: Harper, 1961, 2 vols.).

BACKGROUND READING: THE POLITICAL AND LITERARY SCENE

Articles: Politics, Religion, Education, and Literature

Anon., *La présidence entre Ledru-Rollin et Raspail: Appel aux sentiments de l'unité démocratique et sociale* (Paris: Dépôt central chez Chapuy, n.d. [1848]).

Berthelot, M., "Notice sur les origines et sur l'histoire de la société philomatique," *Mémoires publiés par la société philomatique à l'occasion du centenaire de sa fondation, 1788–1888* (Paris: Gauthier-Villars & fils, 1888).

Bossu, J., "Il y eut en 1848 Hubert et Huber," Chronique et bibliographie, *La révolution de 1848*, XXXVI (1939), 77–78.

Du Camp, M., "Souvenirs littéraires," Pt. V in *Revue des deux mondes* XLVII (Oct. 1, 1881), 485–86.

Durand, Abbé A., "Un ami de l'évêque Périer: Fouché, d'après un livre récent," *Mémoires de l'Académie de Vaucluse*, 2ème série, III (1903), 237–40.

Dutacq, F., "L'élection d'un représentant du Rhône à l'assemblée nationale au mois de septembre 1848," *Revue d'histoire de Lyon*, VII (1908), 443–69.

Gerbod, P., "La vie universitaire à Paris sous la restauration de 1820 à 1830," *Revue d'histoire moderne et contemporaine*, XIII (1966), 5–48.

Hanotaux, G., "La politique intérieure sous Napoléon: 3ème partie: L'organisation de l'empire," *Revue des deux mondes*, 95ème année (Oct. 15, 1925), 817–39.

Hermant, A., "De la prévision rationnelle du temps—Les astronomes et les astrologues," *Revue contemporaine*, 2ème série, XLVIII (Nov.-Dec. 1865), 753–73.

Lebey, A., "Blanqui et Raspail à Doullens," *La révolution de 1848*, VII (1910–1911), 181–95.

Lévy-Schneider, L., "Les préliminaires du 15 mai 1848," *Ibid.*, 219–32.

Mathiez, A., "F.-V. Raspail chez Albertine Marat," *Annales révolutionnaires*, IV (1911), 660–66.

Maurras, Ch., "La politique. 'Et Raspail?'—'Et Denain?'," *Action française*, July 13, 1913.

Nordenfalk, C., "Van Gogh and Literature," *Journal of the Warburg and Courtauld Institutes*, X (1947), 132–47.

Paillet, A., "Les cours prévôtales, 1816–1818," *Revue des deux mondes,* IV, Year LXXXI, 6ème période (July 1, 1911), 123–49.

Raspail, Benjamin, "Lettre de Benjamin Raspail," *La révolution de 1848,* XXI–XXII (1925–1926), 684–86.

Vauthier, G., "Les congrégations religieuses sous l'empire," *Revue des études napoléoniennes,* XII (1917), 233–45.

Zavaès, A., "Les proscrits français en 1848 et 1851 à Londres," *La révolution de 1848,* XX (1923–1924), 343–75; XXI (1924–1925), 94–114.

Background reading: the medical and scientific scene

Articles: Medicine, Science, Public Health, Pharmacy, and the Law

Ackerknecht, E. H., "Anticontagionism between 1821 and 1867," *Bulletin of the History of Medicine,* XXII (1948), 562–93. "Beiträge zur Geschichte der Medizinalreform von 1848," *Sudhoff's Archiv für Geschichte der Medizin,* XXV (1932), 61–183. "Broussais or a Forgotten Medical Revolution," *Bulletin of the History of Medicine,* XXVII (1953), 320–43. "Elisha Bartlett and the Philosophy of the Paris Clinical School," *Ibid.,* XXIV (1950), 45–60. "Hygiene in France, 1815–1848," *Ibid.,* XXII (1948), 117–55. "Typen der medizinischen Ausbildung im 19. Jahrhundert," *Schweizerische Medizinische Wochenschrift,* LXV (1957), 1361–66. "Villermé and Quételet," *Bulletin of the History of Medicine* XXVI (1952), 317–29.

Anon., "Madame Lafarge," bi-weekly in *Figaro,* Feb. 28–May 1, 1864.

Baker, J. R., "The Cell-Theory: a restatement, history, and critique," *Quarterly Journal of Microscopical Science,* Pt. I: LXXXIX (1948), 103–25; Pt. II: XC (1949), 87–108; Pt. III: XCIII (1952), 157–90; Pt. IV: XCIV (1953), 407–40; Pt. V: XCVI (1955), 449–81. "The Discovery of the Uses of Coloring Agents in Biological Micro-technique," *Journal of the Quekett Microscopical Club,* 4th series, I, Pt. 6 (Dec. 1943), 256–75.

Bernard, C., "Glycogénèse animale: évolution du glycogène dans l'oeuf des oiseaux," *Comptes-rendus hebdomadaires des séances de l'Académie des sciences,* LXXV Pt. II (1872), 55–60.

Biot, J.-B., "Sur un caractère optique, à l'aide duquel on reconnaît immédiatement les sucs végétaux qui peuvent donner du sucre analogue au sucre de canne, et ceux qui ne peuvent donner que du sucre semblable au sucre de raisin," *Nouvelles annales du Muséum d'histoire naturelle,* II (1833), 95–108.

Biot, J.-B., and J. F. Persoz, "Mémoires sur les modifications que la fécule et la gomme subissent sous l'influence des acides," *Ibid.*, II (1833), 109–25.

Bizard, L., "Médecine des prisons et des pénitentiaires," in *Histoire de la médecine, de la pharmacie, de l'art dentaire, et de l'art vétérinaire,* M. Laignel-Lavastine, ed. (Paris: A. Michel, 1949), III, 694–712.

Blanchard, R., "Méconnaissance de la nomenclature zoologique et botanique et de l'histoire des sciences biologiques; son influence fâcheuse sur le langage médical," *Bulletin de l'Académie de médecine,* LXXVI (1916), 380–87.

Canguilhem, G., "La théorie cellulaire en biologie. Du sens et de la valeur des théories scientifiques," *Publications de la Faculté des Lettres de l'Université de Strasbourg. Mélanges 1945. IV. Etudes philosophiques.* (Paris: G. Doin, 1946), 143–75.

Cathelin, Dr. F., "Les précurseurs des grands biologistes," *Le Progrès médical, Supplément illustré,* 6ème année, No. 9 (Oct. 1929), 65–70.

Chamot, E. M., and C. W. Mason, "Chemical Microscopy. Its Value in the Training of Chemists," *Journal of Chemical Education,* V, No. 3 (March 1928), 258–68.

Deutsch, A., "Historical Inter-relationship between Medicine and Social Welfare," *Bulletin of the History of Medicine,* XL (1942), 485–502.

Duveen, D. I., and H. S. Klickstein, "Antoine Laurent Lavoisier's Contribution to Medicine and Public Health," *Ibid.*, XXIX (1955), 164–79.

Dykstra, D. L., "The Medical Profession and Patent and Proprietary Medicines during the 19th Century," *Ibid.*, XXIX (1955), 401–19.

Fosseyeux, M., "Histoire de l'hospitalisation des malades en France," in *Histoire de la médecine, de la pharmacie, de l'art dentaire, et de l'art vétérinaire,* M. Laignel-Lavastine, ed. (Paris: A. Michel, 1949), III, 681–93.

Galdston, I., "Humanism and Public Health," *Bulletin of the History of Medicine,* VIII (1940), 1032–39. "Social Medicine and the Epidemic Constitution," *Ibid.*, XXV (1951), 8–21.

Gillispie, C. C., "Science in the French Revolution," *Behavioral Science,* IV (1959), 67–73.

Guerlac, H., "Science as a Social and Historical Phenomenon: Some Aspects of Science during the French Revolution," *The Scientific Monthly,* LXXX (1955), 93–101.

Hausheer, H., "Icarian Medicine: Etienne Cabet's Utopia and its French Medical Background," *Bulletin of the History of Medicine,* IX (1941), 294–310, 401–35, 515–29.

Holmes, O. W., "On the Contagiousness of Puerperal Fever," *New England Quarterly Journal of Medicine,* I (1842–1843), 503 ff.

Léonard, J., "Les études médicales en France entre 1815 et 1848," *Revue d'histoire moderne et contemporaine,* XIII (1966), 87–94.

Ménétrier, P., "Le centenaire de la suppression de la Faculté de médecine de Paris," *Bulletin de la société française d'histoire de la médecine,* XVI (1922), 440–45.

Morelot, S., "Mémoire historique et analytique sur le camphre, "*Recueil périodique de la Société de médecine de Paris,* X (1801), 294–314.

Morin, G., "Raspail et Sainte-Beuve," *Aesculape,* Yr 17, No. 11 (Nov. 1927), 284–87.

Muller, P., "Madame Lafarge sous la 2nde république," *La révolution de 1848,* IX (1912–1913), 447–53.

Policard, A., "Histoire de l'histologie," in *Histoire de la médecine de la pharmacie, de l'art dentaire, et de l'art vétérinaire,* M. Laignel-Lavastine, ed. (Paris: A. Michel, 1938), II, 334–49.

Polk, W. M., "Relation of Medicine to the Problem of Socialism," *Transactions of the New York Academy of Medicine,* 2nd series, VI (1889), 125–38.

Raspail, Julien, "L'Affaire Lafarge," *La Revue,* CIV (Sept. 15 and Oct. 1, 1913), 179–95, 377–95.

Rich, A. R., "The Place of R.-H.-J. Dutrochet in the Development of the Cell Theory," *Bulletin of the Johns Hopkins Hospital,* XXXIX (1926), 330–65.

Rosen, G., "Economic and Social Policy in Public Health," *Journal of the History of Medicine and Allied Sciences,* VIII (1953), 406–30. "An 18th Century Plan for a National Health Service," *Bulletin of the History of Medicine,* XVI (1944), 429–36. "Hospitals, Medical Care and Social Policy in the French Revolution," *Ibid.,* XXX (1956), 124–49. "The Philosophy of Ideology and the Emergence of Modern Medicine in France," *Ibid.,* XX (1946), 328–39. "Problems in the Application of Statistical Analysis to Questions of Health: 1700–1880," *Ibid.,* XXIX (1955), 27–45. Review of Martin Gumpert's *Hahnemann: The Adventurous Career of a Medical Rebel, Ibid.,* XVIII (1945), 461–62.

Schleiden, M. J., "Beiträge zur Phytogenesis," *Archiv für Anatomie, Physiologie, und wissentschaftliche Medizin,* Fr. J. Müller, ed., 1838, 137–76.

Sigerist, H. E., "From Bismarck to Beveridge: Developments and Trends in Social Security Legislation," *Bulletin of the History of Medicine*, XIII (1943), 365–88. "An Outline of the Development of the Hospital," *Ibid.*, IV (1936), 573–81. "The Philosophy of Hygiene," *Ibid.*, I (1933), 323–31. "Surgery at the Time of the Introduction of Antisepsis," *Journal of the Missouri State Medical Association*, XXXII, No. 5 (1935), 169–76.

Studnička, F. K., "Aus der Vorgeschichte der Zellentheorie. H. Milne Edwards, H. Dutrochet, F. Raspail, J. E. Purkinje," *Anatomischer Anzeiger*, LXXIII (1931–1932), 390–416.

Tanon, L., "Histoire de l'hygiène," in *Histoire de la médecine, de la pharmacie, de l'art dentaire, et de l'art vétérinaire*, M. Laignel-Lavastine, ed. (Paris: A. Michel, 1949), III, 475–504.

Temkin, O., "Materialism in French and German Physiology of the Early Nineteenth Century," *Bulletin of the History of Medicine* XX (1946), 322–27. " 'Medicine in 1847: Continental Europe' in 'One Hundred Years Ago: A Symposium' Presented by the Johns Hopkins Institute of the History of Medicine," *Ibid.*, XXI (1947), 466–78. "The Philosophical Background of Magendie's Physiology," *Ibid.*, XX (1946), 10–35.

Trébuchet, A., "Des brevêts d'invention délivrés pour remèdes secrets," *Annales d'hygiène publique et de médecine légale*, XXIX (1843), 203–11.

Williams, L. P., "Science, Education and the French Revolution," *Isis*, XLIV (1953), 311–30. "Science, Education and Napoleon I," *Ibid.*, XLVII (1956), 369–82.

Wilson, J. W., "Cellular Tissue and the Dawn of the Cell Theory," *Ibid.*, XXXV (1944), 168–73. "Dutrochet and the Cell Theory," *Ibid.*, XXXVII (1947), 14–21.

Vaillard, L., "Le rôle de l'académie de médecine dans l'évolution de l'hygiène publique," *Bulletin de l'académie de médecine*, 3ème série, LXXXIV (1920), 401–29.

INDEX

Monnier, M.: hostile witness, 211*n*
Montalembert, Comte C. de, 177
Montalivet, Comte C. de: daughters sent with presents, 169
Montrouge: R. lived at, 161, 201
Montsouris: R. lived at, 159–60
Montyon prize: proposed for, 70, 126–27; withheld, 114*n*
Morel, pharmacist: R.'s partner, 153–55; R. lost lawsuit to, 157; aids in prosecuting R., 194, 196
Mortiller, M. de, publisher, 125*n*
Moskowa, Prince de la: candidate at Club Raspail, 207*n*
Murder trials: R. expert chemist, 165; murders by arsenic, 183–92; Rigal trial, 187; Mercier trial, 187; Affaire Lafarge, 189–92
Muséum of Natural History, 64; professors to Society for Natural History, 65*n*; Cuvier professor, 69; Cordier professor, 71*n*; R. offered position, 71, 167; Decaisne works at, 73; Coste professor, 74; R. publishes in *Memoirs*, 76; visits frequently, 78; Desfontaines professor, 84; work furnishes subject matter for *Almanacs*, 229

Napoleon I, *see* Napoleon Bonaparte
Napoleon III: commutes R.'s sentence, 237; restrained from persecuting Belgian exiles, 239; opposition growing, 253; R. welcomes fall, 258; plebiscite victory, 260; *see also* Louis-Napoleon Bonaparte
Napoleon Bonaparte: admiration for, 12, 47, 55; stepbrothers served, 21; awards Legion of Honor to Victor R., 25*n*; returns from Egypt, 29; Fouché reports, 30; re-establishes Brothers of the Christian Schools, 32*n*; creates lycées, 36; anniversary celebrated, 46; returns from Elba, 49; creates new nobility, 54; death, 56; centralizes education, 64; Corvisart his physician, 67; creates health officers, 137; R. praised by, 196; R. criticizes *Code Napoleon*, 279
Naquet, Dr. Alfred: speaks at R.'s funeral, 266; co-signer of "Raspail bill," 287*n*
National, Le: active in 1848, 200
National Constituent Assembly (1789–1791): annexation of French Papal States, 21, 24; dissolves corporations, 29
National Constituent Assembly (1848–1849): May 15 demonstration, 5, 209–13; election to, 8, 216–

20, 200, 228; popular resentment, 209; Marrast president, 218
National Guard: in Papal States, 24; R. member, 167; Louis Philippe reviews, 168; R. on, 169; disperses crowd, 169*n*; seditious, 174; resigns, 209*n*; arrests R. 218*n*; on May 15, 221, 223*n*
National Legislative Assembly (1849): opinion of May 15 demonstration, 212; Benjamin deputy, 232–34, 287; members former prisoners, 284; fate of political prisoners, 284–85
National Workshops, 220
Natural History of Health and Sickness: plans this synthesis, 109; quoted, 117; drawings praised, 118; analyzed, 119–22; favorable review, 124; sold out, 146; restated in *Elementary Review of Medicine*, 151; special office hours for owners, 162; helped create popularity, 203; revised in Belgian exile, 246–47
Naturphilosophie: encourages speculation in cell theory, 97
Némésis médicale illustrée: Orfila satirized in, 187*n*
Nerval, G. de [Gérard Labrunie], 282*n*
New Caledonia: penal colony, 285
New Journal of Medicine, Surgery, and Pharmacy: publishes in, 76
New Scientific Studies, 246
New System of Organic Chemistry: dedicated to Esseyric, 35; written in jail, 112; analyzed, 114; Montyon prize proposed for, 127; cited, 133
New System of Plant Physiology and Botany: written in jail, 112; analyzed, 114–15
Nicholas I, tsar: crushed Polish revolt, 209
Nitric acid: used as reagent, 105–6
Noir, V.: assassinated, 230, 260
Nouveau système de chimie organique, see New System of Organic Chemistry
Nova Scotia: *Annual* useful in, 148
Noye, Abbé I.: letter to author, 38*n*; help acknowledged, 41*n*, 59*n*

Oil: analyzed in cell, 102–3, 107–8
Oken, L.: publishes notice of R.'s first paper, 81*n*; letter to R., 90; speculates about evolution, 97
Olivier, J.: Ste.-Beuve to O. about R., 151
Olliver, D.: co-sponsors amnesty bill, 286
Olliver d'Angers, C. P., 124
Oppenheim, Banker: R.'s Belgian acquaintance, 249